Printed Test Bank

Laurie Hurley

College Algebra

Third Edition

Judith A. Beecher

Indiana University Purdue University Indianapolis

Judith A. Penna

Indiana University Purdue University Indianapolis

Marvin L. Bittinger

Indiana University Purdue University Indianapolis

Boston San Francisco New York
London Toronto Sydney Tokyo Singapore Madrid
Mexico City Munich Paris Cape Town Hong Kong Montreal

Reproduced by Pearson Addison-Wesley from QuarkXPress® files.

Publishing as Pearson Addison-Wesley, 75 Arlington Street, Boston, MA 02116.

ISBN-13: 978-0-321-46716-4
ISBN-10: 0-321-46716-7

1 2 3 4 5 6 OPM 10 09 08 07

CONTENTS

There are six alternate test forms for each chapter and the final examination. Alternate Test Forms A, B, C, and D are equivalent in length and difficulty. Synthesis questions occur at the end of the Test Forms, and are separated from the rest of the test by a solid line. Synthesis questions are meant to be more challenging than the previous test questions, like those problems found in the last part of each exercise set in the text. The synthesis questions have been placed at the end to make it easy to omit them if the instructor wishes to do so.

All questions on Test Forms E and F are multiple choice. Effort was made to make the wrong answers as logically wrong as possible. In most cases answers were constructed to avoid students doing backward reasoning.

This Printed Test Bank is designed to accompany *College Algebra, 3e* by Beecher/ Penna/ Bittinger.

Gratitude is extended to Jennifer Rosenberg for checking the accuracy of the manuscript, to Mike Penna for producing the graphs, and to Harriet Merkel for typing the manuscript.

CHAPTER R NAME____________________

TEST FORM A CLASS_____SCORE_____GRADE_____

ANSWERS

1. Consider the numbers: $-5, \frac{2}{3}, \sqrt{18}, 0, 0.42, \sqrt[3]{7}, 5\frac{1}{8}, -2.2$.

   a) Which are whole numbers?

   b) Which are irrational numbers?

1. a)____________

   b)____________

Simplify.

2. $\left|\frac{-3}{11}\right|$

3. $\left|4x^2 y\right|$

2. ____________

3. ____________

4. a) Write interval notation for $\{x \mid -3 \le x < 2\}$;

   b) Graph the interval from part a.

4. a)____________

   b) See graph.

5. Find the distance between -2 and 3 on the number line.

5. ____________

6. Calculate: $100 \div 5^2 \cdot 3 - 6$.

6. ____________

7. Convert to decimal notation: 8.5×10^{-5}.

7. ____________

8. Compute and write scientific notation for the answer:

   $\frac{4.2 \times 10^{-6}}{7 \times 10^{8}}$.

8. ____________

CHAPTER R NAME________________________

TEST FORM A

ANSWERS
9. ____________
10. ____________
11. ____________
12. ____________
13. ____________
14. ____________
15. ____________
16. ____________
17. ____________
18. ____________
19. ____________
20. ____________

Simplify.

9. $x^8 \cdot x^{-12}$

10. $(3a^2)^2(2b)^3$

11. $(-2a^4b^{-6})(3a^{-2}b^4)$

12. $(5x^4 - 2x^3 + x) - (3x^4 - 6x^3 + 7x)$

13. $(x-5)(4x+3)$

14. $(5n-3)^2$

15. $\dfrac{\frac{x}{y} - \frac{y}{x}}{\frac{3}{x} - \frac{3}{y}}$

16. $\sqrt{24}$

17. $\sqrt[4]{32}$

18. $2\sqrt{18} + 5\sqrt{8}$

19. $\sqrt{6}\sqrt{15}$

20. $(5+\sqrt{2})(8-\sqrt{2})$

CHAPTER R NAME________________________

TEST FORM A

ANSWERS

Factor.

21. $4x^2 - 17x - 15$

22. $m^3 - 64$

23. $5m^2 - 45$

24. $x^3 - 2x^2 + x$

25. Multiply and simplify: $\dfrac{x^2 - 9}{x^2 + 5x + 6} \cdot \dfrac{x^2 + 6x + 8}{x^2 - 12x + 27}$.

26. Subtract and simplify: $\dfrac{x}{x^2 + 13x + 42} - \dfrac{6}{x^2 + 11x + 30}$.

27. Rationalize the denominator: $\dfrac{4}{2 + \sqrt{5}}$.

28. Convert to radical notation: $x^{4/5}$.

29. An airplane is 12,000 ft horizontally from the airport. The slanted distance to the airport is 13,000 ft. What is the plane's altitude?

21. ______________

22. ______________

23. ______________

24. ______________

25. ______________

26. ______________

27. ______________

28. ______________

29. ______________

CHAPTER R NAME______________________________

TEST FORM A

ANSWERS	Simplify.
30. ______________	30. $6x - 3 = 15$
31. ______________	31. $4(y-5)+8 = 12-(y+3)$
32. ______________	32. $4x^2 - 17x - 15 = 0$
33. ______________	33. $w^2 - 13 = 0$
34. ______________	34. Multiply: $\left(a^{2x} + a^{-2x}\right)^2$.

CHAPTER R NAME____________________

TEST FORM B CLASS_____SCORE_____GRADE_____

---

1. Consider the numbers: $-5, \frac{3}{4}, \sqrt{13}, 0.6, 0, \sqrt[3]{16}, 3\frac{1}{4}, -2.9$.
   a) Which are integers?
   b) Which are rational numbers but not whole numbers?

Simplify.

2. $\left|\frac{5}{6}\right|$

3. $|-2ac|$

4. a) Write interval notation for $\{x \mid -2 \le x < 1\}$;
   b) Graph the interval from part a.

5. Find the distance between -2 and 7 on the number line.

6. Calculate: $24 \div 2^3 \cdot 5 + 2$.

7. Convert to scientific notation: 0.0052.

8. Compute and write scientific notation for the answer: $(4.2 \times 10^{-2})(3.5 \times 10^{8})$.

ANSWERS

1. a)____________
   b)____________

2. ____________

3. ____________

4. a)____________
   b) See graph.

5. ____________

6. ____________

7. ____________

8. ____________

CHAPTER R **NAME**____________________________

TEST FORM B

ANSWERS

9. ______________

10. ______________

11. ______________

12. ______________

13. ______________

14. ______________

15. ______________

16. ______________

17. ______________

18. ______________

19. ______________

20. ______________

Simplify.

9. $y^{-4} \cdot y^{12}$

10. $(4x)^2(3y^4)^3$

11. $(-4a^2b^{-5})(2a^3b^4)$

12. $(6x^3 + 5x^2 - 2) - (11x^3 - 2x + 8)$

13. $(x+2)(5x-6)$

14. $(2k-3)^2$

15. $\dfrac{\dfrac{8}{y} - \dfrac{y}{8}}{y+8}$

16. $\sqrt{80}$

17. $\sqrt[3]{24}$

18. $\sqrt{48} + \sqrt{75}$

19. $\sqrt{8}\sqrt{50}$

20. $(2+\sqrt{7})(8-3\sqrt{7})$

CHAPTER R NAME______________________________

TEST FORM B

Factor.

21. $2y^2 - 9y - 5$

22. $k^3 - 27$

23. $7x^2 - 175$

24. $x^3 - 12x^2 + 36x$

25. Multiply and simplify: $\dfrac{x^2 - 1}{x^2 - 5x - 36} \cdot \dfrac{x^2 - 6x - 27}{x^2 + 5x + 4}$

26. Subtract and simplify: $\dfrac{x}{x^2 + 5x + 6} - \dfrac{2}{x^2 + 3x + 2}$.

27. Rationalize the denominator: $\dfrac{2}{\sqrt{5} + 3}$.

28. Convert to radical notation: $x^{2/3}$.

29. A 15-foot ladder leans up against the side of a building. Its base is 2 ft from the wall of the building. How high up the wall does the ladder reach? Round to the nearest tenth of a foot.

ANSWERS

21. ____________

22. ____________

23. ____________

24. ____________

25. ____________

26. ____________

27. ____________

28. ____________

29. ____________

CHAPTER R **NAME**________________________

TEST FORM B

ANSWERS

30. ____________

31. ____________

32. ____________

33. ____________

34. ____________

Solve.

30. $4x - 2 = 19$

31. $6(y+1) - 10 = 4 - (y+6)$

32. $6x^2 - 19x - 20 = 0$

33. $w^2 - 6 = 0$

---

34. Multiply: $(x^a + y^b)(x^a - y^b)$.

CHAPTER R NAME______________________

TEST FORM C CLASS_____ SCORE_____ GRADE_____

---

1. Consider the numbers: $-8, \frac{7}{6}, \sqrt{5}, 0, 0.53, \sqrt[3]{2}, 4\frac{1}{5}, -6.7$

   a) Which are whole numbers?

   b) Which are rational numbers but not integers?

Simplify.

2. $\left|-\frac{2}{3}\right|$

3. $|-0.1x|$

4. a) Write interval notation for $\{x \mid -1 \leq x < 3\}$;

   b) Graph the interval from part a.

5. Find the distance between -5 and 10 on the number line.

6. Calculate: $36 \div 2^2 \cdot 5 + 4$.

7. Convert to decimal notation: 5.96×10^{-7}.

8. Compute and write scientific notation for the answer: $\frac{7.2 \times 10^{-4}}{8.0 \times 10^{6}}$.

ANSWERS

1. a) ____________

   b) ____________

2. ____________

3. ____________

4. a) ____________

   b) See graph.

5. ____________

6. ____________

7. ____________

8. ____________

CHAPTER R **NAME**____________________________

TEST FORM C

ANSWERS

9. ____________
10. ____________
11. ____________
12. ____________
13. ____________
14. ____________
15. ____________
16. ____________
17. ____________
18. ____________
19. ____________
20. ____________

Simplify.

9. $x^5 \cdot x^{-3}$

10. $(3x^2)^3(2y)^2$

11. $(-2m^2n^{-3})(5m^{-8}n^6)$

12. $(2x^4 - 3x^3 + 5x) - (7x^4 - 4x^2 - x)$

13. $(x+3)(3x-4)$

14. $(7n-2)^2$

15. $\dfrac{\dfrac{4}{x} - \dfrac{4}{y}}{\dfrac{y^2 - x^2}{4}}$

16. $\sqrt{27}$

17. $\sqrt[3]{81}$

18. $4\sqrt{12} + 2\sqrt{75}$

19. $\sqrt{5}\sqrt{15}$

20. $(4+\sqrt{2})(5-3\sqrt{2})$

CHAPTER R NAME________________________

TEST FORM C

Factor.

21. $3y^2 - 14y - 24$

22. $m^3 + 1$

23. $5n^2 - 320$

24. $x^3 - 10x^2 + 25x$

25. Multiply and simplify: $\frac{x^2 - 2x - 15}{x^2 + x - 6} \cdot \frac{x^2 - 4}{x^2 - 2x - 35}$.

26. Add and simplify: $\frac{x}{x^2 - 3x + 2} + \frac{2}{x^2 - 5x + 6}$.

27. Rationalize the denominator: $\frac{2}{3 + \sqrt{7}}$.

28. Convert to radical notation: $y^{1/4}$.

29. A 24-foot ladder leans up against the side of a building. Its base is 2 ft from the wall of the building. How high up the wall does the ladder reach? Round to the nearest tenth of a foot.

ANSWERS

21. ______________

22. ______________

23. ______________

24. ______________

25. ______________

26. ______________

27. ______________

28. ______________

29. ______________

CHAPTER R **NAME**______________________________

TEST FORM C

ANSWERS

30. ________________

31. ________________

32. ________________

33. ________________

34. ________________

Solve.

30. $3x + 8 = 14$

31. $2(y - 6) + 5 = 10 - (y + 4)$

32. $3x^2 + 16x - 12 = 0$

33. $w^2 - 8 = 0$

---

34. Multiply: $(x^a + y^{-a})(x^a - y^{-a})$.

CHAPTER R NAME______________________

TEST FORM D CLASS____SCORE____GRADE____

ANSWERS

1. Consider the numbers: $6, \frac{2}{3}, \sqrt{5}, 0, 6.2, \sqrt[3]{6}, 4\frac{1}{2}, -8.3$.
   a) Which are natural numbers?
   b) Which are rational numbers but not integers?

1. a)______________
   b)______________

Simplify.

2. $\left|\frac{3}{4}\right|$

3. $\left|-3xy^2\right|$

2. ______________

3. ______________

4. a) Write interval notation for $\{x \mid -3 < x \leq 2\}$;
   b) Graph the interval from part a.

4. a)______________
   b) See graph.

5. Find the distance between -8 and 5 on the number line.

5. ______________

6. Calculate: $48 \div 2^3 \cdot 3 - 9$.

6. ______________

7. Convert to scientific notation: 23,400,000.

7. ______________

8. Compute and write scientific notation for the answer: $\left(4.2\times10^5\right)\left(3.1\times10^{-2}\right)$.

8. ______________

CHAPTER R **NAME**________________________

TEST FORM D

ANSWERS
9. ____________
10. ____________
11. ____________
12. ____________
13. ____________
14. ____________
15. ____________
16. ____________
17. ____________
18. ____________
19. ____________
20. ____________

Simplify.

9. $x^{-6} \cdot x^4$

10. $(2x^4)^3(3y)^2$

11. $(5a^{-4}b^5)(-2a^2b^{10})$

12. $(5x^4 - x^2 + 1) - (9x^4 + 2x^3 - 3x^2)$

13. $(x-9)(7x+2)$

14. $(2m-5)^2$

15. $\dfrac{\frac{a}{b}+\frac{b}{a}}{a+b}$

16. $\sqrt{120}$

17. $\sqrt[3]{250}$

18. $5\sqrt{20} - 2\sqrt{125}$

19. $\sqrt{18}\sqrt{45}$

20. $(3+\sqrt{5})(7-2\sqrt{5})$

CHAPTER R NAME______________________________

TEST FORM D

Factor.

21. $2y^2 - 7y - 30$

22. $n^3 - 125$

23. $8m^2 - 32$

24. $x^3 + 16x^2 + 64x$

25. Multiply and simplify: $\frac{x^2 + 13x + 40}{x^2 - x - 6} \cdot \frac{x^2 - 9}{x^2 + 11x + 24}$.

26. Add and simplify: $\frac{x}{x^2 - 3x + 2} + \frac{3}{x^2 + x - 2}$.

27. Rationalize the denominator: $\frac{3}{5 - \sqrt{6}}$.

28. Convert to radical notation: $x^{4/5}$.

29. One end of a 36-foot guy wire is attached to the top of a 30-foot pole. The other end is staked in the ground. How far from the base of the pole is the other end of the guy wire? (Round answer to the nearest tenth of a foot.)

ANSWERS

21. ______________

22. ______________

23. ______________

24. ______________

25. ______________

26. ______________

27. ______________

28. ______________

29. ______________

CHAPTER R **NAME**______________________________

TEST FORM D

ANSWERS	Solve.
30. ______________	30. $3x - 5 = 19$
31. ______________	31. $4(y-2)+5 = 3-(y+1)$
32. ______________	32. $4x^2 + 11x - 20 = 0$
33. ______________	33. $w^2 - 5 = 0$
34. ______________	34. Factor: $x^{4a} - x^a$.

CHAPTER R NAME________________

TEST FORM E CLASS____ SCORE____ GRADE____

Consider the numbers $-4, \frac{2}{3}, \sqrt{8}, 0, -6.1, \sqrt[3]{5}, 12, 3\frac{5}{8}$ for Exercises 1 and 2.

1. Which are integers?

   a) $-4, 0, 12$ b) $0, 12$

   c) 12 d) $-4, 12$

2. Which are rational numbers?

   a) $-4, -6.1$ b) $\frac{2}{3}, -6.1, 3\frac{5}{8}$

   c) $-4, \frac{2}{3}, 0, -6.1, 12, 3\frac{5}{8}$ d) $\sqrt{8}, \sqrt[3]{5}$

3. Simplify: $\left|-\frac{2}{3}x\right|$.

   a) $-\frac{2}{3}x$ b) $\frac{3}{2}x$ c) $-\frac{3}{2}x$ d) $\frac{2}{3}x$

4. Find the distance between -4 and 3 on a number line.

   a) -1 b) 12 c) 5 d) 7

5. Write interval notation for $\{x \mid -2 \le x < 4\}$.

   a) $[-2, 4]$ b) $(-2, 4)$ c) $[-2, 4)$ d) $(-2, 4]$

6. Calculate: $15 - 6 \div 2 + 4 \cdot 3$.

   a) $\frac{51}{2}$ b) 24 c) $\frac{3}{4}$ d) 48

7. Compute and write scientific notation for the answer: $\frac{3.2 \times 10^{-5}}{2.5 \times 10^{8}}$.

   a) 1.28×10^{-3} b) 1.28×10^{-13}

   c) $1.28 \times 10^{-5/8}$ d) 7.0×10^{-14}

ANSWERS

1. ____________
2. ____________
3. ____________
4. ____________
5. ____________
6. ____________
7. ____________

CHAPTER R **NAME**______________________________

TEST FORM E

ANSWERS

8. ____________

9. ____________

10. ____________

11. ____________

12. ____________

13. ____________

14. ____________

15. ____________

8. Multiply: $(5x^2)^3(2x)^2$.

 a) $60x^8$ b) $500x^7$ c) $60x^7$ d) $500x^8$

9. Simplify: $\sqrt[3]{72}$.

 a) $2\sqrt[3]{9}$ b) 24 c) $4\sqrt[3]{9}$ d) $2\sqrt[3]{3}$

10. Subtract: $(6x^3 - 3x^2 + 2x) - (8x^3 - 3x + 4)$.

 a) $-2x^3 - 2x - 4$ b) $-2x^3 - 3x^2 + 5x - 4$

 c) $-2x^3 - 3x^2 - x + 4$ d) $-2x^3 - 3x^2 - 5x + 4$

11. Multiply: $(x+2)(3x-5)$.

 a) $3x^2 + x + 10$ b) $3x^2 - 10$

 c) $3x^2 + x - 10$ d) $3x^2 + 6x - 5$

12. Multiply: $(3y-2)^2$.

 a) $9y^2 - 12y + 4$ b) $9y^2 - 6x + 4$

 c) $9y^2 - 4$ d) $9y^2 - 12y - 4$

13. Multiply: $(2+\sqrt{6})(5-\sqrt{6})$.

 a) 4 b) $16 + 3\sqrt{6}$

 c) $10 - \sqrt{12}$ d) $4 + 3\sqrt{6}$

14. Add: $5\sqrt{12} + 3\sqrt{3}$.

 a) $23\sqrt{3}$ b) $13\sqrt{3}$ c) 90 d) $8\sqrt{15}$

15. Simplify: $\dfrac{5 - \frac{2}{x}}{7 + \frac{2}{x}}$.

 a) $\dfrac{1}{2}$ b) $\dfrac{5+x}{7-x}$ c) $\dfrac{5x^2-2}{7x^2+2}$ d) $\dfrac{5x-2}{7x+2}$

CHAPTER R **NAME**________________________

TEST FORM E

16. Which is a factor of $2n^2 + 5n - 42$?

    a) $2n + 7$ b) $n - 6$ c) $n + 6$ d) $n - 3$

17. Which is a factor of $4x^2 - 324$?

    a) $x - 3$ b) $x - 9$ c) $x + 3$ d) $x - 18$

18. Which is a factor of $x^3 - 64$?

    a) $x + 4$ b) $x + 8$
    c) $x - 4$ d) $x - 8$

19. Which is a factor of $4x^3 - 24x^2 + x - 6$?

    a) $4x - 1$ b) $x - 2$
    c) $x + 6$ d) $x - 6$

20. Multiply and simplify: $\frac{x^2 - 2x - 15}{x^2 + x - 6} \cdot \frac{x^2 - 4x - 21}{x^2 - 25}$

    a) $\frac{(x+3)(x-7)}{(x-2)(x+5)}$ b) $\frac{(x-3)(x-7)}{(x+2)(x+5)}$
    c) $\frac{(x-5)^2(x+5)}{(x-7)(x-2)(x+3)}$ d) $\frac{(x+3)(x-7)}{(x-2)(x-5)}$

21. Subtract and simplify: $\frac{x}{x^2 + 9x + 20} - \frac{5}{x^2 + 11x + 30}$.

    a) $\frac{x-5}{(x+5)(x+6)}$ b) $\frac{x-20}{x+4}$
    c) $\frac{x-4}{(x+4)(x+6)}$ d) $\frac{x-5}{(x+4)(x+5)(x+6)}$

22. Convert to radical notation: $x^{5/6}$.

    a) $\sqrt[5]{x^6}$ b) $x\sqrt[5]{x}$ c) $\sqrt[6]{x^5}$ d) $6x^5$

ANSWERS

16. __________

17. __________

18. __________

19. __________

20. __________

21. __________

22. __________

CHAPTER R **NAME**____________________

TEST FORM E

ANSWERS

23. __________

24. __________

25. __________

26. __________

27. __________

28. __________

23. Rationalize the denominator: $\dfrac{6}{2+\sqrt{3}}$.

    a) $12+6\sqrt{3}$ b) $12-6\sqrt{3}$ c) $-12+6\sqrt{3}$ d) $\dfrac{12-6\sqrt{3}}{7}$

24. An airplane is 25,000 ft horizontally from the airport. Its altitude is 10,000 ft. Find its slanted distance to the airport. Round to the nearest foot.

    a) 26,926 ft b) 18,708 ft c) 35,000 ft d) 22,919 ft

25. Solve: $4x-3=12$.

    a) $\dfrac{9}{4}$ b) $\dfrac{15}{4}$ c) 60 d) $\dfrac{4}{15}$

26. Solve: $2x^2+9x-18=0$.

    a) $-6, \dfrac{2}{3}$ b) $-\dfrac{3}{2}, 6$ c) $-6, \dfrac{3}{2}$ d) $-\dfrac{2}{3}, 6$

27. Solve: $w^2-3=0$.

    a) $-\sqrt{3}, \sqrt{3}$ b) –3, 3 c) –9, 9 d) 0, 3

---

28. Factor: $x^{12a}-x^{2a}$.

    a) $x^{2a}(6x-1)$
    b) $2a(x+1)(x-1)(x^2+x+1)(x^2-x+1)$
    c) $x^{2a}(x^{5a}+1)(x^{5a}-1)$
    d) $x^{2a}(x^{3a}+1)(x^{3a}-1)$

CHAPTER R NAME________________________

TEST FORM F CLASS_____ SCORE_____ GRADE_____

ANSWERS

1. ____________
2. ____________
3. ____________
4. ____________
5. ____________
6. ____________
7. ____________
8. ____________

Consider the numbers $-5, \frac{2}{3}, \sqrt{2}, 0, -3.4, \sqrt[4]{4}, 8, 2\frac{1}{2}$ for Exercises 1 and 2.

1. Which are integers?

   a) $\sqrt{2}, \sqrt[4]{4}$ b) $\frac{2}{3}, -3.4, 2\frac{1}{2}$

   c) $-5, 0, 8$ d) -5

2. Which are rational numbers?

   a) $\frac{2}{3}, -3.4, 2\frac{1}{2}$ b) $\sqrt{2}, \sqrt[4]{4}$

   c) $-5, 0, 8$ d) $-5, \frac{2}{3}, 0, -3.4, 8, 2\frac{1}{2}$

3. Simplify: $\left|-0.4xy^2\right|$.

   a) $0.4xy^2$ b) $-0.4xy^2$ c) $\frac{1}{0.4xy^2}$ d) $2.5xy^2$

4. Find the distance between -4 and 12 on a number line.

   a) 8 b) $\sqrt{160}$ c) 16 d) 36

5. Write interval notation for $\{x \mid -2 < x \leq 1\}$.

   a) $(-2, 1)$ b) $(-2, 1]$ c) $[2, 1]$ d) $[-2, 1)$

6. Calculate: $3^3 - 2 \cdot 3 \div 3$.

   a) 7 b) 1 c) 24 d) 25

7. Compute and write scientific notation for the answer: $(5.1 \times 10^4)(3.5 \times 10^{-6})$.

   a) 8.6×10^{-2} b) 1.785×10^{-1}

   c) 1.785×10^{-2} d) 1.785×10^{-23}

8. Multiply: $(-2a^{-5}b^6)(7a^4b^{-3})$.

   a) $-14a^{-1}b^3$ b) $-14a^{-20}b^{-18}$

   c) $5a^{-1}b^3$ d) $5a^{-20}n^{-18}$

CHAPTER R

NAME________________________________

TEST FORM F

ANSWERS

9. ______________

10. ______________

11. ______________

12. ______________

13. ______________

14. ______________

15. ______________

9. Simplify: $\sqrt[3]{250}$.

a) $5\sqrt{10}$ b) $25\sqrt[3]{2}$ c) $5\sqrt[3]{2}$ d) $83\frac{1}{3}$

10. Subtract: $(4x^3 - 6x^2 + 3x) - (-8x^3 + 4x^2 + 2)$.

a) $12x^3 - 10x^2 + x$
b) $12x^3 - 10x^2 + 3x - 2$
c) $12x^3 - 2x^2 + 3x - 2$
d) $32x^6 - 64x^5 + 48x^4 - 20x^3 + 12x^2 - 6x$

11. Multiply: $(x+5)(3x-2)$.

a) $3x^2 + 15x - 2$ b) $3x^2 + 13x - 10$
c) $3x^2 + 3x - 10$ d) $3x^2 - 10$

12. Multiply: $(4y-3)^2$.

a) $16y^2 - 24y + 9$ b) $16y^2 - 12y + 9$
c) $16y^2 - 9$ d) $16y^2 - 24y - 9$

13. Multiply: $(2+\sqrt{6})(5-2\sqrt{6})$.

a) $-62 - 2\sqrt{6}$ b) $-2 + \sqrt{6}$
c) $10 - 2\sqrt{6}$ d) $-2 - 2\sqrt{6}$

14. Add: $4\sqrt{150} - 2\sqrt{54}$.

a) $28\sqrt{6}$ b) $14\sqrt{6}$ c) -720 d) $16\sqrt{6}$

15. Simplify: $\dfrac{\dfrac{a^2 - b^2}{ab}}{a^2 + 2ab + b^2}$.

a) $\dfrac{(a+b)^3(a-b)}{ab}$ b) $\dfrac{a-b}{ab(a+b)}$
c) $\dfrac{ab(a+b)}{a-b}$ d) $\dfrac{a-b}{a+b}$

CHAPTER R NAME______________________

TEST FORM F

---

16. Which is a factor of $5x^2 + 22x - 15$?

a) $x+5$ b) $x+3$ c) $5x+1$ d) $5x+3$

17. Which is a factor of $7x^2 - 175$?

a) $x-25$ b) $x+25$ c) $x+5$ d) $x-15$

18. Which is a factor of $n^3 - 729$?

a) $x-3$ b) $x+3$ c) $x+9$ d) $x-9$

19. Which is a factor of $3x^3 - 15x^2 + 4x - 20$?

a) $3x^2 - 5$ b) $x+5$ c) $3x^2 + 4$ d) $x-4$

20. Multiply and simplify: $\frac{x^2 + x - 6}{x^2 - 4x - 5} \cdot \frac{x^2 - 3x - 4}{x^2 - 4}$

a) $\frac{(x+2)(x+3)(x-2)^2}{(x-5)(x-4)(x-11)^2}$ b) $\frac{(x+3)(x-4)}{(x+2)(x-5)}$

c) $\frac{(x+3)(x-4)}{(x-2)(x-5)}$ d) $\frac{(x-3)(x-4)}{(x-2)(x-5)}$

21. Subtract and simplify: $\frac{x}{x^2 + 5x + 6} - \frac{2}{x^2 + 3x + 2}$.

a) $\frac{x-3}{(x+1)(x+3)}$ b) $\frac{x^2 + 3x + 6}{(x+1)(x+2)(x+3)}$

c) $\frac{x-2}{(x+1)(x+2)(x+3)}$ d) $\frac{x^2 - x + 6}{(x+1)(x+2)(x+3)}$

22. Convert to radical notation: $x^{3/4}$.

a) $\sqrt[3]{x^4}$ b) $x\sqrt[3]{x}$ c) $4x^3$ d) $\sqrt[4]{x^3}$

ANSWERS

16. ____________

17. ____________

18. ____________

19. ____________

20. ____________

21. ____________

22. ____________

CHAPTER R **NAME**______________________________

TEST FORM F

ANSWERS

23. ______________

24. ______________

25. ______________

26. ______________

27. ______________

28. ______________

23. Rationalize the denominator: $\dfrac{6}{\sqrt{3}+5}$.

a) $\dfrac{15+3\sqrt{3}}{11}$ b) $\dfrac{-15+3\sqrt{3}}{16}$

c) $\dfrac{15-3\sqrt{3}}{11}$ d) $\dfrac{-15+3\sqrt{3}}{17}$

24. A guy wire is extended from the top of a 12-ft pole to a place on the ground 6 ft from the base of the pole. How long is the guy wire? Round your answer to the nearest tenth of a foot.

a) 18 ft b) 13.4 ft c) 11.3 ft d) 16.2 ft

25. Solve: $3x-6=5$.

a) $\dfrac{11}{3}$ b) $-\dfrac{1}{3}$ c) 33 d) $\dfrac{3}{11}$

26. Solve: $2x^2-x-15=0$.

a) $-3, \dfrac{5}{2}$ b) $-\dfrac{2}{5}, 3$ c) $-3, \dfrac{2}{5}$ d) $-\dfrac{5}{2}, 3$

27. Solve: $x^2-7=0$.

a) –7, 7 b) –49, 49 c) $-\sqrt{7}, \sqrt{7}$ d) 0, 7

28. Factor completely: $k^{3x}-k^{9x}$.

a) $k^{3x}\left(1-k^{3x}\right)$

b) $k^{3x}\left(1+k^{x}\right)\left(1-k^{x}\right)\left(1+k^{x}+k^{2x}\right)\left(1-k^{x}+k^{2x}\right)$

c) $k^{3x}\left(1-k^{x}\right)^2\left(1+k^{x}\right)^2$

d) $k^{3x}\left(1+k^{x}\right)\left(1-k^{x}\right)\left(1+2k^{x}+k^{2x}\right)\left(1-2k^{x}+k^{2x}\right)$

CHAPTER 1 NAME________________

TEST FORM A CLASS____ SCORE____ GRADE____

1. Graph: $3x - 2y = 6$.

2. Find the distance between (4, 8) and (–7, 6).

3. Find the midpoint of the segment with endpoints (1, 0) and (5, –8).

4. Find an equation of the circle with center (–2, 3) and radius $\sqrt{11}$.

5. Find the center and the radius of the circle $(x+6)^2 + y^2 = 9$.

6. a) Determine whether the relation $\{(-5, 5), (-4, 4), (3, -3), (1, 1)\}$ is a function. Answer "yes" or "no."

   b) Find the domain of the relation.

7. Given that $f(x) = x^2 - 6x + 2$, find
   a) $f(-1)$; b) $f(x+3)$.

8. a) Graph: $f(x) = |x-1| + 4$.

   b) Visually estimate the range of $f(x)$.

ANSWERS

1. See graph.
2. ________
3. ________
4. ________
5. ________
6. a) ________
   b) ________
7. a) ________
   b) ________
8. a) See graph.
   b) ________

CHAPTER 1 **NAME**____________________________

TEST FORM A

ANSWERS

9. _______________

10. a) _______________
    b) _______________

11. _______________

12. _______________

13. _______________

14. _______________

15. _______________

16. _______________

17. _______________

9. Find the domain of $f(x)=\dfrac{2+x}{4-x}$.

10. Determine whether each graph is that of a function. Answer "yes" or "no."

a) b)

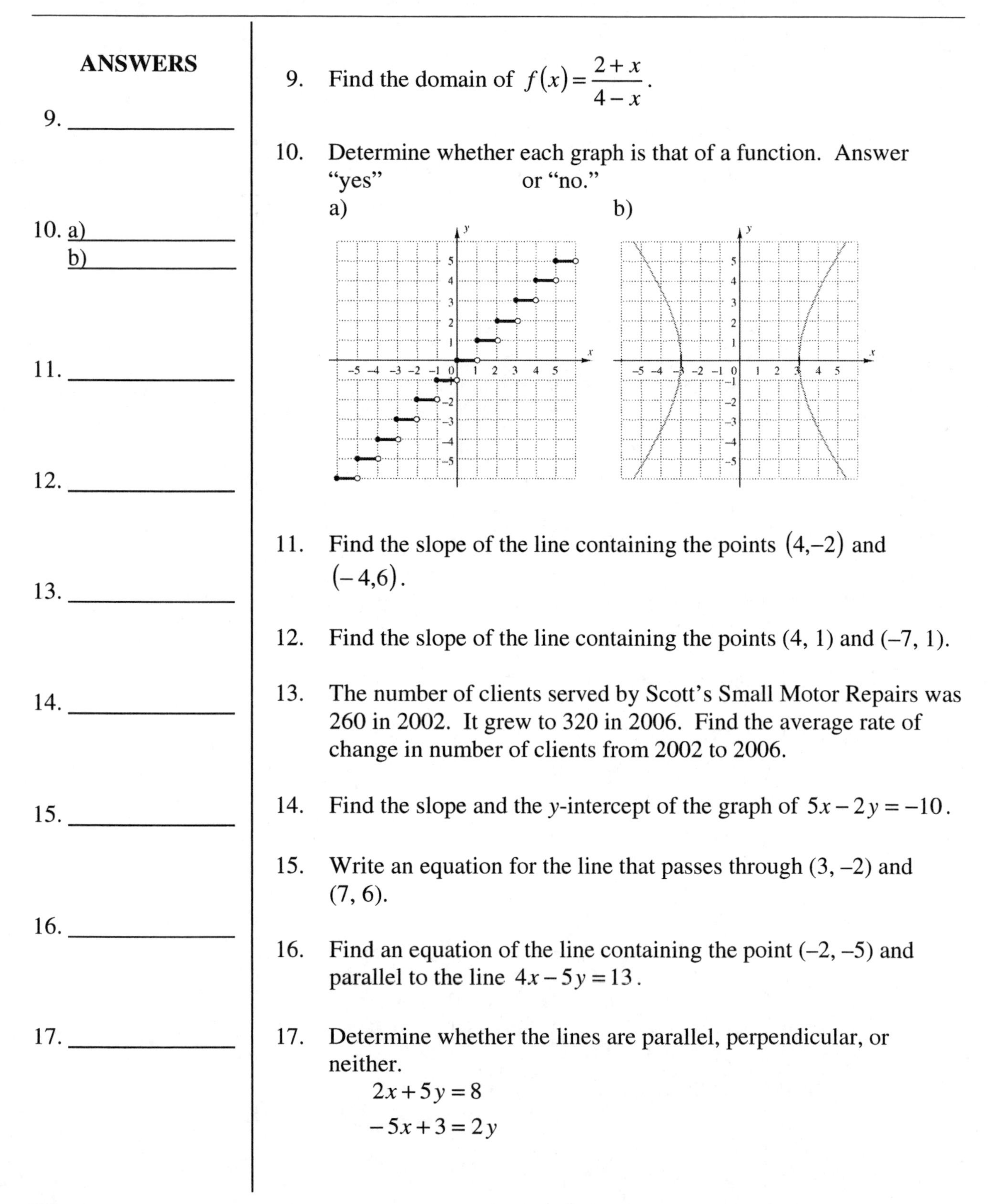

11. Find the slope of the line containing the points $(4,-2)$ and $(-4,6)$.

12. Find the slope of the line containing the points (4, 1) and (–7, 1).

13. The number of clients served by Scott's Small Motor Repairs was 260 in 2002. It grew to 320 in 2006. Find the average rate of change in number of clients from 2002 to 2006.

14. Find the slope and the *y*-intercept of the graph of $5x-2y=-10$.

15. Write an equation for the line that passes through (3, –2) and (7, 6).

16. Find an equation of the line containing the point (–2, –5) and parallel to the line $4x-5y=13$.

17. Determine whether the lines are parallel, perpendicular, or neither.

$$2x+5y=8$$
$$-5x+3=2y$$

CHAPTER 1 NAME________________________________

TEST FORM A

---

18. The table below shows the average price, in dollars, of a computer at Johnson Office Supply in several recent years.

Year, x	Average Price, P
1994, 0	1560
1997, 3	1450
2000, 6	1250
2003, 9	1025
2006, 12	800

Model the data with a linear function using years 3 and 9 and predict the average price in 2010 using this function.

19. Graph:

$$f(x)=\begin{cases}-2x, \text{ for } x<-2,\\ -x^2, \text{ for } -2\le x\le 2,\\ 5, \text{ for } x>2.\end{cases}$$

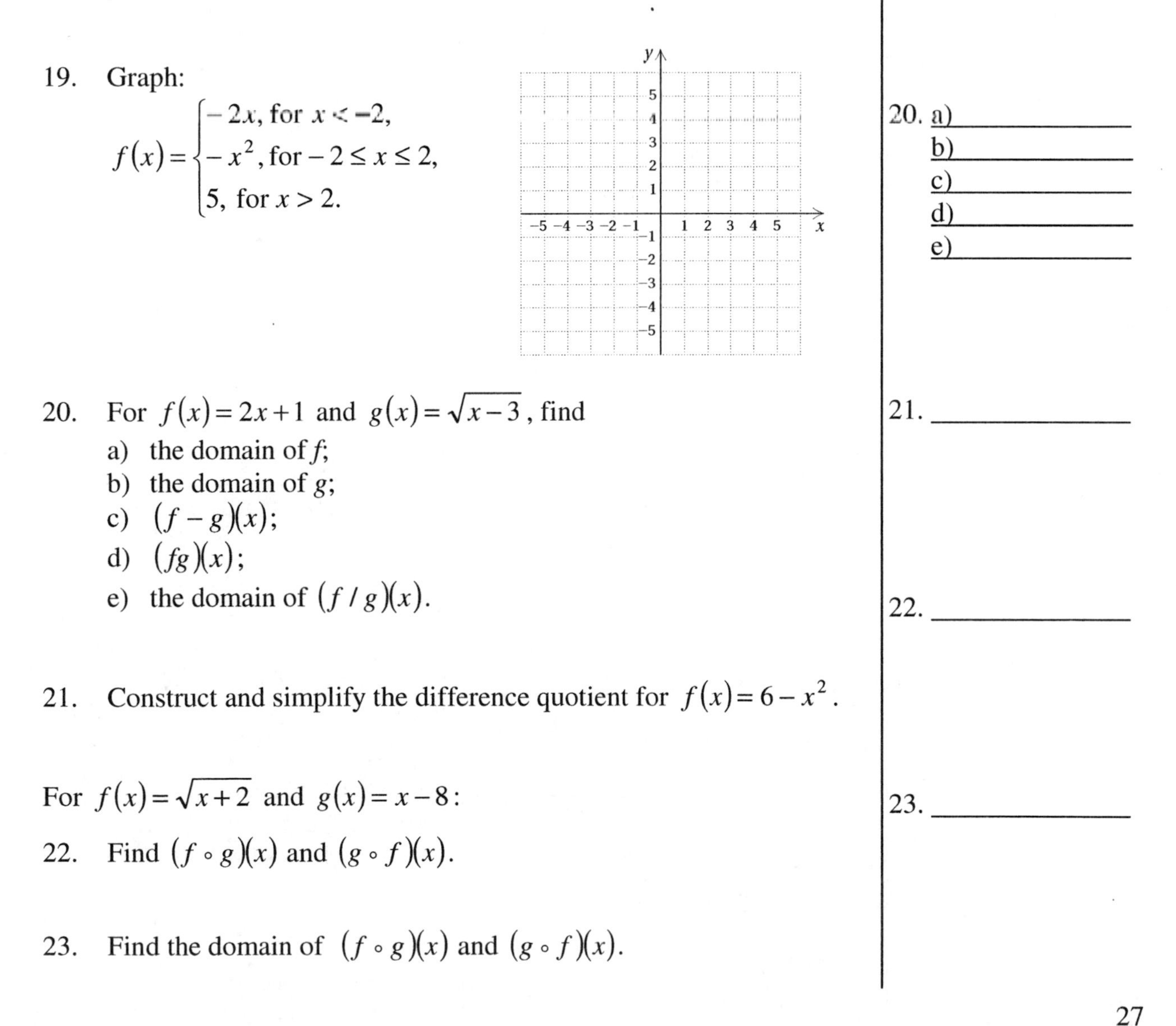

20. For $f(x)=2x+1$ and $g(x)=\sqrt{x-3}$, find
   a) the domain of f;
   b) the domain of g;
   c) $(f-g)(x)$;
   d) $(fg)(x)$;
   e) the domain of $(f/g)(x)$.

21. Construct and simplify the difference quotient for $f(x)=6-x^2$.

For $f(x)=\sqrt{x+2}$ and $g(x)=x-8$:

22. Find $(f\circ g)(x)$ and $(g\circ f)(x)$.

23. Find the domain of $(f\circ g)(x)$ and $(g\circ f)(x)$.

ANSWERS

18. ______________

19. See graph.

20. a) ______________
   b) ______________
   c) ______________
   d) ______________
   e) ______________

21. ______________

22. ______________

23. ______________

CHAPTER 1 **NAME**______________________________

TEST FORM A

ANSWERS

24. _______________

25. _______________

26. _______________

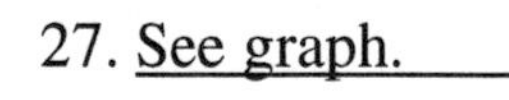

27. See graph.

28. _______________

---

24. Determine whether the graph of $y = \dfrac{3x}{x^2 - 4}$ is symmetric with respect to the x-axis, the y-axis, and/or the origin.

25. Test algebraically whether the function $f(x) = 5x - x^3$ is even, odd, or neither even nor odd. Show your work.

26. Write an equation for a function that has the shape of $y = x^2$, but shifted right 5 units and down 3 units.

27. The graph of a function $y = f(x)$ is shown below. No formula for f is given. Make a graph of $y = f(-x)$.

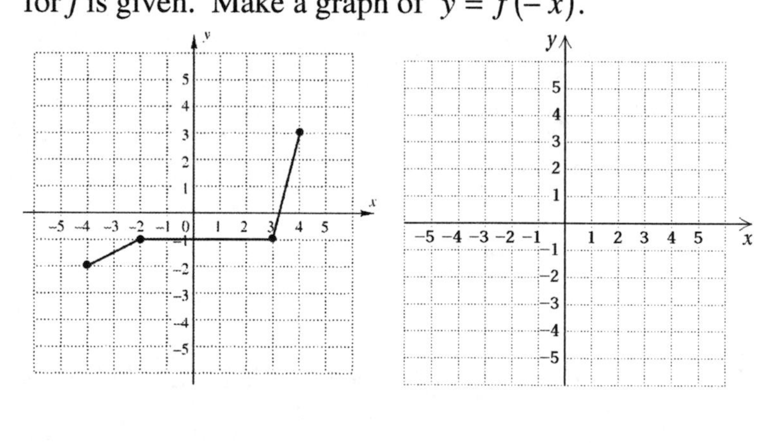

---

28. If (–3, 6) is a point on the graph of $y = f(x)$, what point do you know is on the graph of $y = f(x+3)$?

CHAPTER 1 NAME______________________________

TEST FORM B CLASS_____SCORE_____GRADE_____

---

1. Graph: $x - 4y = 4$.

2. Find the distance between (4, –3) and (6, 1).

3. Find the midpoint of the segment with endpoints (4, –6) and (–3, –12).

4. Find an equation of the circle with center (8, –1) and radius $\sqrt{3}$.

5. Find the center and the radius of the circle $(x+5)^2 + (y+2)^2 = 100$.

6. a) Determine whether the relation $\{(-2, 0), (-1, 1), (-2, 4), (1, 3)\}$ is a function. Answer "yes" or "no."

   b) Find the domain of the relation.

7. Given that $f(x) = x^2 + x + 1$, find
   a) $f(-2)$; b) $f(x-3)$.

8. a) Graph: $f(x) = \sqrt{x^2 - 4}$.

   b) Visually estimate the range of $f(x)$.

ANSWERS

1. See graph.
2. ______________
3. ______________
4. ______________
5. ______________
6. a) ______________
   b) ______________
7. a) ______________
   b) ______________
8. a) See graph.
   b) ______________

CHAPTER 1 **NAME**______________________

TEST FORM B

ANSWERS

9. ____________

10. a) ____________
    b) ____________

11. ____________

12. ____________

13. ____________

14. ____________

15. ____________

16. ____________

17. ____________

9. Find the domain of $f(x) = \dfrac{2x}{x-6}$.

10. Determine whether each graph is that of a function. Answer "yes" or "no."

a) b)

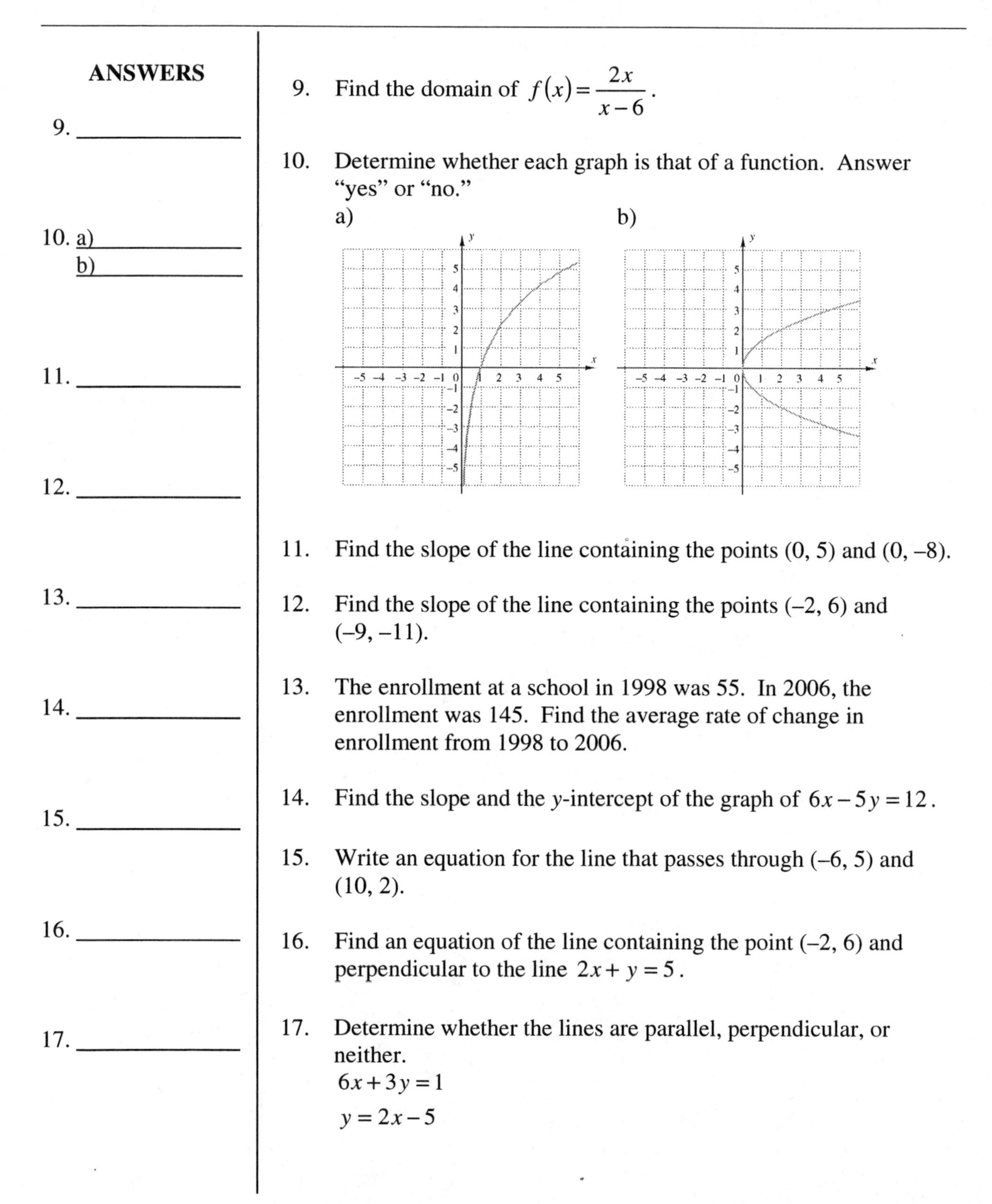

11. Find the slope of the line containing the points (0, 5) and (0, –8).

12. Find the slope of the line containing the points (–2, 6) and (–9, –11).

13. The enrollment at a school in 1998 was 55. In 2006, the enrollment was 145. Find the average rate of change in enrollment from 1998 to 2006.

14. Find the slope and the *y*-intercept of the graph of $6x - 5y = 12$.

15. Write an equation for the line that passes through (–6, 5) and (10, 2).

16. Find an equation of the line containing the point (–2, 6) and perpendicular to the line $2x + y = 5$.

17. Determine whether the lines are parallel, perpendicular, or neither.

$6x + 3y = 1$

$y = 2x - 5$

CHAPTER 1 **NAME**______________________

TEST FORM B

---

18. The table below shows the average number of lunches per day, sold for various years.

Year, x	Lunches Sold, L
2003, 0	50
2004, 1	65
2005, 2	70
2006, 3	88

Model the data with a linear function using years 1 and 3 and predict the average number of lunches sold per day in 2009 using this function.

19. Graph:

$$f(x)=\begin{cases}\sqrt{x+5}, \text{ for } x<-1,\\ x^2, \text{ for } -1\le x\le 2,\\ -|x|, \text{ for } x>2.\end{cases}$$

20. For $f(x)=x^2$ and $g(x)=\sqrt{2x}$, find

a) the domain of f;
b) the domain of g;
c) $(f-g)(x)$;
d) $(fg)(x)$;
e) the domain of $(f/g)(x)$.

21. Construct and simplify the difference quotient for $f(x)=5x^2+2$.

For $f(x)=3x-2$ and $g(x)=\sqrt{x}$:

22. Find $(f\circ g)(x)$ and $(g\circ f)(x)$.

23. Find the domain of $(f\circ g)(x)$ and $(g\circ f)(x)$.

ANSWERS

18. ______________

19. See graph.

20. a) ______________
b) ______________
c) ______________
d) ______________
e) ______________

21. ______________

22. ______________

23. ______________

CHAPTER 1 **NAME**__________________________

TEST FORM B

ANSWERS

24. ____________

25. ____________

26. ____________

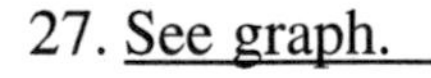

27. See graph.

28. ____________

---

24. Determine whether the graph of $y = x^4 - 2x^2$ is symmetric with respect to the x-axis, the y-axis, and/or the origin.

25. Test algebraically whether the function $f(x) = \dfrac{x^2}{x-1}$ is even, odd, or neither even nor odd. Show your work.

26. Write an equation for a function that has the shape of $y = |x|$, but shifted right 4 units and up 2 units.

27. The graph of a function $y = f(x)$ is shown below. No formula for f is given. Make a graph of $y = f(x-1)$.

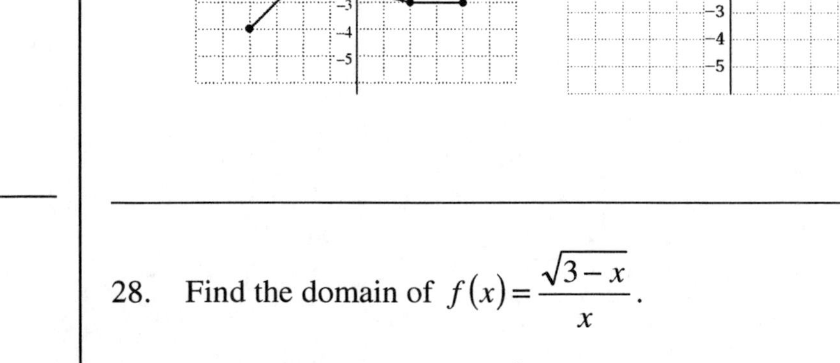

---

28. Find the domain of $f(x) = \dfrac{\sqrt{3-x}}{x}$.

CHAPTER 1 NAME________________________

TEST FORM C CLASS_____SCORE_____GRADE_____

---

1. Graph: $-2x+3y=6$.

2. Find the distance between (–5, 8) and (3, –2).

3. Find the midpoint of the segment with endpoints (7, –2) and (10, 4).

4. Find an equation of the circle with center (–2, 0) and radius 16.

5. Find the center and the radius of the circle $(x+3)^2+(y-6)^2=11$.

6. a) Determine whether the relation $\{(2, 1), (3, 2), (-1, 1), (0, -2)\}$ is a function. Answer "yes" or "no."

   b) Find the domain of the relation.

7. Given that $f(x)=2x^2+6$, find
   a) $f(-3)$; b) $f(x+a)$.

8. a) Graph: $f(x)=|x+3|-2$.

   b) Visually estimate the range of $f(x)$.

ANSWERS

1. See graph.
2. ______________
3. ______________
4. ______________
5. ______________
6. a) ______________
   b) ______________
7. a) ______________
   b) ______________
8. a) See graph.
   b) ______________

CHAPTER 1 **NAME**____________________

TEST FORM C

ANSWERS

9. __________

10. a) __________
    b) __________

11. __________

12. __________

13. __________

14. __________

15. __________

16. __________

17. __________

9. Find the domain of $f(x) = \dfrac{4-x}{3+x}$.

10. Determine whether each graph is that of a function. Answer "yes" or "no."
    a) b)

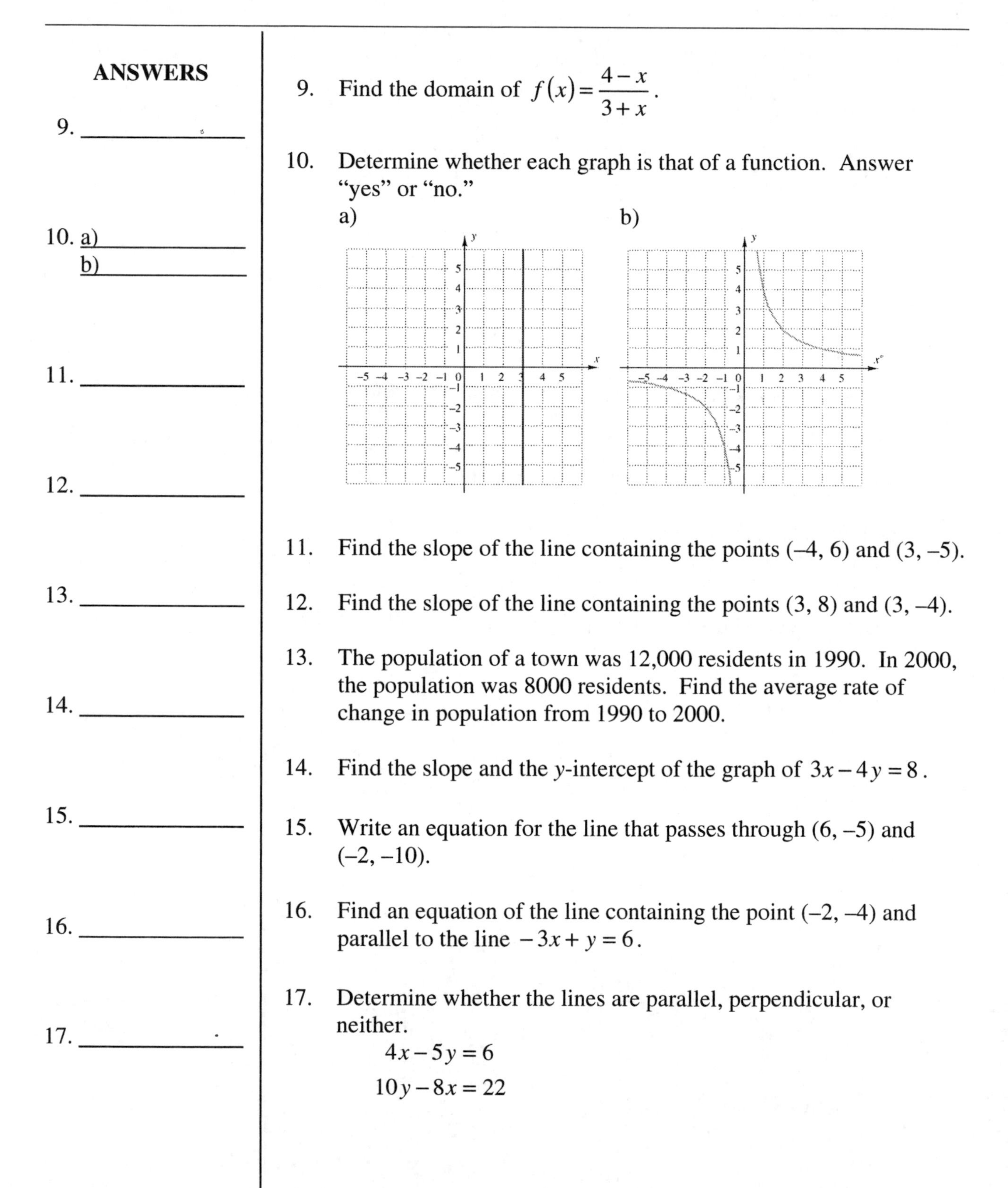

11. Find the slope of the line containing the points (–4, 6) and (3, –5).

12. Find the slope of the line containing the points (3, 8) and (3, –4).

13. The population of a town was 12,000 residents in 1990. In 2000, the population was 8000 residents. Find the average rate of change in population from 1990 to 2000.

14. Find the slope and the *y*-intercept of the graph of $3x - 4y = 8$.

15. Write an equation for the line that passes through (6, –5) and (–2, –10).

16. Find an equation of the line containing the point (–2, –4) and parallel to the line $-3x + y = 6$.

17. Determine whether the lines are parallel, perpendicular, or neither.

$$4x - 5y = 6$$
$$10y - 8x = 22$$

CHAPTER 1 **NAME**____________________________

TEST FORM C

18. The table below shows the comparison of the cost, in dollars, of a $100,000 life insurance policy for female nonsmokers at certain ages.

Age, a	Cost, C
31	170
32	172
33	176
34	178
35	182

Model the data with a linear function using age 32 and 35. Then predict the cost of life insurance for a female non-smoker of age 40.

19. Graph:

$$f(x)=\begin{cases} |x|, \text{ for } x<-2, \\ x^2, \text{ for } -2\le x\le 1, \\ -3x, \text{ for } x>1. \end{cases}$$

20. For $f(x)=-2x+4$ and $g(x)=\frac{1}{x}$, find

a) the domain of f;
b) the domain of g;
c) $(f-g)(x)$;
d) $(fg)(x)$;
e) the domain of $(f/g)(x)$.

21. Construct and simplify the difference quotient for $f(x)=x^3-x$.

For $f(x)=x^2$ and $g(x)=x-3$:

22. Find $(f\circ g)(x)$ and $(g\circ f)(x)$.

23. Find the domain of $(f\circ g)(x)$ and $(g\circ f)(x)$.

ANSWERS

18. ________________

19. See graph.

20. a) ________________
b) ________________
c) ________________
d) ________________
e) ________________

21. ________________

22. ________________

23. ________________

CHAPTER 1 NAME________________________________

TEST FORM C

ANSWERS

24. ______________

25. ______________

26. ______________

27. See graph.

28. ______________

24. Determine whether the graph of $y = 3x^6 - 2x^4$ is symmetric with respect to the x-axis, the y-axis, and/or the origin.

25. Test algebraically whether the function $f(x) = -3x + 1$ is even, odd, or neither even nor odd. Show your work.

26. Write an equation for a function that has the shape of $y = x^3$, but shifted left 4 units and up 6 units.

27. The graph of a function $y = f(x)$ is shown below. No formula for f is given. Make a graph of $y = f(x - 2)$.

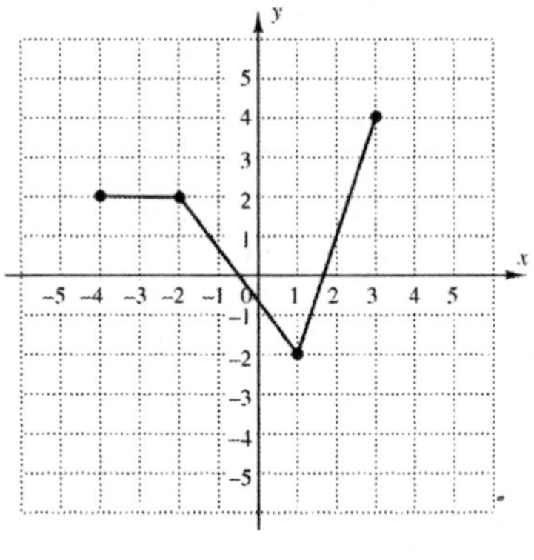

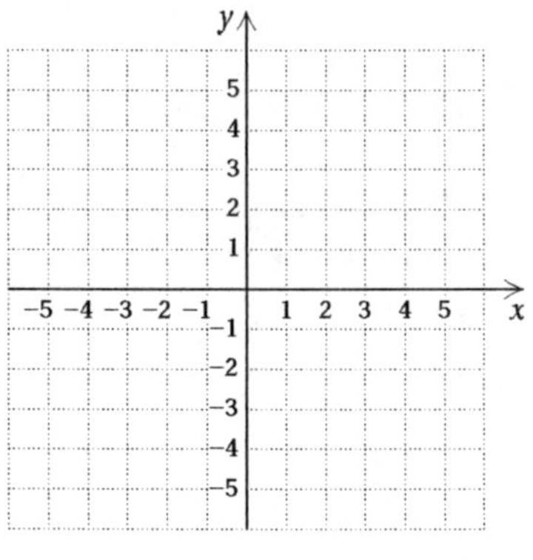

---

28. Find the domain of $f(x) = \dfrac{\sqrt{16 - x}}{x^3}$

CHAPTER 1 NAME______________________________

TEST FORM D CLASS_____ SCORE_____ GRADE_____

---

1. Graph: $x - 5y = 5$.

2. Find the distance between (4, –6) and (–7, –9).

3. Find the midpoint of the segment with endpoints (3, 1) and (–8, 3).

4. Find an equation of the circle with center (0, 16) and radius $\sqrt{11}$.

5. Find the center and the radius of the circle $(x-6)^2 + (y+5)^2 = 4$.

6. a) Determine whether the relation $\{(-4, 1), (-3, 2), (-5, 1), (-2, -1)\}$ is a function. Answer "yes" or "no."

   b) Find the domain of the relation.

7. Given that $f(x) = x^2 + 3x - 4$, find

   a) $f(-2)$; b) $f(x+5)$.

8. a) Graph: $f(x) = \sqrt{x^2 - 9}$.

   b) Visually estimate the range of $f(x)$.

ANSWERS

1. See graph.
2. ______________
3. ______________
4. ______________
5. ______________
6. a) ______________
   b) ______________
7. a) ______________
   b) ______________
8. a) See graph.
   b) ______________

ANSWERS

9. ______________

10. a) ______________
    b) ______________

11. ______________

12. ______________

13. ______________

14. ______________

15. ______________

16. ______________

17. ______________

9. Find the domain of $f(x) = \dfrac{x-3}{x+6}$.

10. Determine whether each graph is that of a function. Answer "yes" or "no."

a) b)

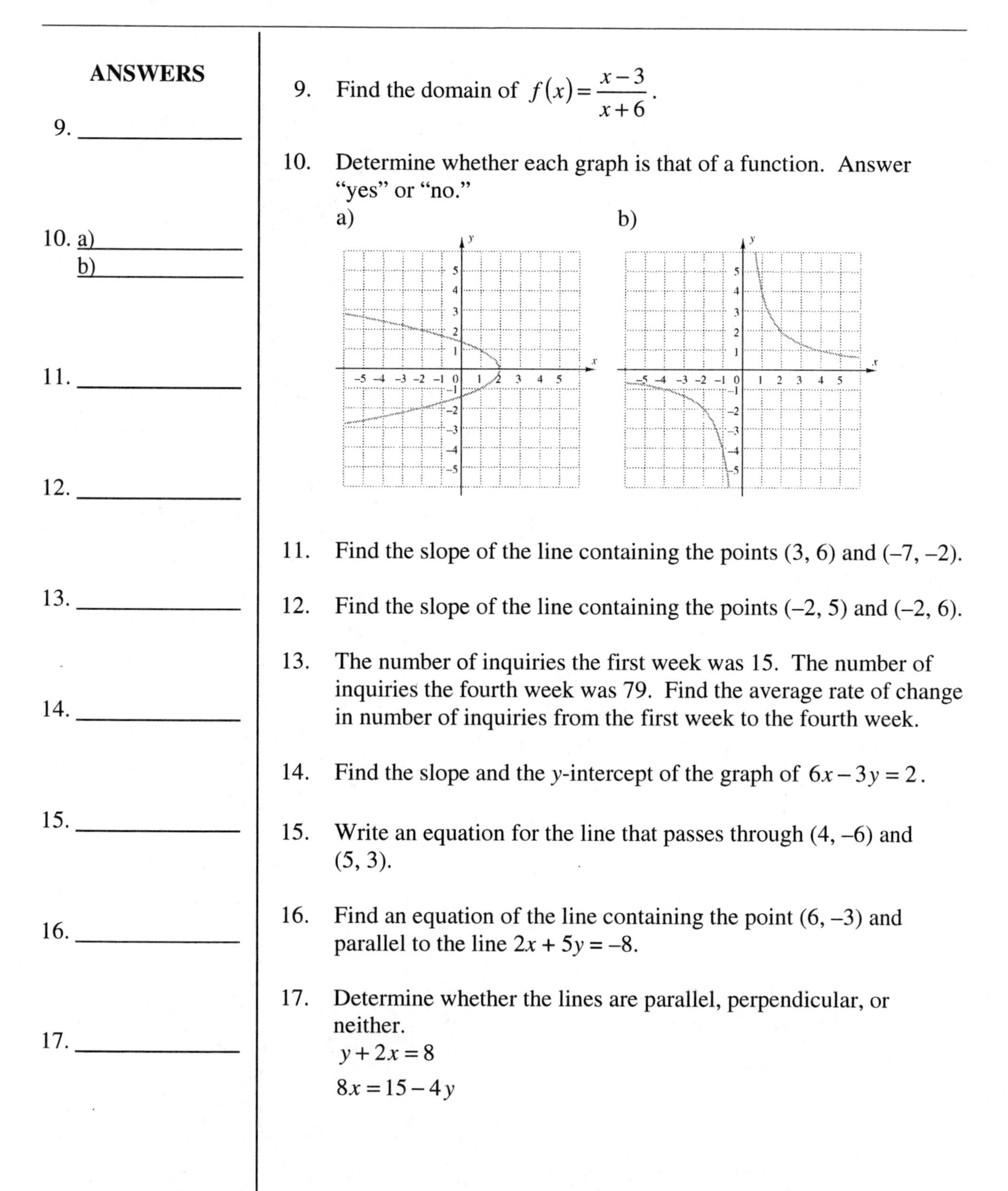

11. Find the slope of the line containing the points (3, 6) and (–7, –2).

12. Find the slope of the line containing the points (–2, 5) and (–2, 6).

13. The number of inquiries the first week was 15. The number of inquiries the fourth week was 79. Find the average rate of change in number of inquiries from the first week to the fourth week.

14. Find the slope and the y-intercept of the graph of $6x - 3y = 2$.

15. Write an equation for the line that passes through (4, –6) and (5, 3).

16. Find an equation of the line containing the point (6, –3) and parallel to the line $2x + 5y = -8$.

17. Determine whether the lines are parallel, perpendicular, or neither.

$y + 2x = 8$

$8x = 15 - 4y$

CHAPTER 1 NAME______________________________

TEST FORM D

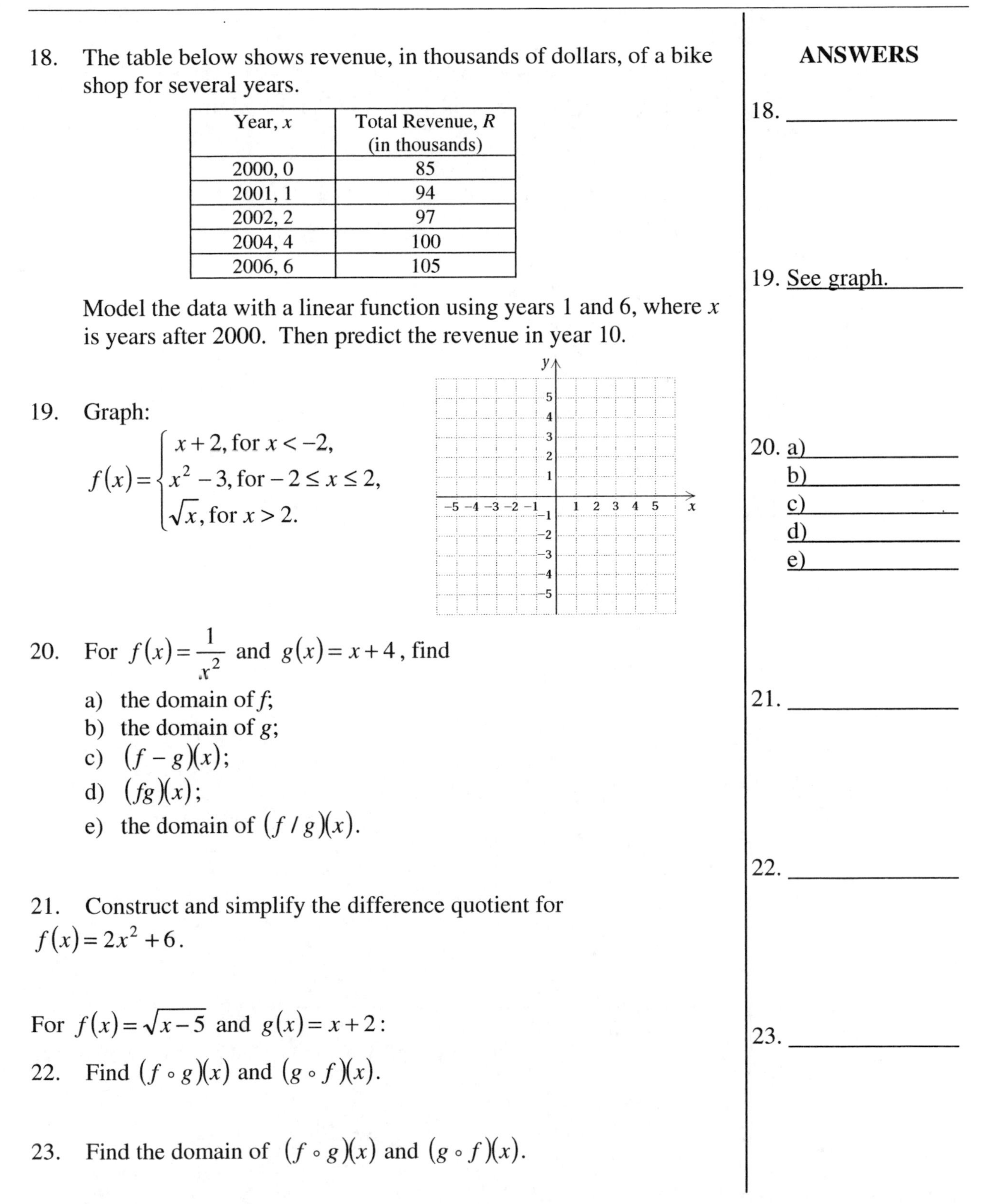

18. The table below shows revenue, in thousands of dollars, of a bike shop for several years.

Year, x	Total Revenue, R (in thousands)
2000, 0	85
2001, 1	94
2002, 2	97
2004, 4	100
2006, 6	105

Model the data with a linear function using years 1 and 6, where x is years after 2000. Then predict the revenue in year 10.

19. Graph:

$$f(x)=\begin{cases} x+2, \text{ for } x<-2, \\ x^2-3, \text{ for } -2\le x\le 2, \\ \sqrt{x}, \text{ for } x>2. \end{cases}$$

20. For $f(x)=\dfrac{1}{x^2}$ and $g(x)=x+4$, find

a) the domain of f;
b) the domain of g;
c) $(f-g)(x)$;
d) $(fg)(x)$;
e) the domain of $(f/g)(x)$.

21. Construct and simplify the difference quotient for $f(x)=2x^2+6$.

For $f(x)=\sqrt{x-5}$ and $g(x)=x+2$:

22. Find $(f\circ g)(x)$ and $(g\circ f)(x)$.

23. Find the domain of $(f\circ g)(x)$ and $(g\circ f)(x)$.

ANSWERS

18. ______________

19. See graph.

20. a) ______________
b) ______________
c) ______________
d) ______________
e) ______________

21. ______________

22. ______________

23. ______________

CHAPTER 1 **NAME**______________________________

TEST FORM D

ANSWERS

24. ______________

25. ______________

26. ______________

27. See graph.

28. ______________

24. Determine whether the graph of $y = x^3 - 2x$ is symmetric with respect to the x-axis, the y-axis, and/or the origin.

25. Test algebraically whether the function $f(x) = 8x - |x|$ is even, odd, or neither even nor odd. Show your work.

26. Write an equation for a function that has the shape of $y = \sqrt{x}$, but shifted left 5 units and down 3 units.

27. The graph of a function $y = f(x)$ is shown below. No formula for f is given. Make a graph of $y = -f(x)$.

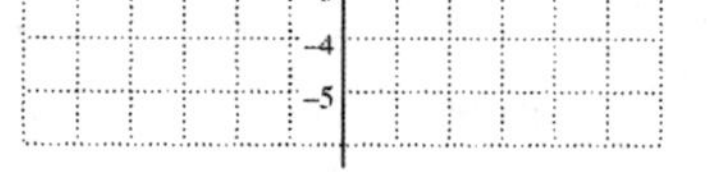

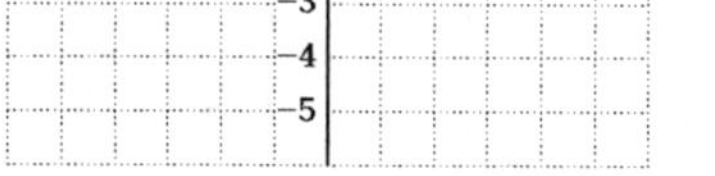

---

28. If (–10, 10) is on the graph of $y = f(x)$, what point do you know is on the graph of $y = f\left(\frac{1}{2}x\right)$?

CHAPTER 1 NAME______________________________

TEST FORM E CLASS_____ SCORE_____ GRADE_____

1. Which of the following represents the graph of $3x - 2y = -6$?

a) b) c) d)

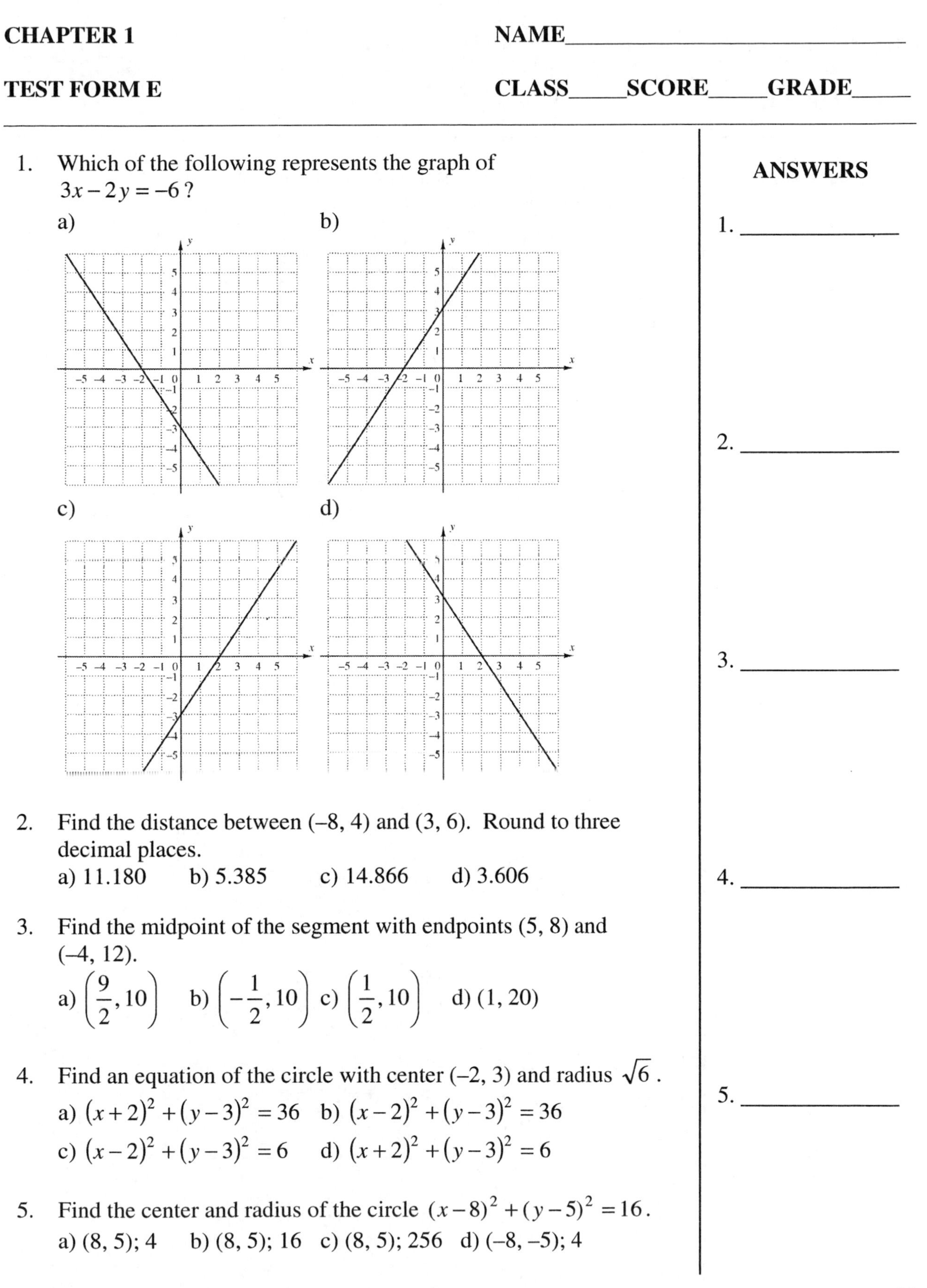

2. Find the distance between (–8, 4) and (3, 6). Round to three decimal places.
a) 11.180 b) 5.385 c) 14.866 d) 3.606

3. Find the midpoint of the segment with endpoints (5, 8) and (–4, 12).
a) $\left(\frac{9}{2}, 10\right)$ b) $\left(-\frac{1}{2}, 10\right)$ c) $\left(\frac{1}{2}, 10\right)$ d) (1, 20)

4. Find an equation of the circle with center (–2, 3) and radius $\sqrt{6}$.
a) $(x+2)^2 + (y-3)^2 = 36$ b) $(x-2)^2 + (y-3)^2 = 36$
c) $(x-2)^2 + (y-3)^2 = 6$ d) $(x+2)^2 + (y-3)^2 = 6$

5. Find the center and radius of the circle $(x-8)^2 + (y-5)^2 = 16$.
a) (8, 5); 4 b) (8, 5); 16 c) (8, 5); 256 d) (–8, –5); 4

ANSWERS

1. ____________
2. ____________
3. ____________
4. ____________
5. ____________

CHAPTER 1 **NAME**______________________________

TEST FORM E

ANSWERS

6. ______________

7. ______________

8. ______________

9. ______________

10. ______________

6. Determine which relation is not a function.
   a) $\{(7,6),(8,5),(-4,2),(7,3)\}$
   b) $\{(6,5),(3,-2),(-4,5),(-2,1)\}$
   c) $\{(-1,-1),(2,3),(5,-8),(-4,2)\}$
   d) $\{(-8,-6),(-6,-8),(5,3),(3,5)\}$

7. Find the domain of the function $\{(-5,6),(2,-8),(7,12),(-2,-8)\}$.
   a) $\{6,-8,12\}$ b) $\{-5,6,2,-8,7,12,-2\}$
   c) $\{-5,2,7,-2\}$ d) $\{6,2,7,12\}$

8. Given that $f(x)=4-x^3$, find $f(-3)$.
   a) 13 b) 31 c) –23 d) –5

9. Given that $f(x)=4-x^2$, find $f(x-2)$.
   a) $8-2x$ b) $-x^2$
   c) $4x-x^2$ d) $-x^2-4x$

10. Which of the following represents the graph of $f(x)=|x-4|+2$?

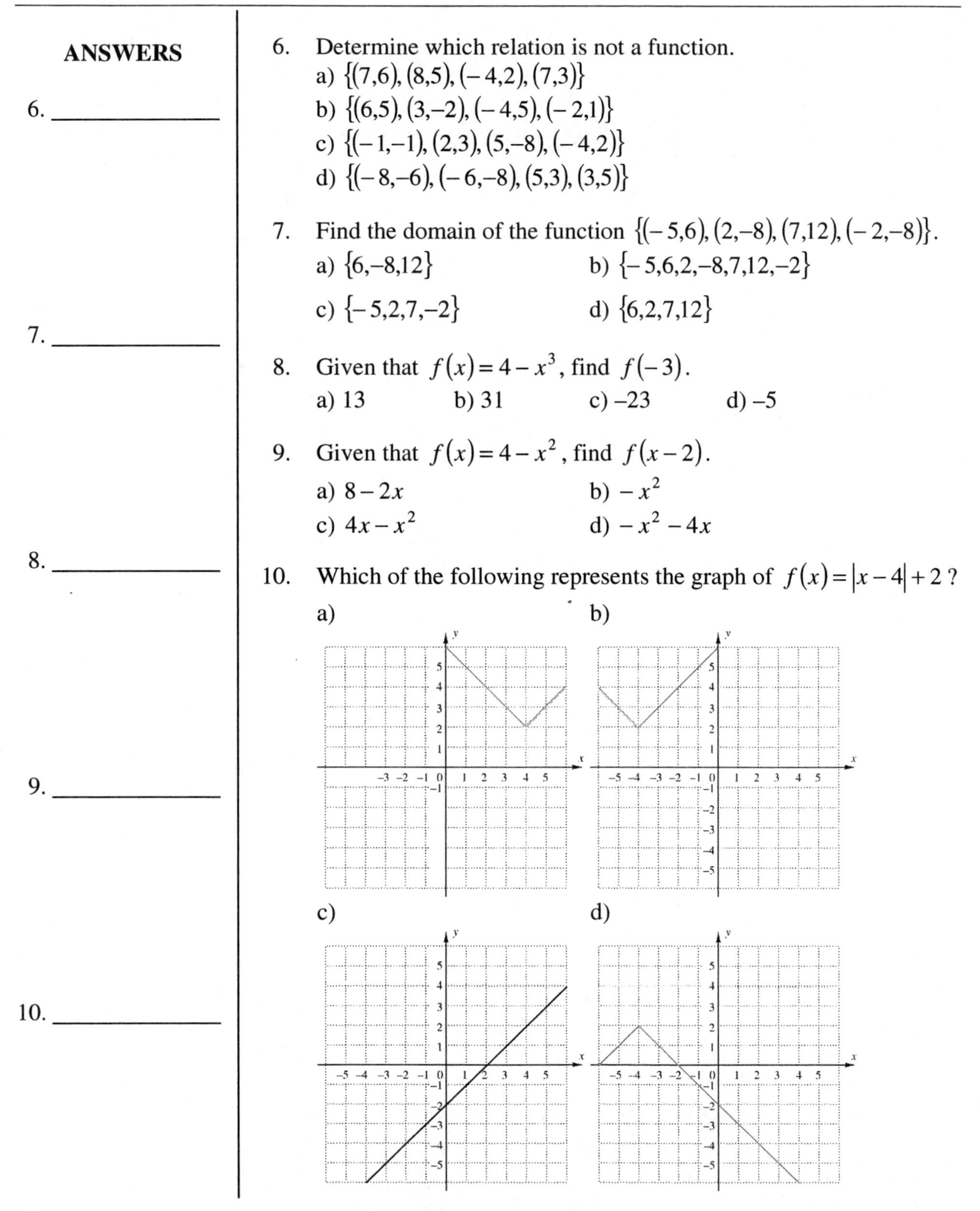

CHAPTER 1 **NAME**______________________

TEST FORM E

---

11. Find the domain of $f(x)=\dfrac{x-5}{2-x}$.

    a) $(-\infty,5)\cup(5,\infty)$ b) $(-\infty,-2)\cup-(2,\infty)$
    c) $(-\infty,2)\cup(2,5)\cup(5,\infty)$ d) $(-\infty,2)\cup(2,\infty)$

12. Determine which of the following graphs does not represent a function.

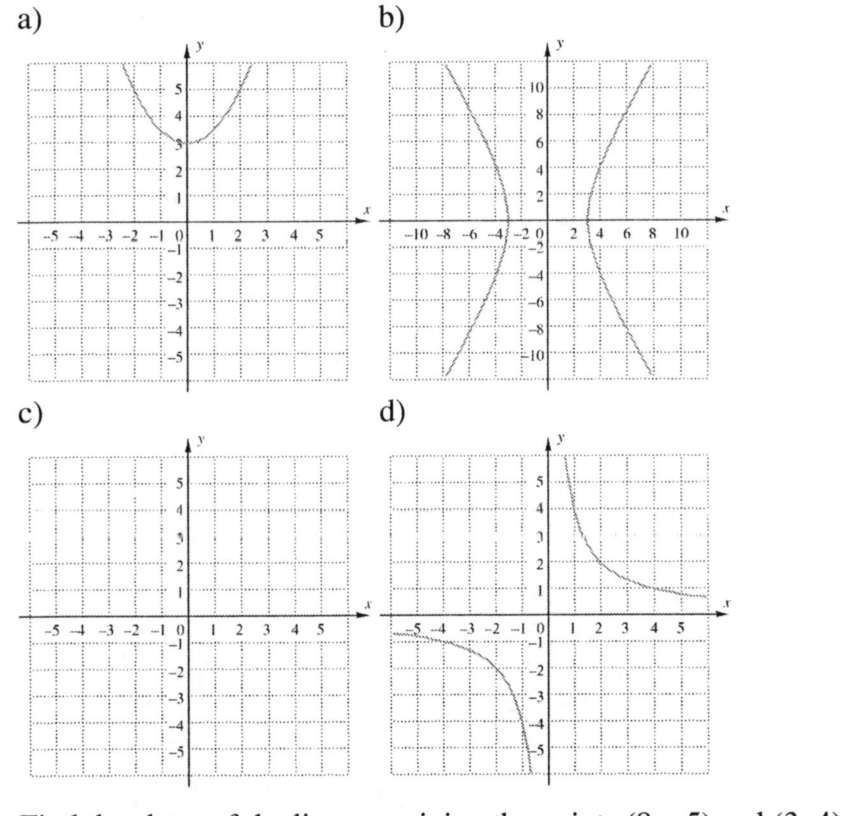

13. Find the slope of the line containing the points (8, –5) and (3, 4).

    a) $-\dfrac{5}{9}$ b) $-\dfrac{1}{5}$ c) $\dfrac{9}{5}$ d) $-\dfrac{9}{5}$

14. Jess had packed 6 crates by 8 a.m. By 11 a.m., she had packed 24 crates. Find the average rate of change in crates packed from 8 a.m. to 11 a.m.

    a) 4.5 crates/hr b) 18 crates/hr
    c) 8 crates/hr d) 6 crates/hr

ANSWERS

11. ______________

12. ______________

13. ______________

14. ______________

ANSWERS

15. ______________

16. ______________

17. ______________

18. ______________

19. ______________

15. Find the y-intercept of the graph $6x-4y=-5$.

a) $\left(0,-\frac{5}{4}\right)$ b) $\left(-\frac{5}{6},0\right)$ c) $\left(0,-\frac{4}{5}\right)$ d) $\left(0,\frac{5}{4}\right)$

16. Find the equation of the line that passes through $(4,-3)$ and $(8,-5)$.

a) $y=-\frac{1}{2}x-1$ b) $y=-2x+11$

c) $y=-2x+5$ d) $y=\frac{1}{2}x+1$

17. Find the equation of the line containing the point $(-1,-3)$ and perpendicular to the line $-2x+3y=6$.

a) $y=\frac{2}{3}x-\frac{7}{3}$ b) $y=-\frac{3}{2}x-\frac{3}{2}$

c) $y=-\frac{3}{2}x-\frac{9}{2}$ d) $y=\frac{3}{2}x-\frac{3}{2}$

18. The table below shows the study time for a particular chapter in a math class and the corresponding test grade for that chapter.

Study Time (in min), t	Test Grade (in percent), G
40	77
60	83
120	85
200	91
300	95

Model the data with a linear function using 60 min and 120 min.

a) $G(t)=\frac{1}{30}t+83$ b) $G(t)=\frac{1}{30}t+81$

c) $G(t)=30t+81$ d) $G(t)=\frac{1}{20}t+83$

19. Use the function in Exercise 18 to predict the test grade for a student who studies 240 min.

a) 89 b) 87 c) 95 d) 91

CHAPTER 1 NAME______________________

TEST FORM E

ANSWERS

20. For $f(x)=x^2-5$ and $g(x)=\sqrt{x}$, find $h(x)=(fg)(x)$.
    a) $h(x)=x^2-5+\sqrt{x}$ b) $h(x)=x-5$
    c) $h(x)=x^2\sqrt{x}-5\sqrt{x}$ d) $h(x)=\sqrt{x^2-5}$

20. ____________

21. Construct and simplify the difference quotient for $f(x)=3+5x$.
    a) $5h$ b) 5
    c) $3+5x-5h$ d) 3

21. ____________

22. For $f(x)=x+4$ and $g(x)=2x^2$, find $h(x)=(g\circ f)(x)$.
    a) $h(x)=2x^2+4$ b) $h(x)=2x^3+8x^2$
    c) $h(x)=2x^2+16x+32$ d) $h(x)=2x^2+x+4$

22. ____________

23. Which of the following functions is symmetric with respect to the y-axis?
    a) $f(x)=5-x^2$ b) $f(x)=x$
    c) $f(x)=5x^3$ d) $f(x)=\sqrt{x}$

23. ____________

24. Which of the following functions is even?
    a) $y=16-x^2$ b) $y=2x^3$
    c) $y=4x-6$ d) $y=\sqrt{x}$

24. ____________

25. Write an equation for a function that has the shape of $y=|x|$, but is shifted right 2 units and down 6 units.
    a) $f(x)=|x+2|-6$ b) $f(x)=|x-2|+6$
    c) $f(x)=|x+2|+6$ d) $f(x)=|x-2|-6$

25. ____________

ANSWERS

26. _______________

27. _______________

26. The graph of $y = f(x)$ is given. Which graph below represents the graph of $y = f(x) + 3$?

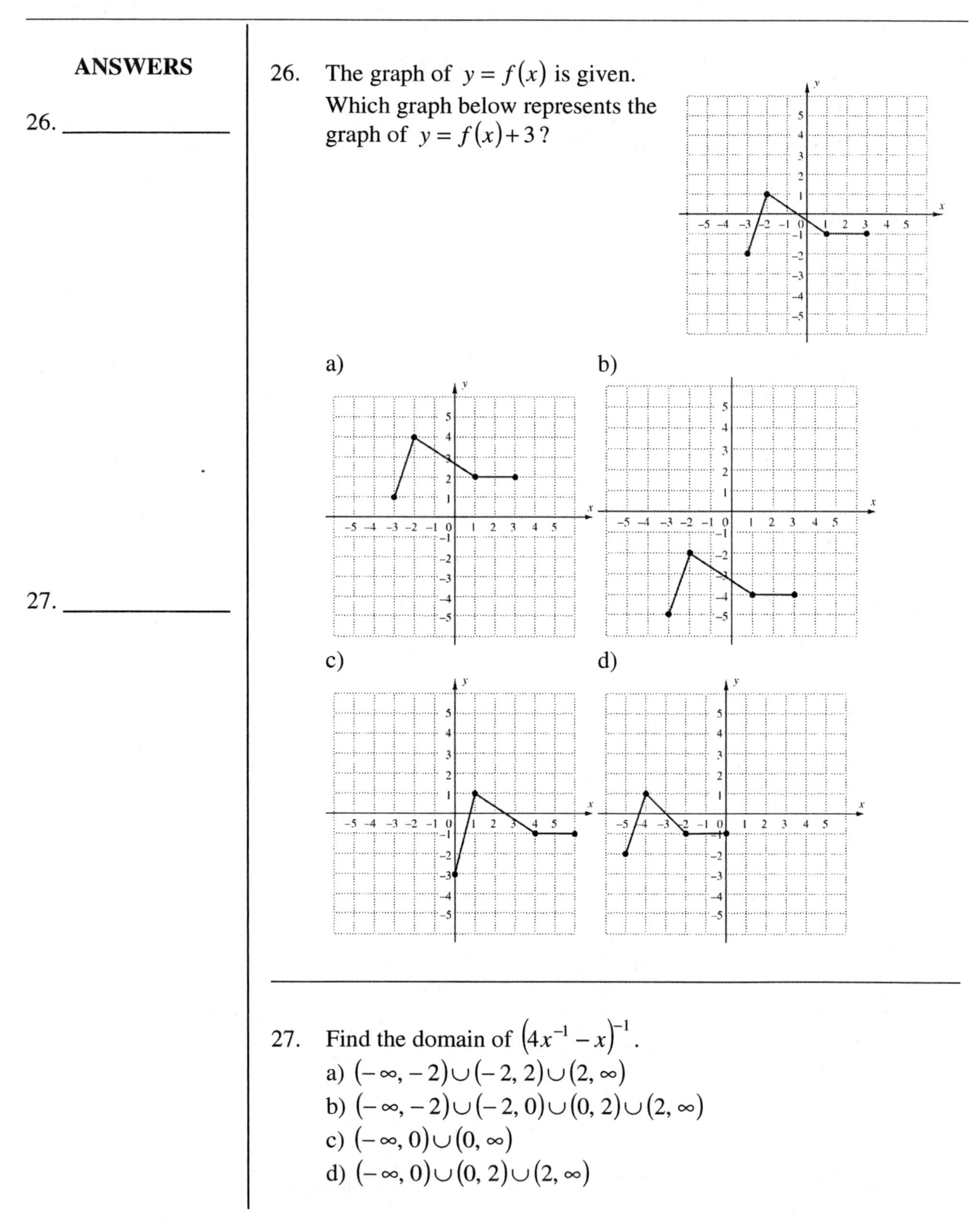

a)

b)

c)

d)

27. Find the domain of $\left(4x^{-1} - x\right)^{-1}$.

a) $(-\infty, -2) \cup (-2, 2) \cup (2, \infty)$

b) $(-\infty, -2) \cup (-2, 0) \cup (0, 2) \cup (2, \infty)$

c) $(-\infty, 0) \cup (0, \infty)$

d) $(-\infty, 0) \cup (0, 2) \cup (2, \infty)$

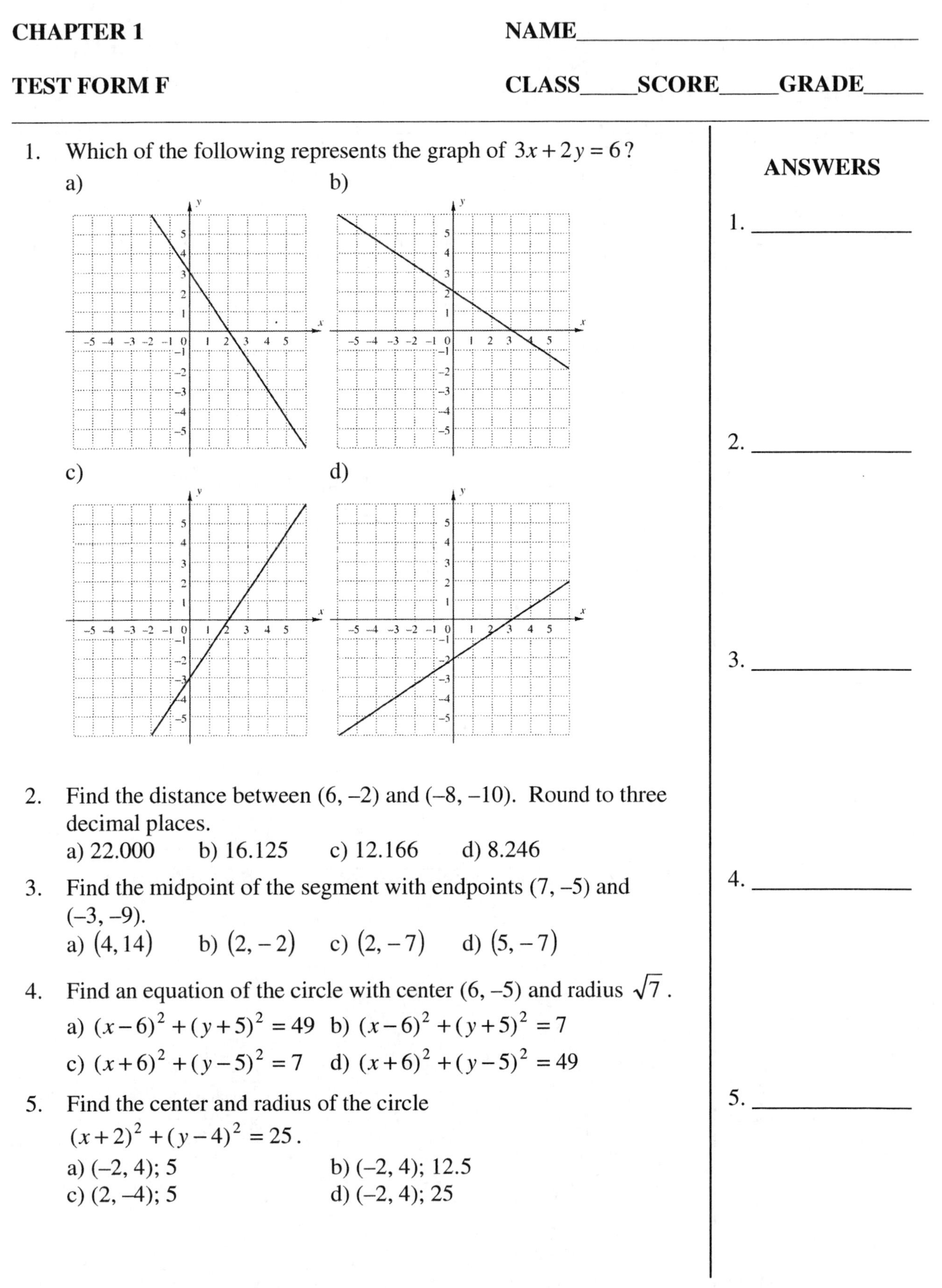

CHAPTER 1 NAME______________________

TEST FORM F CLASS____ SCORE____ GRADE____

1. Which of the following represents the graph of $3x+2y=6$?

   a) b)

   c) d)

2. Find the distance between (6, –2) and (–8, –10). Round to three decimal places.

   a) 22.000 b) 16.125 c) 12.166 d) 8.246

3. Find the midpoint of the segment with endpoints (7, –5) and (–3, –9).

   a) $(4, 14)$ b) $(2, -2)$ c) $(2, -7)$ d) $(5, -7)$

4. Find an equation of the circle with center (6, –5) and radius $\sqrt{7}$.

   a) $(x-6)^2+(y+5)^2=49$ b) $(x-6)^2+(y+5)^2=7$

   c) $(x+6)^2+(y-5)^2=7$ d) $(x+6)^2+(y-5)^2=49$

5. Find the center and radius of the circle $(x+2)^2+(y-4)^2=25$.

   a) (–2, 4); 5 b) (–2, 4); 12.5

   c) (2, –4); 5 d) (–2, 4); 25

ANSWERS

1. ____________
2. ____________
3. ____________
4. ____________
5. ____________

CHAPTER 1 NAME______________________

TEST FORM F

ANSWERS

6. ______________

7. ______________

8. ______________

9. ______________

10. ______________

6. Determine which relation is a function.
a) $\{(5,-8),(6,3),(5,4),(2,0)\}$
b) $\{(0,1),(1,2),(-1,2),(0,-1)\}$
c) $\{(3,-4),(8,-4),(5,-2),(2,4)\}$
d) $\{(2,4),(5,8),(5,3),(7,6)\}$

7. Find the domain of the function $\{(4,-8),(-2,1),(6,-5),(-3,-6)\}$.
a) $\{8,1,-5,-6\}$ b) $\{4,8,2,1,6,-5,-3,-6\}$
c) $\{4,-2,6,-3\}$ d) $\{1,4,6,8\}$

8. Given that $f(x)=6x^2+x-1$, find $f(-2)$.
a) -27 b) 25 c) 141 d) 21

9. Given that $f(x)=6x^2+x-1$, find $f(x+1)$.
a) $6x^2+x+6$ b) $6x^2+13x+6$
c) $6x^2+x+1$ d) $6x^2+13x+5$

10. Which of the following represents the graph of $f(x)=x^3-2$?

a)

y
5 4 3 2 1
x
−5 −4 −3 −2 −1 0 1 2 3 4 5
−1 −2 −3 −4 −5

b)

y
5 4 3 2 1
x
−5 −4 −3 −2 −1 0 1 2 3 4 5
−1 −2 −3 −4 −5

c)

y
5 4 3 2 1
x
−5 −4 −3 −2 −1 0 1 2 3 4 5
−1 −2 −3 −4 −5

d)

y
5 4 3 2 1
x
−5 −4 −3 −2 −1 0 1 2 3 4 5
−1 −2 −3 −4 −5

CHAPTER 1 **NAME**________________________

TEST FORM F

ANSWERS

11. __________

12. __________

13. __________

14. __________

---

11. Find the domain of $f(x)=\dfrac{4-x}{x+2}$.

a) $(-\infty,-2)\cup(-2,\infty)$ b) $(-\infty,-2)\cup(-2,4)\cup(4,\infty)$
c) $(-\infty,4)\cup(4,\infty)$ d) $(-\infty,2)\cup(2,\infty)$

12. Determine which of the following graphs does not represent a function.

a) b)

c) d)

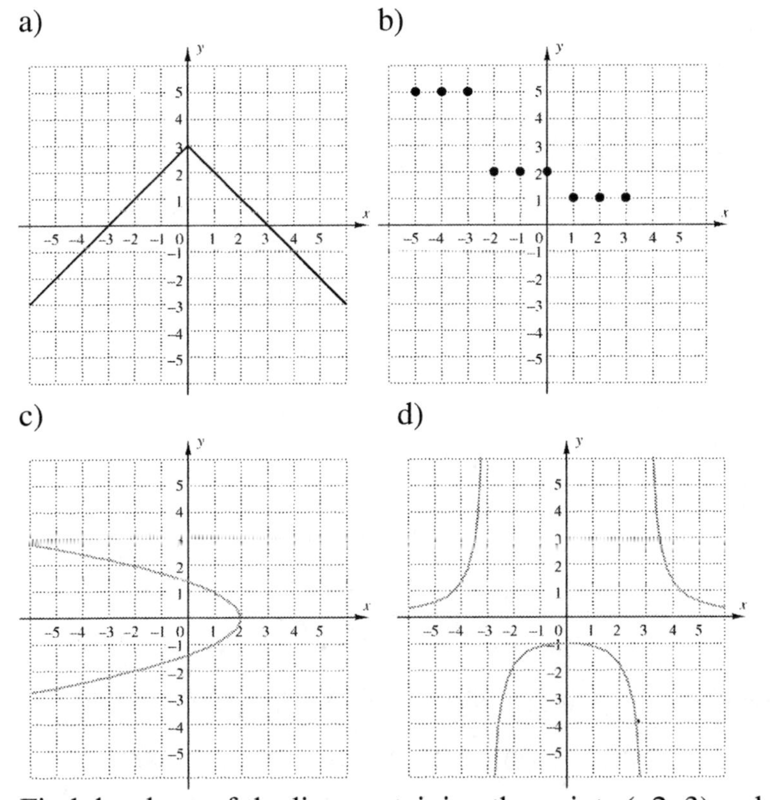

13. Find the slope of the line containing the points (–2, 3) and (–8, –6).

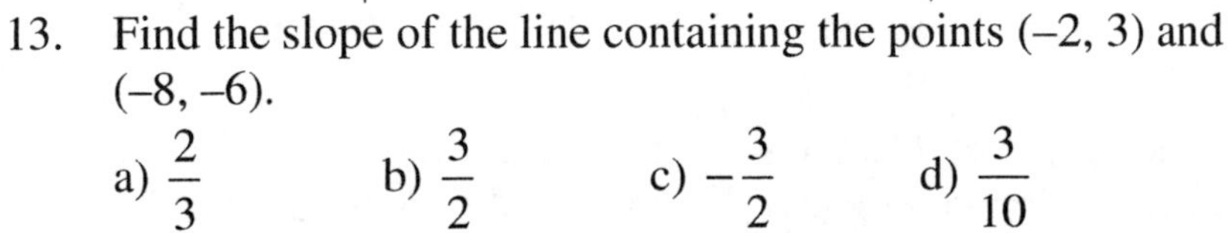

a) $\dfrac{2}{3}$ b) $\dfrac{3}{2}$ c) $-\dfrac{3}{2}$ d) $\dfrac{3}{10}$

14. Joe's Used Cars sold 50 cars in 2001. In 2006, they sold 180 cars. Find the average rate of change in cars sold from 2001 to 2006.

a) increased 32.5 cars/yr b) increased 21.7 cars/yr
c) increased 130 cars/yr d) increased 26 cars/yr

ANSWERS

15. ____________

16. ____________

17. ____________

18. ____________

19. ____________

15. Find the y-intercept of the graph $-3x+4y=-8$.

a) (0, –2) b) (0, 2) c) $\left(\frac{8}{3}, 0\right)$ d) $\left(0, \frac{8}{3}\right)$

16. Find the equation of the line that passes through $(7,6)$ and $(8,9)$.

a) $y=-3x+27$ b) $y=\frac{1}{3}x+\frac{11}{3}$

c) $y=3x-15$ d) $y=3x+15$

17. Find the equation of the line containing the point (–2, 6) and parallel to the line $4x+5y=12$.

a) $y=-\frac{4}{5}x-\frac{14}{5}$ b) $y=-\frac{4}{5}x+\frac{22}{5}$

c) $y=\frac{4}{5}x+\frac{38}{5}$ d) $y=-\frac{4}{5}x-\frac{22}{5}$

18. The table below shows the average yearly income, in dollars, of individuals based on years of schooling.

Years of Schooling, x	Average Income, I
8	$16,000
10	$19,000
12	$25,000
14	$28,000

Model the data with a linear function using 10 years and 14 years.

a) $I(x)=2250x-3500$ b) $I(x)=2250x+16{,}000$

c) $I(x)=2250x+19{,}000$ d) $I(x)=9000x=3500$

19. Use the function in Exercise 18 to estimate the average yearly income for an individual with 16 years of schooling.

a) $52,000 b) $37,600 c) $34,000 d) $32,500

CHAPTER 1 **NAME**____________________

TEST FORM F

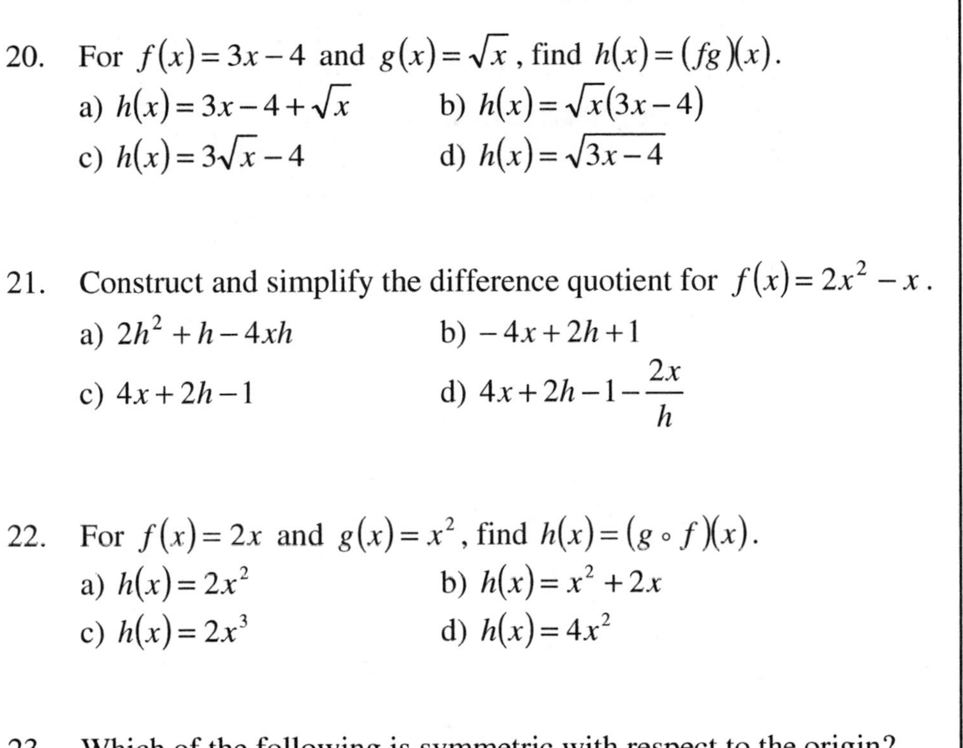

20. For $f(x)=3x-4$ and $g(x)=\sqrt{x}$, find $h(x)=(fg)(x)$.
   a) $h(x)=3x-4+\sqrt{x}$ b) $h(x)=\sqrt{x}(3x-4)$
   c) $h(x)=3\sqrt{x}-4$ d) $h(x)=\sqrt{3x-4}$

21. Construct and simplify the difference quotient for $f(x)=2x^2-x$.
   a) $2h^2+h-4xh$ b) $-4x+2h+1$
   c) $4x+2h-1$ d) $4x+2h-1-\dfrac{2x}{h}$

22. For $f(x)=2x$ and $g(x)=x^2$, find $h(x)=(g\circ f)(x)$.
   a) $h(x)=2x^2$ b) $h(x)=x^2+2x$
   c) $h(x)=2x^3$ d) $h(x)=4x^2$

23. Which of the following is symmetric with respect to the origin?
   a) $y=(x-4)^2$ b) $x=y^2$
   c) $y=-|x|-2$ d) $y=x-x^3$

24. Which of the following functions is even?
   a) $f(x)=2x+8$ b) $f(x)=\sqrt{4-x^2}$
   c) $f(x)=x^2+x$ d) $f(x)=\sqrt[4]{x}$

25. Write an equation for a function that has the shape of $y=x^2$, but is shifted left 3 units and up 4 units.
   a) $f(x)=(x+3)^2+4$ b) $f(x)=(x-3)^2+4$
   c) $f(x)=(x-3)^2-4$ d) $f(x)=(x+3)^2-4$

ANSWERS

20. __________

21. __________

22. __________

23. __________

24. __________

25. __________

ANSWERS

26. ______________

27. ______________

26. The graph of $y = f(x)$ is given. Which graph below represents the graph of $y = f(x) - 1$?

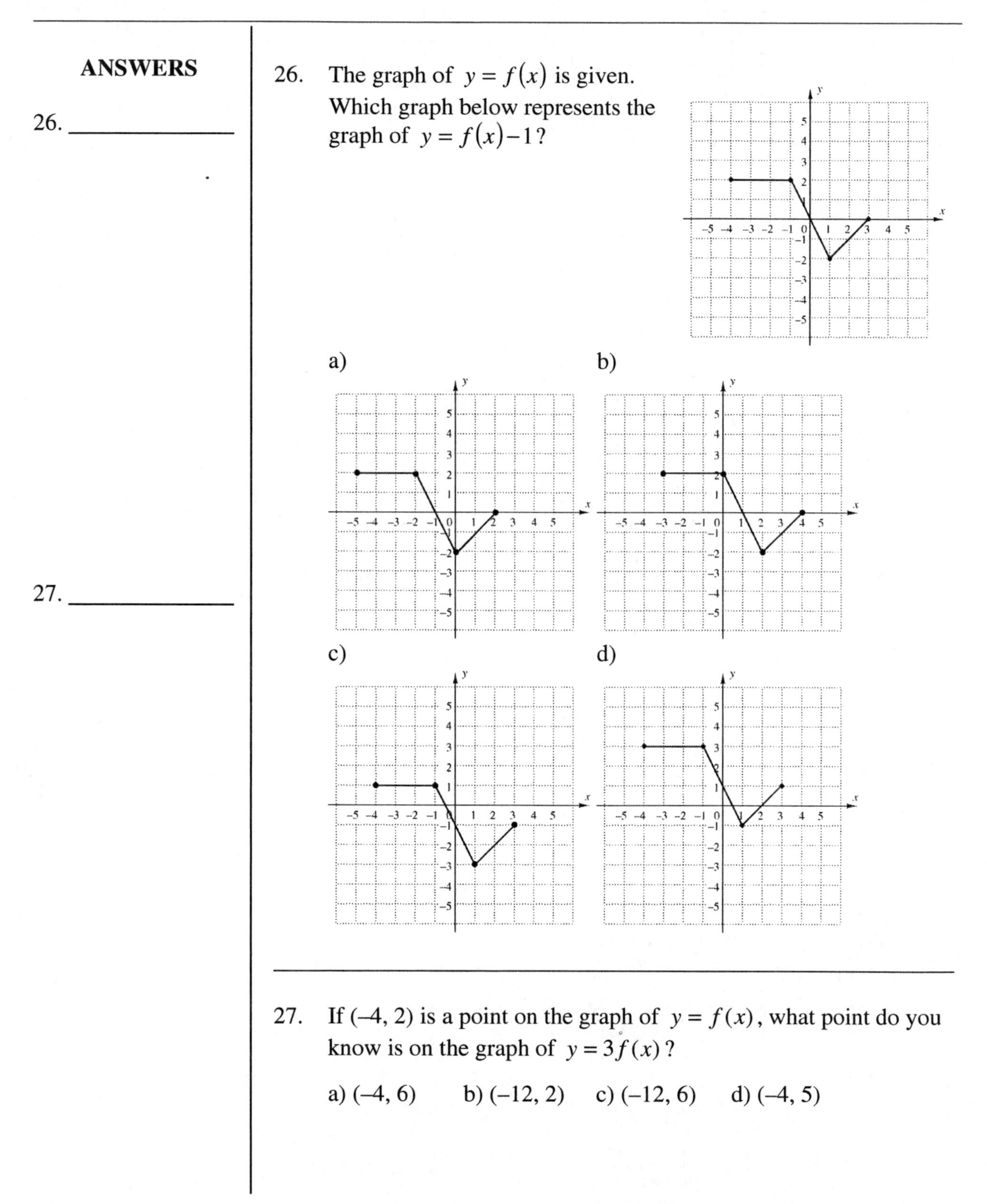

a) b) c) d)

27. If (–4, 2) is a point on the graph of $y = f(x)$, what point do you know is on the graph of $y = 3f(x)$?

a) (–4, 6) b) (–12, 2) c) (–12, 6) d) (–4, 5)

CHAPTER 2 NAME____________________

TEST FORM A CLASS_____ SCORE_____ GRADE_____

Solve. Find exact solutions.

1. $-3x+2=15$
2. $9(y-2)=8y+14$
3. $(2x-5)(x+8)=0$
4. $4x^2-64=0$
5. $y^2+25=0$
6. $x^2+5x-24=0$
7. $3x^2-2x-6=0$
8. $5m^2+2m+2=0$
9. $x-5\sqrt{x}-24=0$
10. $\dfrac{3}{x+5}-\dfrac{11}{3x-1}=-1$
11. $\sqrt{6+2n}-2=2$
12. $\sqrt{4x-11}+2=\sqrt{6x-5}$
13. $|5x+4|=13$

Solve and write interval notation for the solution set.

14. $-1<3x-5\le 8$
15. $3x-2\le -3$ *or* $4x+1\ge 2$
16. $|x+5|<8$
17. $|x+6|\ge 10$
18. Solve $P=2w+2l$ for w.
19. Solve $\dfrac{1}{a}+\dfrac{1}{b}=8$ for b.
20. Solve $x^2-3x=12$ by completing the square. Find exact solutions. Show your work.
21. A boat travels 10 mi upstream and 10 mi downstream. The total time for both parts of the trip is $5\frac{1}{3}$ hr. The speed of the stream is 1 mph. What is the speed of the boat in still water?

ANSWERS

1. ______________
2. ______________
3. ______________
4. ______________
5. ______________
6. ______________
7. ______________
8. ______________
9. ______________
10. ______________
11. ______________
12. ______________
13. ______________
14. ______________
15. ______________
16. ______________
17. ______________
18. ______________
19. ______________
20. ______________
21. ______________

CHAPTER 2 NAME________________________________

TEST FORM A

ANSWERS

22. ______________
23. ______________
24. ______________
25. ______________
26. ______________
27. ______________
28. ______________
29. ______________
30. ______________
31. ______________
32. a) ______________
    b) ______________
    c) ______________
    d) ______________
    e) See graph.
33. ______________
34. ______________

22. A parking lot has a perimeter of 500 ft. The width is 20 ft less than the length. Find the dimensions.

Express in terms of i.

23. $\sqrt{-13}$

24. $-\sqrt{-121}$

Simplify.

25. $(5-3i)-(6+2i)$

26. $(7+6i)(4-3i)$

27. $\dfrac{3-2i}{7+i}$

28. i^{18}

Find the zero(s) of each function.

29. $f(x)=3x+1$

30. $f(x)=3x^2+25x-18$

31. $f(x)=x^2+6x-15$

32. For the graph of the function $f(x)=x^2-6x+4$,
    a) find the vertex;
    b) find the line of symmetry;
    c) state whether there is a maximum or minimum value and find that value;
    d) find the range;
    e) graph the function.

33. A homeowner wants to fence a rectangular garden using 60 ft of fencing. An existing stone wall will be used as one side of the rectangle. Find the dimensions for which the area is a maximum.

---

34. Find a such that $f(x)=ax^2+5x+6$ has a minimum value of $7\frac{1}{24}$.

CHAPTER 2 NAME______________________

TEST FORM B CLASS_____ SCORE_____ GRADE_____

Solve. Find exact solutions.

1. $-8x+3=-24$
2. $3(y+4)=8y-13$
3. $(4x+5)(x-9)=0$
4. $8x^2-24=0$
5. $y^2+49=0$
6. $x^2-8x+12=0$
7. $4x^2-9x+2=0$
8. $x^2-x+5=0$
9. $x+5\sqrt{x}-24=0$
10. $\dfrac{70}{x-6}+\dfrac{42}{2x+1}=-13$
11. $\sqrt{8x+28}-6=-4$
12. $\sqrt{3x+7}-\sqrt{10-x}=3$
13. $|3x+2|=11$

Solve and write interval notation for the solution set.

14. $-4\le 3x+1<7$
15. $5x+3<-4$ or $3x+5\ge 6$
16. $|x-3|<10$
17. $|x-4|\ge 2$
18. Solve $A=P+Prt$ for t.
19. Solve $\dfrac{3}{m}-2n=6$ for m.
20. Solve $x^2-4x=2$ by completing the square. Find exact solutions. Show your work.
21. The speed of the current in a river is 2 mph. Jay travels 20 mi upstream and then 20 mi downstream in a total time of $5\frac{1}{3}$ hr. Find the speed of his boat.

ANSWERS

1. ____________
2. ____________
3. ____________
4. ____________
5. ____________
6. ____________
7. ____________
8. ____________
9. ____________
10. ____________
11. ____________
12. ____________
13. ____________
14. ____________
15. ____________
16. ____________
17. ____________
18. ____________
19. ____________
20. ____________
21. ____________

CHAPTER 2 **NAME**__________________________

TEST FORM B

ANSWERS

22. ______________
23. ______________
24. ______________
25. ______________
26. ______________
27. ______________
28. ______________
29. ______________
30. ______________
31. ______________
32. a) ______________
    b) ______________
    c) ______________
    d) ______________
    e) See graph.
33. ______________
34. ______________

22. The hypotenuse of a right triangle is 65 ft. One leg is 35 ft longer than the other. What are the lengths of the legs?

Express in terms of i.

23. $\sqrt{-6}$

24. $-\sqrt{-100}$

Simplify.

25. $(4-2i)-(8+3i)$

26. $(4-i)(6+i)$

27. $\dfrac{3+6i}{5+i}$

28. i^{34}

Find the zero(s) of each function.

29. $f(x)=6x+3$

30. $f(x)=6x^2+13x-15$

31. $f(x)=5x^2-3x-3$

32. For the graph of the function $f(x)=2x^2-12x+20$,
    a) find the vertex;
    b) find the line of symmetry;
    c) state whether there is a maximum or minimum value and find that value;
    d) find the range;
    e) graph the function.

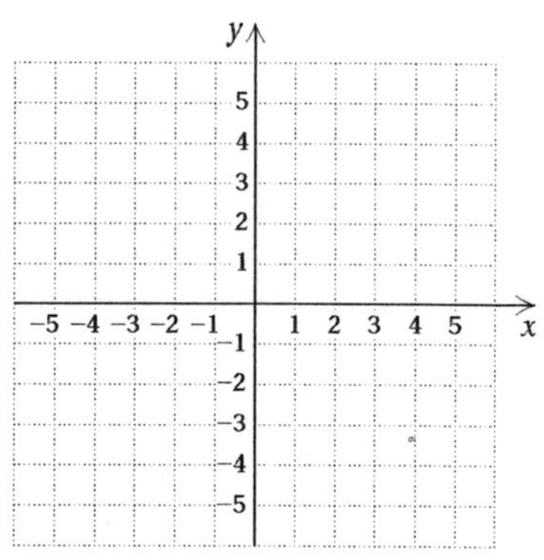

33. Doreen's Catering charges \$150 for set up plus \$12 per person for parties under 100 people. Jackson's Catering charges \$18 per person for parties under 100 people. For what size party is Jackson's a better deal? Assume that the party will be under 100 people.

---

34. Solve $(x-2)^{5/4}=32$.

CHAPTER 2 NAME________________________

TEST FORM C CLASS_____ SCORE_____ GRADE_____

Solve. Find exact solutions.

1. $4x-6=8$
2. $3y+8=2(y-12)$
3. $(4x-3)(2x+1)=0$
4. $6x^2-24=0$
5. $x^2+16=0$
6. $x^2-2x-8=0$
7. $5x^2+17x+6=0$
8. $x^2-4x+6=0$
9. $x-10\sqrt{x}+24=0$
10. $\dfrac{12}{x-2}+\dfrac{26}{2x+1}=5$
11. $\sqrt{3x+4}+5=9$
12. $\sqrt{x+6}+1=\sqrt{2x-11}$
13. $|8m-3|=7$

Solve and write interval notation for the solution set.

14. $-6 \le 2x-3 < 5$
15. $2x \ge 9$ or $3x-5 \le -2$
16. $|x-6| < 3$
17. $|x+2| \ge 6$
18. Solve $A=\frac{1}{2}bh$ for h.
19. Solve $A=2.5\sqrt{n}$ for n.
20. Solve $x^2-6x=8$ by completing the square. Find exact solutions. Show your work.
21. It cost $27.95 per day plus $0.15 per mile to rent a car. How many miles was a car driven that was rented for one day and had a rental bill of $45.95?

ANSWERS

1. ____________
2. ____________
3. ____________
4. ____________
5. ____________
6. ____________
7. ____________
8. ____________
9. ____________
10. ____________
11. ____________
12. ____________
13. ____________
14. ____________
15. ____________
16. ____________
17. ____________
18. ____________
19. ____________
20. ____________
21. ____________

CHAPTER 2 **NAME**____________________

TEST FORM C

ANSWERS

22. ______________
23. ______________
24. ______________
25. ______________
26. ______________
27. ______________
28. ______________
29. ______________
30. ______________
31. ______________
32. a) ______________
    b) ______________
    c) ______________
    d) ______________
    e) See graph.
33. ______________
34. ______________

22. The edges of a 20 ft by 30 ft garden are to be torn up to install a walking path of uniform width around its perimeter. The area of the new garden is three fourths of the old area. How wide is the walking path?

Express in terms of i.

23. $\sqrt{-11}$

24. $\sqrt{-12}$

Simplify.

25. $(3-2i)-(6+5i)$

26. $(3+2i)(4-i)$

27. $\dfrac{4-3i}{5+i}$

28. i^{23}

Find the zero(s) of each function.

29. $f(x)=-2x+4$

30. $f(x)=4x^2+11x+6$

31. $f(x)=2x^2+x-5$

32. For the graph of the function $f(x)=-x^2+6x-8$,
    a) find the vertex;
    b) find the line of symmetry;
    c) state whether there is a maximum or minimum value and find that value;
    d) find the range;
    e) graph the function.

y
5
4
3
2
1
−5 −4 −3 −2 −1 1 2 3 4 5 x
−1
−2
−3
−4
−5

33. The formula $F=\dfrac{9}{5}C+32$ can be used to convert Celsius temperatures to Fahrenheit temperatures. For what Celsius temperatures is the Fahrenheit temperature below 60° F?

---

34. Solve $\sqrt{\sqrt{\sqrt{x}}}=3$.

CHAPTER 2 NAME____________________

TEST FORM D CLASS____ SCORE____ GRADE____

Solve. Find exact solutions.

1. $5x - 3 = 6$
2. $3(y+4) = 6y - 9$
3. $(2x-5)(5x+3) = 0$
4. $-4x^2 + 36 = 0$
5. $x^2 + 36 = 0$
6. $x^2 - 12x + 35 = 0$
7. $x^2 - 6x + 3 = 0$
8. $x^2 - 3x + 7 = 0$
9. $x + 7\sqrt{x} - 18 = 0$
10. $\dfrac{14}{x-3} + \dfrac{10}{x+6} = 3$
11. $\sqrt{x+6} + 8 = 11$
12. $\sqrt{x+7} + 5 = 2\sqrt{6x+4}$
13. $|5 - x| = 8$

Solve and write interval notation for the solution set.

14. $-3 \le 5x + 2 < 10$
15. $4x + 6 \le 8$ or $3x > 2$
16. $|x + 2| \ge 4$
17. $|x - 5| < 14$
18. Solve $PV = nrt$ for r.
19. Solve $T = \sqrt{12.5k}$ for k.
20. Solve $x^2 + 4x = 9$ by completing the square. Find exact solutions. Show your work.
21. Rosie's Books prices its books by raising the wholesale price 40% and adding 50¢. What is the wholesale price on a book that sells for $39.95? Round to the nearest cent.

ANSWERS

1. ____________
2. ____________
3. ____________
4. ____________
5. ____________
6. ____________
7. ____________
8. ____________
9. ____________
10. ____________
11. ____________
12. ____________
13. ____________
14. ____________
15. ____________
16. ____________
17. ____________
18. ____________
19. ____________
20. ____________
21. ____________

CHAPTER 2 **NAME**________________________

TEST FORM D

ANSWERS

22. _______________

23. _______________

24. _______________

25. _______________

26. _______________

27. _______________

28. _______________

29. _______________

30. _______________

31. _______________

32. a) _______________
    b) _______________
    c) _______________
    d) _______________
    e) See graph.

33. _______________

34. _______________

22. Two trains leave the same city at the same time at right angles. One train travels at a speed of 75 km/h. In 2 hr the trains are 250 km apart. How fast is the other train traveling?

Express in terms of *i*.

23. $\sqrt{-25}$

24. $-\sqrt{-49}$

Simplify.

25. $(8-6i)-(-5+4i)$

26. $(4-3i)(4+3i)$

27. $\frac{2-i}{3+i}$

28. i^{15}

Find the zero(s) of each function.

29. $f(x)=4x-5$

30. $f(x)=2x^2-13x+6$

31. $f(x)=x^2-8x+5$

32. For the graph of the function $f(x)=-x^2-4x$,
    a) find the vertex;
    b) find the line of symmetry;
    c) state whether there is a maximum or minimum value and find that value;
    d) find the range;
    e) graph the function.

y
5
4
3
2
1
−5 −4 −3 −2 −1 1 2 3 4 5 x
−1
−2
−3
−4
−5

33. The sum of the base and the height of a triangle is 72 in. Find the base for which the area is a maximum.

---

34. Solve $(x-2)^2-40=3(x-2)$.

CHAPTER 2 NAME____________________

TEST FORM E CLASS_____ SCORE_____ GRADE_____

ANSWERS

1. Solve: $4(y-2)=10y+5$.

   a) $-\frac{6}{13}$ b) $-\frac{13}{6}$ c) $-\frac{7}{6}$ d) $\frac{1}{2}$

   1. ______________

2. Solve: $15x^2-7x-4=0$.

   a) $-\frac{1}{3},\frac{5}{4}$ b) $-\frac{4}{5},\frac{1}{3}$ c) $\frac{5}{4},-3$ d) $\frac{4}{5},-\frac{1}{3}$

   2. ______________

3. Solve: $2m^2-m+9=0$.

   a) $\frac{1\pm\sqrt{73}}{4}$ b) $\frac{1\pm\sqrt{35}i}{4}$ c) $\frac{1\pm\sqrt{71}i}{4}$ d) $\frac{1\pm\sqrt{71}i}{4}$

   3. ______________

4. Solve: $x+3\sqrt{x}-18=0$.

   a) 3 b) 81 c) $\pm\sqrt{3}$ d) 9

   4. ______________

5. Solve: $y^2+1=0$.

   a) $-i, i$ b) $-i, 1$ c) i d) $-i$

   5. ______________

6. Find one of the solutions of $\frac{5}{2x+6}+\frac{46}{7x}=2$.

   a) $\frac{1}{4}$ b) $\frac{69}{28}$ c) 4 d) 2

   6. ______________

7. Solve: $\sqrt{5x+14}+3=5$.

   a) 10 b) –2 c) $\frac{144}{25}$ d) $\frac{18}{5}$

   7. ______________

8. Solve: $|5m-6|=20$.

   a) $-\frac{14}{5},\frac{26}{5}$ b) $-\frac{26}{5},\frac{26}{5}$ c) –70, 130 d) $\frac{26}{5}$

   8. ______________

9. Solve: $|x+6|\geq 5$.

   a) $(-\infty,-11]\cup[-1,\infty)$ b) $[-11,-1]$
   c) $(-\infty,1]\cup[11,\infty)$ d) $[1,11]$

   9. ______________

10. Solve: $-10<3x+3\leq 4$.

   a) □$-\frac{13}{3},\frac{1}{3}$□ b) □$-\frac{1}{3},\frac{13}{3}$□ c) □$-\frac{13}{3},\frac{1}{3}$□ d) □$-\frac{7}{3},\frac{1}{3}$□

   10. ______________

CHAPTER 2 **NAME**______________________

TEST FORM E

ANSWERS

11. ____________
12. ____________
13. ____________
14. ____________
15. ____________
16. ____________
17. ____________
18. ____________
19. ____________
20. ____________
21. ____________

11. Solve $P = Irt$ for t.

    a) $t = P - Ir$ b) $t = PIr$ c) $t = \frac{Ir}{P}$ d) $t = \frac{P}{Ir}$

12. Find the zero of $f(x) = 3x - 4$.

    a) $-\frac{4}{3}$ b) $\frac{4}{3}$ c) $-\frac{3}{4}$ d) $\frac{3}{4}$

13. Find the zeros of $f(x) = 4x^2 - 17x - 15$.

    a) $-\frac{4}{3}, 5$ b) $-5, \frac{3}{4}$ c) $-5, \frac{4}{3}$ d) $-\frac{3}{4}, 5$

14. Solve $x^2 - 4x = 6$ by completing the square.

    a) $2 \pm \sqrt{10}$ b) $2 \pm 2\sqrt{2}i$ c) $\frac{4 \pm \sqrt{22}}{2}$ d) $2 \pm 2\sqrt{10}$

15. Express $\sqrt{-6}$ in terms of i.

    a) $\sqrt{6}i$ b) $6i$ c) $-\sqrt{6}i$ d) $-\sqrt{6}$

16. Simplify: $(5 - 2i)(8 + i)$.

    a) $38 - 11i$ b) $42 - 11i$ c) $40 + 2i$ d) 42

17. Simplify: i^{12}.

    a) i b) -1 c) $-i$ d) 1

18. For the graph of the function $f(x) = 2x^2 - 12x + 14$ find the vertex.

    a) (3, 4) b) (6, 14) c) (–4, 3) d) (3, –4)

19. For the graph of the function $f(x) = 4x^2 - 8x - 1$ find the line of symmetry.

    a) $x = 1$ b) $x = 2$ c) $x = -5$ d) $x = \frac{1}{4}$

20. The sum of the base and the height of a triangle is 54 in. Find the base for which the area is a maximum.

    a) $b = \frac{27}{2}$ in. b) $b = 18$ in. c) $b = 27$ in. d) $b = 36$ in.

---

21. Find b such that $f(x) = -2x^2 + bx - 30$ has a maximum value of 2 and the vertex is located in the second quadrant.

    a) –16 b) 4 c) –8 d) –4

CHAPTER 2 NAME______________________

TEST FORM F CLASS_____SCORE_____GRADE_____

---

1. Solve: $2(x+6)=3x+8$.

   a) -2 b) -20 c) $-\frac{4}{5}$ d) 4

2. Solve: $2x^2+x-28=0$.

   a) $-4, \frac{2}{7}$ b) $-4, 7$ c) $-4, \frac{7}{2}$ d) $4, -\frac{7}{2}$

3. Solve: $x^2-6x+1=0$.

   a) $3\pm 2\sqrt{2}$ b) $1, 5$ c) $3\pm\sqrt{10}$ d) $3\pm\sqrt{2}$

4. Solve: $3x-7\sqrt{x}-20=0$.

   a) 4 b) $-\frac{5}{3}, 4$ c) $\frac{25}{9}, 16$ d) 16

5. Solve: $x^2+81=0$.

   a) $-9, 9$ b) $-9i, 9i$ c) -81 d) $-81i$

6. Solve: $\frac{12}{3x-2}-\frac{5}{x+4}=1$.

   a) $\frac{22}{3}, -3$ b) $\frac{58}{3}$ c) $-\frac{22}{3}, 3$ d) $-\frac{3}{22}, 3$

7. Solve: $\sqrt{5x-11}+2=5$.

   a) 4 b) 100 c) $-\frac{2}{5}$ d) 2

8. Solve: $|3x-4|=17$.

   a) $-39, 63$ b) $-\frac{13}{3}, 7$ c) $-\frac{13}{3}$ d) 7

9. Solve: $|15+x|>2$.

   a) $(-\infty,-17]\cup[13,\infty)$ b) $(-17, 13)$

   c) $(\infty, 13)\cup(17, \infty)$ d) $(-\infty, -17)\cup(-13, \infty)$

10. Solve: $-2<2x+1\le 6$.

    a) $\square\frac{3}{2}, \frac{5}{2}\square$ b) $(-4.3]$ c) $\square-\frac{1}{2}, \frac{7}{2}\square$ d) $\square-\frac{3}{2}, \frac{5}{2}\square$

11. Solve $S=\sqrt{8mn}$ for m.

    a) $m=\frac{S^2}{8n}$ b) $m=\frac{S^2}{64n^2}$ c) $m=\frac{\sqrt{S}}{8n}$ d) $m=\frac{8n}{S^2}$

ANSWERS

1. ____________
2. ____________
3. ____________
4. ____________
5. ____________
6. ____________
7. ____________
8. ____________
9. ____________
10. ____________
11. ____________

CHAPTER 2 NAME______________________________

TEST FORM F

ANSWERS

12. ______________

13. ______________

14. ______________

15. ______________

16. ______________

17. ______________

18. ______________

19. ______________

20. ______________

21. ______________

12. Find the zero of $f(x)=6-5x$.
a) $-\frac{6}{5}$ b) $\frac{6}{5}$ c) $-\frac{5}{6}$ d) $\frac{5}{6}$

13. Find the zeros of $f(x)=4x^2-19x-30$.
a) $-6, \frac{5}{4}$ b) $-\frac{4}{5}, 6$ c) $-\frac{5}{4}, 6$ d) $-6, \frac{4}{5}$

14. Solve $x^2+5x=8$ by completing the square.
a) $\frac{-5\pm\sqrt{7}i}{2}$ b) $\frac{-5\pm\sqrt{7}}{2}$ c) $\frac{-5\pm\sqrt{22}i}{2}$ d) $\frac{-5\pm\sqrt{57}}{2}$

15. Express $\sqrt{-8}$ in terms of i.
a) $-2\sqrt{2}$ b) $2\sqrt{2}i$ c) $4\sqrt{2}i$ d) $-2\sqrt{2}i$

16. Simplify: $(4+3i)(5-i)$.
a) $23+11i$ b) $17+11i$ c) $23-11i$ d) $20+3i$

17. Simplify: i^{21}.
a) i b) -1 c) $-i$ d) 1

18. For the graph of the function $f(x)=-3x^2+18x-31$ find the vertex.
a) $(3, 4)$ b) $(6, 14)$ c) $(-4, 3)$ d) $(3, -4)$

19. For the graph of the function $f(x)=x^2-2x+3$ find the line of symmetry.
a) $x=1$ b) $x=2$ c) $x=3$ d) $x=\frac{1}{2}$

20. The Cotes have 30 feet of picket fence with which to enclose a flower garden. What dimensions should the garden have in order to maximize area?
a) 15 ft by 15 ft b) 7 ft by 8 ft
c) 7.5 ft by 7.5 ft d) 20 ft by 5 ft

---

21. Find the value of a such that $f(x)=ax^2+16x+38$ has a minimum value of 6.
a) –2 b) $\frac{96}{19}$ c) 2 d) $-\frac{96}{19}$

CHAPTER 3 NAME______________________________

TEST FORM A CLASS_____ SCORE_____ GRADE_____

---

1. For the polynomial $f(x)=6x^3-5x^2+x$,
   a) classify $f(x)$ as constant, linear, quadratic, cubic, or quartic;
   b) find the leading term;
   c) find the leading coefficient;
   d) find the degree of the polynomial.

2. Find the zeros of the polynomial function $f(x)=x^2(3x+2)(x-6)^3$ and state the multiplicity of each.

3. Sketch the graph of the polynomial function $f(x)=x^3-4x^2+x+6$.

4. Use the intermediate value theorem to determine, if possible, whether $g(x)=-2x^3-3x+10$ has a real zero between -1 and 0. If it is not possible to make a determination using this method, state this.

5. Use long division to find the quotient $Q(x)$ and the remainder $R(x)$ when $P(x)$ is divided by $d(x)$, and express $P(x)$ in the form $d(x)\cdot Q(x)+R(x)$. Show your work.
   $P(x)=x^4-2x^3+x-6$,
   $d(x)=x+3$

ANSWERS

1. a)____________
   b)____________
   c)____________
   d)____________

2. See graph.

3. ____________

4. ____________

5. ____________

CHAPTER 3 **NAME**____________________________

TEST FORM A

ANSWERS

6. _______________

7. _______________

8. _______________

9. _______________

10. _______________

11. _______________

12. _______________

6. Use synthetic division to find the quotient and remainder. Show your work.

$$(5x^4 - 3x^3 + x - 2) \div (x + 2)$$

7. Use synthetic division to find $P(-3)$ for $P(x) = 4x^3 + 5x^2 - 2x + 1$.

8. Use synthetic division to determine if 2 is a zero of $P(x) = x^3 - 2x^2 - 13x - 10$. Answer "yes" or "no." Show your work.

9. Find a polynomial of degree 4 with –2 as a zero of multiplicity 2 and 0 and 3 as zeros of multiplicity 1.

10. Suppose that a polynomial function of degree 5 with rational coefficients has $4, \sqrt{3}, 7 - 2i$ as zeros. Find the other zeros.

11. Find a polynomial function of lowest degree with rational coefficients and $5, -\sqrt{7}$ as some of its zeros.

12. Use the rational zeros theorem to list all possible rational zeros of $P(x) = 5x^3 - x^2 + 4x - 2$.

CHAPTER 3 NAME________________________

TEST FORM A

ANSWERS

13. For the polynomial function $P(x) = x^4 - 9x^2 + 4x + 12$
a) solve $P(x) = 0$;
b) express $P(x)$ as a product of linear factors.

13. a)______________
b)______________

14. For $f(x) = -4x^5 - 5x^4 + 6x^2 - 10$, what does Descartes' rule of signs tell you about
a) the number of positive real zeros;
b) the number of negative real zeros?

14. a)______________
b)______________

15. Make a graph of $f(x) = \dfrac{6}{(x-2)^2}$. Label all the asymptotes and the y-intercept. List the domain and the x-intercepts.

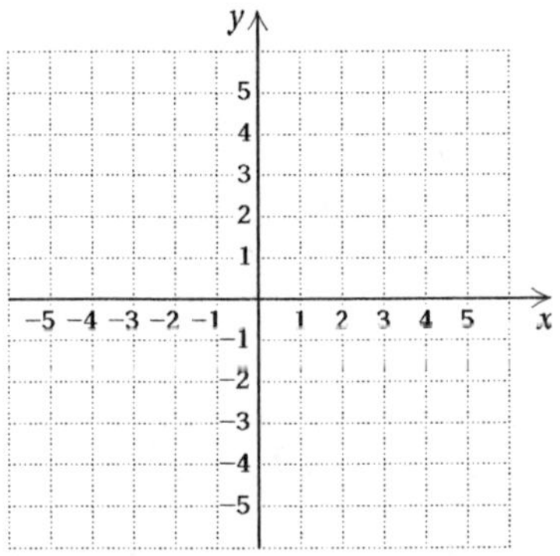

y
5
4
3
2
1
−5 −4 −3 −2 −1 1 2 3 4 5 x
−1
−2
−3
−4
−5

15. See graph.
domain: ________
x-intercepts:_____

16. Find a rational function that has $x = -2$ and $x = 6$ as vertical asymptotes, and $(-3, 0)$ as an x-intercept.

16. ______________

Solve.

17. $3x^2 < 17x - 10$

18. $\dfrac{x-5}{x+1} \le 5$

17. ______________

18. ______________

CHAPTER 3 **NAME**________________________

TEST FORM A

ANSWERS

19. ____________

20. ____________

21. ____________

22. ____________

23. ____________

24. ____________

19. An object launched upward with an initial velocity of 4.9 m/s from a height of 9.8 m will have a height of $s(t) = -4.9t^2 + 4.9t + 9.8$, where s is in meters and t is in seconds. How long will it take the object to hit the ground?

20. The population of a certain organism, in thousands, is given by the function $P(t) = \dfrac{30t}{2t^2 + 9}$, where t is time, in days. Find the interval on which the population is less than 1000.

21. Find an equation of variation in which y varies inversely as x, and $y = 18$ when $x = 5$.

22. The volume of a 6-in. tall cone varies directly as the square of the radius. The volume is 14.1 in^3 when the radius is 1.5 in. Find the volume when the radius is 3 in.

23. Find an equation of variation where y varies jointly as x and z and inversely as the square of w, and $y = 20$ when $x = 0.5$, $z = 4$, and $w = 5$.

---

24. Find the domain of $f(x) = \sqrt{x^2 + 7x - 60}$.

CHAPTER 3 NAME______________________

TEST FORM B CLASS_____ SCORE_____ GRADE_____

1. For the polynomial $f(x) = 81 - 3x^4$,
   a) classify $f(x)$ as constant, linear, quadratic, cubic, or quartic;
   b) find the leading term;
   c) find the leading coefficient;
   d) find the degree of the polynomial.

2. Find the zeros of the polynomial function $f(x) = x^2(2x+1)(x-1)^3$ and state the multiplicity of each.

3. Sketch the graph of the polynomial function $f(x) = x^3 + 3x^2 - 6x - 8$.

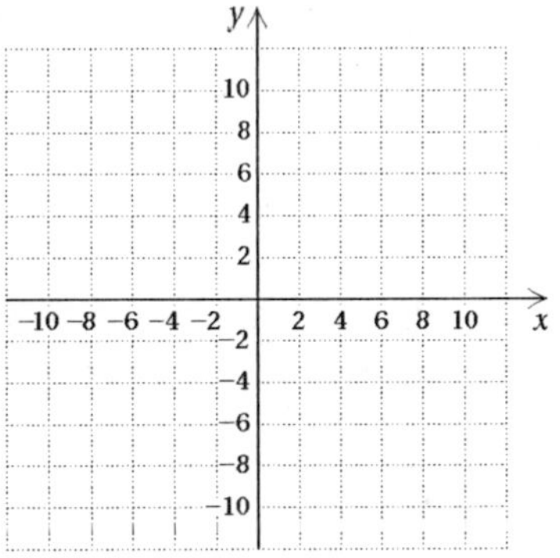

4. Use the intermediate value theorem to determine, if possible, whether $g(x) = 4x^3 - 3x + 3$ has a real zero between -2 and -1. If it is not possible to make a determination using this method, state this.

5. Use long division to find the quotient $Q(x)$ and the remainder $R(x)$ when $P(x)$ is divided by $d(x)$, and express $P(x)$ in the form $d(x) \cdot Q(x) + R(x)$. Show your work.
   $P(x) = x^4 - 2x^2 + 3x - 5$,
   $d(x) = x - 4$

ANSWERS

1. a) ______________
   b) ______________
   c) ______________
   d) ______________

2. See graph.

3. ______________

4. ______________

5. ______________

ANSWERS

6. ____________

7. ____________

8. ____________

9. ____________

10. ____________

11. ____________

12. ____________

6. Use synthetic division to find the quotient and remainder. Show your work.
$$(4x^3 - 2x^2 + 8x - 5) \div (x - 2)$$

7. Use synthetic division to find $P(-1)$ for $P(x) = 4x^3 - 5x^2 + 6x - 8$.

8. Use synthetic division to determine if -3 is a zero of $P(x) = -2x^3 - 3x^2 + 11x + 6$. Answer "yes" or "no." Show your work.

9. Find a polynomial of degree 4 with 3 as a zero of multiplicity 2 and –4 and 6 as zeros of multiplicity 1.

10. Suppose that a polynomial function of degree 5 with rational coefficients has $3, \sqrt{2}, 7 + 4i$ as zeros. Find the other zeros.

11. Find a polynomial function of lowest degree with rational coefficients and $3, -\sqrt{6}$ as some of its zeros.

12. Use the rational zeros theorem to list all possible rational zeros of $P(x) = 2x^3 - 6x^2 + 4x - 3$.

CHAPTER 3 **NAME**__________________________

TEST FORM B

13. For the polynomial function $P(x) = x^3 + 2x^2 - 5x - 10$
a) solve $P(x) = 0$;
b) express $P(x)$ as a product of linear factors.

14. For $f(x) = 2x^4 - 3x^3 + 6x^2 - 8$, what does Descartes' rule of signs tell you about
a) the number of positive real zeros;
b) the number of negative real zeros?

15. Make a graph of $f(x) = \dfrac{3}{(x+3)^2}$. Label all the asymptotes and the y-intercept. List the domain and the x intercept.

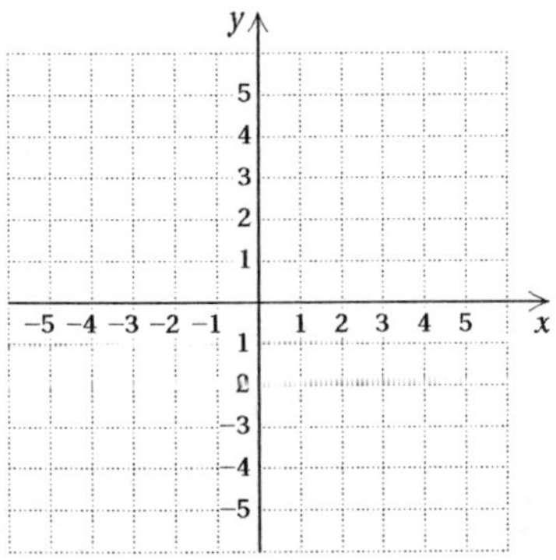

16. Find a rational function that has $x = -3$ and $x = 5$ as vertical asymptotes, and $(4, 0)$ as an x-intercept.

Solve.

17. $2x^2 < -5x + 12$

18. $\dfrac{x+1}{x-5} \geq 6$

ANSWERS

13. a)______________
b)______________

14. a)______________
b)______________

15. See graph.
domain: ________
x-intercepts:_____

16. ______________

17. ______________

18. ______________

ANSWERS

19. ____________

20. ____________

21. ____________

22. ____________

23. ____________

24. ____________

19. An object launched upward with an initial velocity of 9.8 m/s from a height of 73.5 m will have a height of $s(t) = -4.9t^2 + 9.8t + 73.5$, where s is in meters and t is in seconds. How long will it take the object to hit the ground?

20. The population of a certain organism, in thousands, is given by the function $P(t) = \frac{50t}{5t^2 + 12}$, where t is time, in years. Find the interval on which the population is less than 2000.

21. Find an equation of variation in which y varies directly as x, and $y = 14$ when $x = 6$.

22. The current I in an electrical conductor varies inversely as the resistance R of the conductor. Suppose I is 0.2 ampere when the resistance is 200 ohms. Find the current when the resistance is 250 ohms.

23. Find an equation of variation where y varies jointly as the square of x and the square of z and inversely as w, and $y = 50$ when $x = 2$, $z = 3$, and $w = 10$.

---

24. Find the domain of $f(x) = \frac{1}{\sqrt{2 - |x|}}$.

CHAPTER 3 NAME____________________

TEST FORM C CLASS_____ SCORE_____ GRADE_____

1. For the polynomial $f(x) = 2 + 3x - x^2$,
   a) classify $f(x)$ as constant, linear, quadratic, cubic, or quartic;
   b) find the leading term;
   c) find the leading coefficient;
   d) find the degree of the polynomial.

2. Find the zeros of the polynomial function $f(x) = x^2(x-3)^2(4x+5)$ and state the multiplicity of each.

3. Sketch the graph of the polynomial function $f(x) = x^3 - x^2 - 4x + 4$.

y
10
8
6
4
2
−10 −8 −6 −4 −2 2 4 6 8 10 x
−2
−4
−6
−8
−10

4. Use the intermediate value theorem to determine, if possible, whether $g(x) = 2x^3 - 3x^2 + 4$ has a real zero between -2 and -1. If it is not possible to make a determination using this method, state this.

5. Use long division to find the quotient $Q(x)$ and the remainder $R(x)$ when $P(x)$ is divided by $d(x)$, and express $P(x)$ in the form $d(x) \cdot Q(x) + R(x)$. Show your work.
   $P(x) = x^4 - 3x^2 + x - 6$,
   $d(x) = x + 2$

ANSWERS

1. a)____________
   b)____________
   c)____________
   d)____________

2. See graph.

3. ____________

4. ____________

5. ____________

CHAPTER 3 **NAME**____________________________

TEST FORM C

ANSWERS

6. ____________

7. ____________

8. ____________

9. ____________

10. ____________

11. ____________

12. ____________

6. Use synthetic division to find the quotient and remainder. Show your work.
$$(5x^4 - x^2 + x - 2) \div (x + 1)$$

7. Use synthetic division to find $P(-2)$ for $P(x) = 3x^3 + 2x^2 - x + 4$.

8. Use synthetic division to determine if 1 is a zero of $P(x) = 3x^3 - 2x^2 + x - 2$. Answer "yes" or "no." Show your work.

9. Find a polynomial of degree 4 with 0 as a zero of multiplicity 2 and –3 and 5 as zeros of multiplicity 1.

10. Suppose that a polynomial function of degree 5 with rational coefficients has $2, -\sqrt{5}, 3+i$ as zeros. Find the other zeros.

11. Find a polynomial function of lowest degree with rational coefficients and $-4, 2i$ as some of its zeros.

12. Use the rational zeros theorem to list all possible rational zeros of $P(x) = 6x^3 - 4x^2 + 5x + 1$.

CHAPTER 3 NAME______________________

TEST FORM C

ANSWERS

13. For the polynomial function $P(x)=x^4-2x^3-5x^2+4x+6$
    a) solve $P(x)=0$;
    b) express $P(x)$ as a product of linear factors.

14. For $f(x)=-x^3+6x^2-x-2$, what does Descartes' rule of signs tell you about
    a) the number of positive real zeros;
    b) the number of negative real zeros?

15. Make a graph of $f(x)=\dfrac{x+3}{x^2-3x-4}$. Label all the asymptotes and the y intercept. List the domain and the x intercepts.

y, x; −5 −4 −3 −2 −1 1 2 3 4 5; 5 4 3 2 1 −1 −2 −3 −4 −5

16. Find a rational function that has $x=-3$ and $x=1$ as vertical asymptotes, and $(0, 0)$ as an x-intercept.

Solve.

17. $3x^2 \le 10-x$

18. $\dfrac{x-2}{x+5} \ge 3$

13. a) ______________
    b) ______________

14. a) ______________
    b) ______________

15. See graph.
    domain: ________
    x-intercepts: _____

16. ______________

17. ______________

18. ______________

CHAPTER 3 **NAME**________________________

TEST FORM C

ANSWERS

19. ________________

20. ________________

21. ________________

22. ________________

23. ________________

24. ________________

19. The function $s(t) = -4.9t^2 + 4.9t + 58.8$ gives the height s, in meters, of an object launched with a velocity of 4.9 m/s from a height of 58.8 m. How long will it take the object to hit the ground?

20. The population of a certain organism, in thousands, is given by the function $P(t) = \dfrac{25t}{3t^2 + 15}$, where t is time, in days. Find the interval on which the population is greater than 1000.

21. Find an equation of variation in which y varies directly as x, and $y = 1.5$ when $x = 0.3$.

22. The intensity of I of a light from a light bulb varies inversely as the square of the distance d from the bulb. Suppose I is $60\ \text{W/m}^2$ (watts per square meter) when the distance is 5 m. Find the intensity at 20 m.

23. Find an equation of variation where y varies jointly as x and z and inversely as the square root of w, and $y = 20$ when $x = 5$, $z = 2$, and $w = 25$.

---

24. Find the domain of $f(x) = \sqrt{x^2 - 2x - 15}$.

CHAPTER 3 NAME________________

TEST FORM D CLASS____ SCORE____ GRADE____

---

1. For the polynomial $f(x) = 4 - 2x$,
   a) classify $f(x)$ as constant, linear, quadratic, cubic, or quartic;
   b) find the leading term;
   c) find the leading coefficient;
   d) find the degree of the polynomial.

2. Find the zeros of the polynomial function $f(x) = x(4x-3)^2(x+2)$ and state the multiplicity of each.

3. Sketch the graph of the polynomial function $f(x) = x^3 - 5x^2 + 2x + 8$.

y
10
8
6
4
2
−10 −8 −6 −4 −2 2 4 6 8 10 x
−2
−4
−6
−8
−10

4. Use the intermediate value theorem to determine, if possible, whether $g(x) = -2x^3 + 5x + 2$ has a real zero between -2 and -1. If it is not possible to make a determination using this method, state this.

5. Use long division to find the quotient $Q(x)$ and the remainder $R(x)$ when $P(x)$ is divided by $d(x)$, and express $P(x)$ in the form $d(x) \cdot Q(x) + R(x)$. Show your work.

   $P(x) = x^4 + 5x^2 - 3x + 2$,
   $d(x) = x - 2$

ANSWERS

1. a)________
   b)________
   c)________
   d)________

2. See graph.________

3. ________

4. ________

5. ________

CHAPTER 3 **NAME**______________________

TEST FORM D

ANSWERS

6. ____________

7. ____________

8. ____________

9. ____________

10. ____________

11. ____________

12. ____________

6. Use synthetic division to find the quotient and remainder. Show your work.
   $(8x^3 - 5x^2 + 3x) \div (x - 4)$

7. Use synthetic division to find $P(3)$ for $P(x) = -3x^2 + 6x - 5$.

8. Use synthetic division to determine if -2 is a zero of $P(x) = 4x^3 - 5x^2 - 7x + 2$. Answer "yes" or "no." Show your work.

9. Find a polynomial of degree 4 with –1 as a zero of multiplicity 2 and 4 and 0 as zeros of multiplicity 1.

10. Suppose that a polynomial function of degree 5 with rational coefficients has $10, -\sqrt{3}, 5 - 3i$ as zeros. Find the other zeros.

11. Find a polynomial function of lowest degree with rational coefficients and $-2, 1 + i$ as some of its zeros.

12. Use the rational zeros theorem to list all possible rational zeros of $P(x) = 3x^3 - 5x^2 + 4x - 2$.

CHAPTER 3 NAME________________________

TEST FORM D

---

13. For the polynomial function $P(x)=x^3-4x^2-7x+28$
a) solve $P(x)=0$;
b) express $P(x)$ as a product of linear factors.

14. For $f(x)=5x^3+6x^2+4x-2$, what does Descartes' rule of signs tell you about
a) the number of positive real zeros;
b) the number of negative real zeros?

15. Make a graph of $f(x)=\dfrac{x+4}{x^2-2x-3}$. Label all the asymptotes and the y-intercept. List the domain and the x-intercept.

y
5
4
3
2
1
−5 −4 −3 −2 −1 1 2 3 4 5 x
−1
−2
−3
−4
−5

16. Find a rational function that has $x=-2$ and $x=-5$ as vertical asymptotes, and no x-intercept.

Solve.

17. $4x^2 \geq 13x-3$

18. $\dfrac{x-4}{x+2} \geq 3$

ANSWERS

13. a)____________
b)____________

14. a)____________
b)____________

15. See graph.
domain: ________
x-intercepts:_____

16. ______________

17. ______________

18. ______________

ANSWERS

19. ____________

20. ____________

21. ____________

22. ____________

23. ____________

24. ____________

19. The function $s(t) = -4.9t^2 + 9.8t + 73.5$ gives the height s, in meters, of an object launched with a velocity of 9.8 m/s from a height of 73.5 m. How long will it take the object to hit the ground?

20. The population of a certain organism, in thousands, is given by the function $P(t) = \frac{20t}{t^2 + 16}$, where t is time, in years. Find the interval on which the population is greater than 2000.

21. Find an equation of variation in which y varies inversely as x, and $y = 15$ when $x = 6$.

22. The surface area of a balloon varies directly as the square of its radius. The area is 78.5 cm^2 when the radius is 2.5 cm. Find the area when the radius is 3 cm.

23. Find an equation of variation where y varies jointly as x and the square of z and inversely as w, and $y = 40$ when $x = 100$, $z = 0.1$, and $w = 2$.

---

24. Find the domain of $(x-2)^{-3} \geq 0$.

CHAPTER 3 NAME____________________

TEST FORM E CLASS____ SCORE____ GRADE____

ANSWERS

1. Classify the polynomial $P(x) = 4x^2 - 6x + 3$.

   a) quadratic b) quartic
   c) linear d) cubic

2. Determine the leading coefficient of the polynomial $P(x) = -2x^4 + 5x^5 - x^6 + 9$.

   a) –2 b) 9 c) -1 d) 5

3. Determine the degree of the polynomial $P(x) = 12x^3 - 6x^2 + 7x + 2$.

   a) 3 b) 12 c) 4 d) 6

4. Which graph represents the polynomial function $f(x) = x^3 - x^2 - 4x + 4$?

   a)

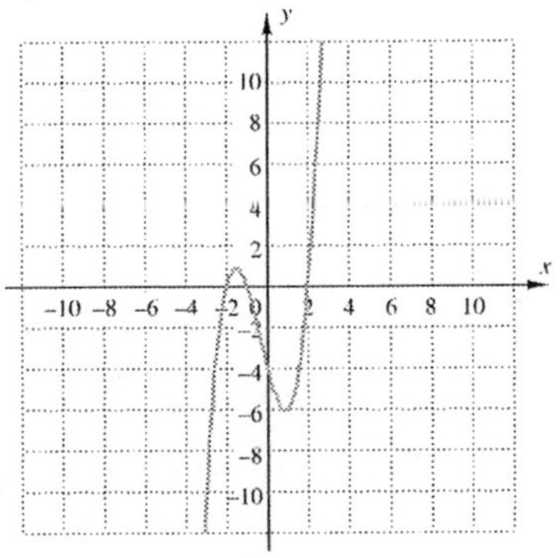

   b)

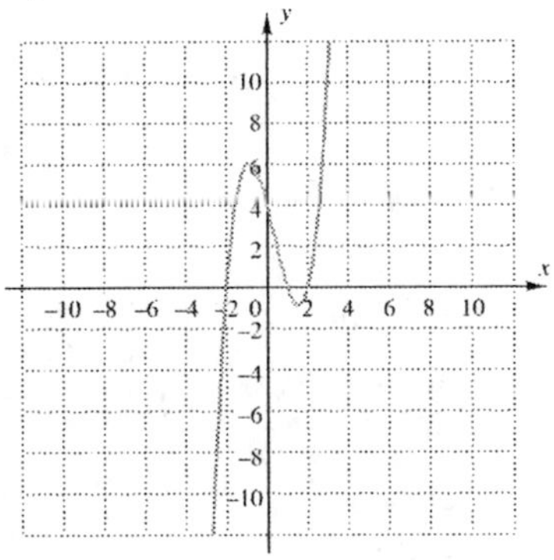

   c)

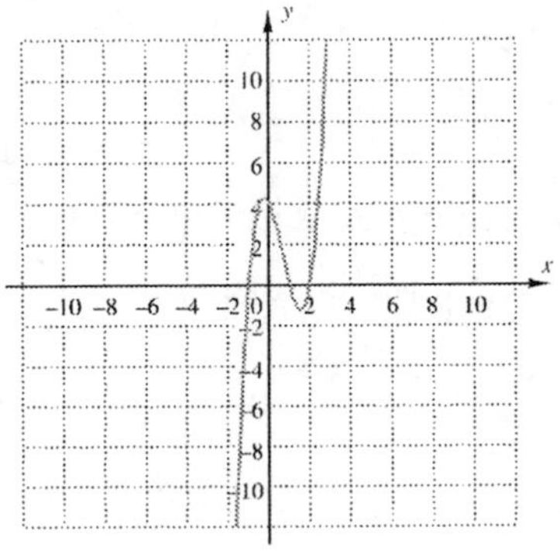

   d)

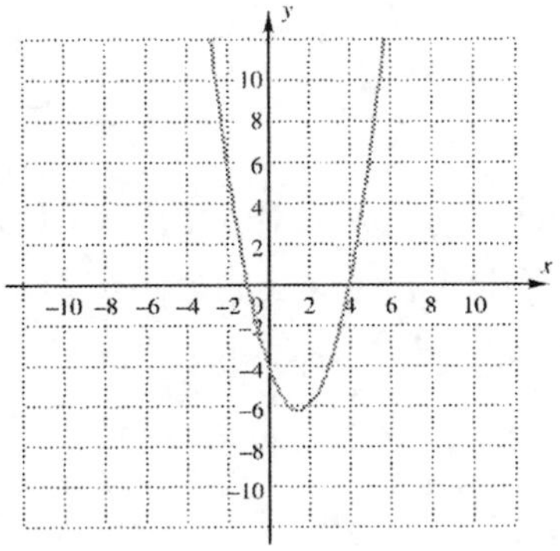

1. ____________

2. ____________

3. ____________

4. ____________

CHAPTER 3 NAME________________________

TEST FORM E

ANSWERS

5. ____________

6. ____________

7. ____________

8. ____________

9. ____________

10. ____________

11. ____________

5. For $f(x) = -2x^4 + 3$, use the intermediate value theorem to determine which interval contains a zero of f.
a) between -1 and 0 b) between 0 and 1
c) between 1 and 2 d) between 2 and 3

6. Use long division to find the quotient and remainder when $x^4 + 2x^3 - 3x + 1$ is divided by $x + 2$.
a) $x^3 - 3$, R 7
b) $x^3 - 3x + 6$, R -11
c) $x^3 + 4x^2 + 8x + 13$, R 27
d) $x^2 - 3$, R 7

7. Use synthetic division to find the quotient and remainder when $5x^3 - 4x^2 + 2x - 10$ is divided by $x - 2$.
a) $5x^2 + 3x + 7$, R -1 b) $5x^2 - 14x + 30$, R -70
c) $5x^2 + 14x + 30$, R 50 d) $5x^2 + 6x + 14$, R 18

8. Use synthetic division to determine which number is a zero of $P(x) = x^4 + 6x^3 - 7x^2 - 36x + 36$.
a) 6 b) 3 c) 2 d) -1

9. Use synthetic division to find $P(-3)$ for $P(x) = 4x^3 - 2x^2 - 3x + 6$.
a) -111 b) 87 c) -39 d) -93

10. Suppose that a polynomial function of degree 5 with rational coefficients has $4, \sqrt{2}$, and $3 - 2i$ as zeros. Find one other zero.
a) -4 b) $-\sqrt{2}$ c) $-3 + 2i$ d) $-3 - 2i$

11. Find a polynomial function of lowest degree with rational coefficients and -5 and $-\sqrt{7}$ as some of its zeros.
a) $f(x) = x^2 - 2x - 35$
b) $f(x) = x^3 + 5x^2 - 7x - 35$
c) $f(x) = x^3 - 5x^2 - 7x + 35$
d) $f(x) = x^2 + \sqrt{7}x + 5x + 5\sqrt{7}$

CHAPTER 3 NAME____________________

TEST FORM E

ANSWERS

12. Use the rational zeros theorem to determine which number cannot be a zero of $P(x)=10x^4+6x^2-5x+2$.

a) $\frac{1}{5}$ b) -2 c) -5 d) $\frac{2}{5}$

12. ____________

13. How many negative real zeros does Descartes' rule of signs indicate $g(x)=2x^5-3x^4-5x^3+2x^2-x+3$ has?

a) 4, 2, or 0 b) 3 or 1
c) 1 d) 2 or 0

13. ____________

14. Find the vertical asymptote for $f(x)=\dfrac{x-2}{(x+8)^2}$.

a) $x = 2$ b) $x = 8$ c) $y=-\frac{1}{4}$ d) $x = -8$

14. ____________

15. Solve: $(x-3)(x+4)(x-2)\le 0$.

a) $(-\infty,-4]\cup[2,3]$ b) $[-4,2]\cup[3,\infty)$
c) $(-\infty,-4]\cup[3,\infty)$ d) $(-\infty-4)\cup(2,3)$

15. ____________

16. Solve: $4x^2>3x+7$.

a) $(-\infty,-1)\cup\left(\frac{4}{7},\infty\right)$ b) $(-\infty,-1)\cup\left(\frac{7}{4},\infty\right)$
c) $\left(-\infty,-\frac{7}{4}\right)\cup(1,\infty)$ d) $\left(-1,\frac{7}{4}\right)$

16. ____________

CHAPTER 3 NAME______________________________

TEST FORM E

ANSWERS

17. ____________

18. ____________

19. ____________

20. ____________

21. ____________

17. Solve: $\dfrac{x+8}{x-2} \geq 3$.

a) $(2, 7)$ b) $[2, 7]$

c) $(2, 7]$ d) $(-\infty, 2) \cup [7, \infty)$

18. Express $x^4 - 9x^2 + 4x + 12$ as a product of linear factors.

a) $(x+1)^2(x-2)(x+3)$

b) $(x-2)^2(x+1)(x+3)$

c) $(x-2)^2(x-1)(x+3)$

d) $(x+2)^2(x-1)(x-3)$

19. If y varies inversely as x and $y = 1.5$ when $x = 8$, find y when $x = 20$.

a) $\dfrac{5}{3}$ b) $\dfrac{15}{4}$ c) $\dfrac{320}{3}$ d) $\dfrac{3}{5}$

20. An object launched upward with an initial velocity of 14.7 m/s from a height of 137.2 m will have a height of $s(t) = -4.9t^2 + 14.7t + 137.2$, where s is in meters and t is in seconds. How long will it take the object to hit the ground?

a) 7 sec b) 3.5 sec c) 3 sec d) 14 sec

21. Solve: $(x+4)^{-5} \leq 0$.

a) $(-\infty, -4]$ b) $(-\infty, -4)$

c) $(-4, \infty)$ d) $(-4, 4)$

CHAPTER 3 **NAME**______________________

TEST FORM F **CLASS**____**SCORE**____**GRADE**____

ANSWERS

1. Classify the polynomial $P(x) = x^3 - x$.
   a) quadratic b) quartic
   c) linear d) cubic

2. Determine the leading coefficient of the polynomial
   $P(x) = 5x + 4x^2 - 6x^3 + x^4$.
   a) 10 b) 4 c) 1 d) 5

3. Determine the degree of the polynomial $P(x) = 3x^4 - 2x^2 + 6$.
   a) 3 b) 1 c) 6 d) 4

4. Which graph represents the polynomial function
   $f(x) = x^3 - 3x^2 - x + 3$?
   a) b)
   c) d)

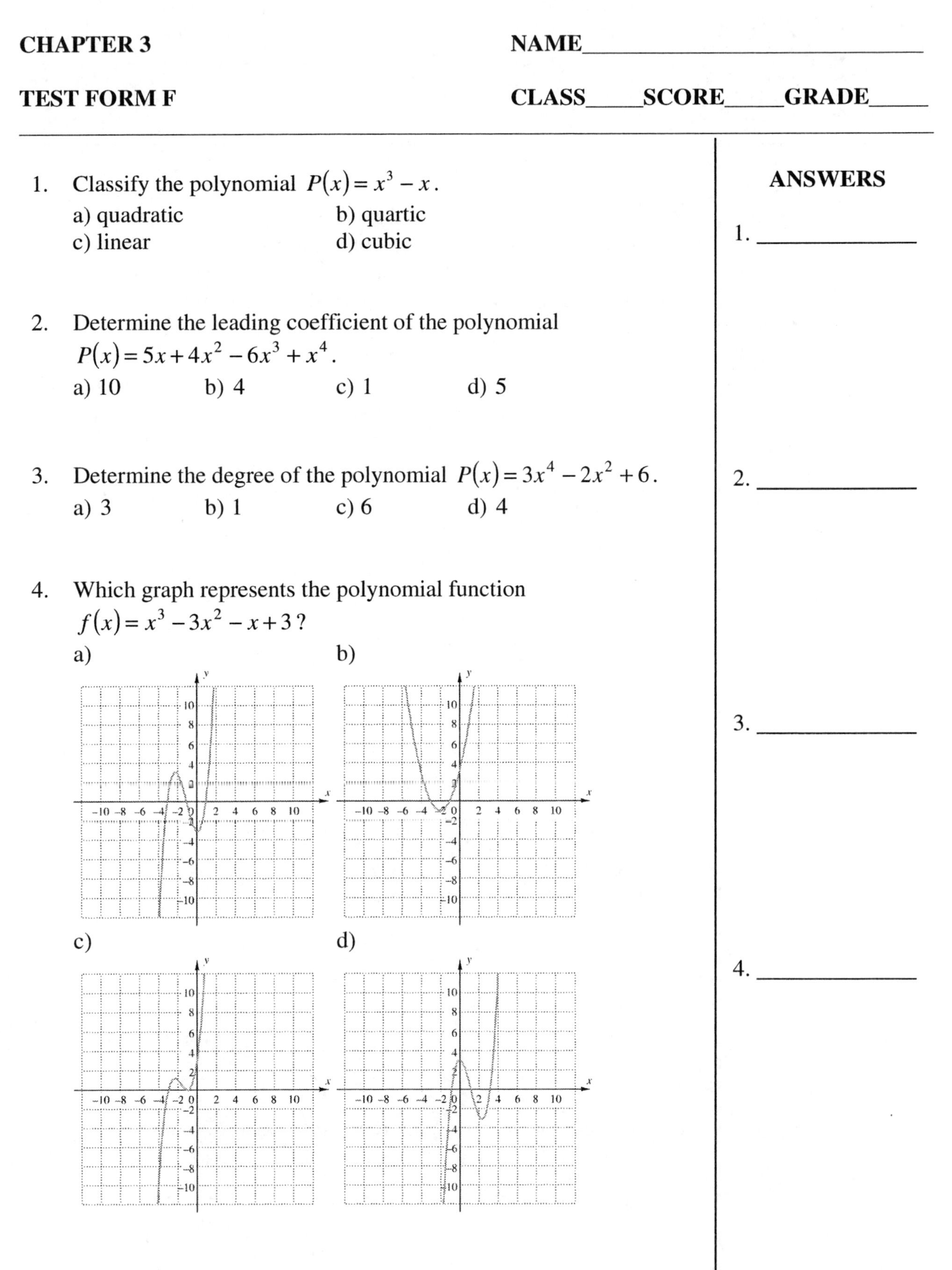

1. ____________

2. ____________

3. ____________

4. ____________

CHAPTER 3 NAME______________________________

TEST FORM F

ANSWERS

5. ______________

6. ______________

7. ______________

8. ______________

9. ______________

10. ______________

5. For $f(x) = -2x^4 + 3x + 1$, use the intermediate value theorem to determine which interval contains a zero of f.
   a) between -2 and -1 b) between -1 and 0
   c) between 0 and 1 d) between 2 and 3

6. Use long division to find the quotient and remainder when $x^4 + 2x^3 - 2x + 4$ is divided by $x - 2$.
   a) $x^3 + 4x^2 + 8x + 14$, R 32
   b) $x^3 - 2$, R 8
   c) $x^3 + 4x^2 + 8x + 18$, R 40
   d) $x^3 + 4x^2 + 6x + 12$, R 28

7. Use synthetic division to find the quotient and remainder when $9x^3 - 6x^2 + 4x - 3$ is divided by $x + 1$.
   a) $9x^2 + 3x + 7$, R 4 b) $9x^2 - 3x + 7$, R - 4
   c) $9x^2 - 3x + 7$, R -10 d) $9x^2 - 15x + 19$, R -22

8. Use synthetic division to determine which number is a zero of $P(x) = x^4 - 37x^2 - 24x + 180$.
   a) 5 b) –6 c) –2 d) –3

9. Use synthetic division to find $P(-3)$ for $P(x) = -2x^4 + 3x^3 - 5x^2 + 2$.
   a) –286 b) –124 c) –34 d) –100

10. Suppose that a polynomial function of degree 5 with rational coefficients has $2, \sqrt{7}$, and $5 + i$ as zeros. Find one other zero.
    a) -2 b) $5 - i$ c) $-5 - i$ d) $-2\sqrt{7}$

CHAPTER 3 NAME_______________________________

TEST FORM F

ANSWERS

11. Find a polynomial function of lowest degree with rational coefficients and -3 and $4i$ as some of its zeros.
    a) $f(x)=x^2+3x-4xi-12i$
    b) $f(x)=x^3+3x^2-16x-48$
    c) $f(x)=x^3-3x^2+16x-48$
    d) $f(x)=x^3+3x^2+16x+48$

11. ______________

12. Use the rational zeros theorem to determine which number cannot be a zero of $P(x)=4x^4+3x^2+x-3$.
    a) $\frac{4}{3}$ b) $\frac{3}{4}$ c) $-\frac{1}{4}$ d) -3

12. ______________

13. How many negative real zeros does Descartes' rule of signs indicate $g(x)=-x^5+4x^4-2x^3+3x^2-6$ has?
    a) 1 b) 3 or 1
    c) 5, 3, or 1 d) 2 or 0

13. ______________

14. Find the vertical asymptote for $f(x)=\dfrac{x-6}{(x+2)^2}$.
    a) $x=-3$ b) $x=6$ c) $x=2$ d) $x=-2$

14. ______________

15. Solve: $(x-3)(x+4)(x-5)\geq 0$.
    a) $(-\infty,-4]\cup[3,5]$ b) $(-\infty,-4]\cup[5,\infty)$
    c) $[-4,3]\cup[5,\infty)$ d) $(-4,3)\cup(5,\infty)$

15. ______________

16. Solve: $3x^2>-x+10$.
    a) $\left(-\infty,-\frac{5}{3}\right)\cup(2,\infty)$ b) $\left(-2,\frac{5}{3}\right)$
    c) $(-\infty,-2)\cup\left(\frac{3}{5},\infty\right)$ d) $(-\infty,-2)\cup\left(\frac{5}{3},\infty\right)$

16. ______________

CHAPTER 3 **NAME**______________________

TEST FORM F

ANSWERS

17. ____________

18. ____________

19. ____________

20. ____________

21. ____________

17. Solve: $\frac{x+2}{x-6} \le 4$.

a) $(-\infty, 6) \cup \left[\frac{26}{3}, \infty\right)$ b) $(-\infty, 6] \cup \left[\frac{26}{3}, \infty\right)$

c) $\left(6, \frac{26}{3}\right]$ d) $(-\infty, -6) \cup \left[-\frac{26}{3}, \infty\right)$

18. Express $x^4 - 9x^2 + 4x + 12$ as a product of linear factors.

a) $(x+1)^2(x-2)(x+3)$

b) $(x-2)^2(x+1)(x+3)$

c) $(x-2)^2(x-1)(x+3)$

d) $(x+2)^2(x-1)(x-3)$

19. If y varies inversely as x and $y = 4$ when $x = 0.2$, find y when $x = 8$.

a) 160 b) 10 c) 0.1 d) 0.4

20. An object launched upward with an initial velocity of 14.7 m/s from a height of 49 m will have a height of $s(t) = -4.9t^2 + 14.7t + 49$, where s is in meters and t is in seconds. How long will it take the object to hit the ground?

a) 5 sec b) 3 sec c) 2.5 sec d) 10 sec

---

21. Find the domain of $f(x) = \sqrt{x^2 + x - 12}$.

a) $(-\infty, 4) \cup (3, \infty)$ b) $(-\infty, -3] \cup [4, \infty)$

c) $(-\infty, -4] \cup [3, \infty)$ d) $[-4, 3]$

CHAPTER 4 NAME________________________

TEST FORM A CLASS_____ SCORE_____ GRADE_____

ANSWERS

1. ______________

2. ______________

3. ______________

4. ______________

5. ______________

6. ______________

7. ______________

1. Find the inverse of the relation $\{(5, 0), (-4, 2), (3, -1), (2, 6)\}$.

2. Determine whether the graph shown below is one-to-one. Answer "yes" or "no."

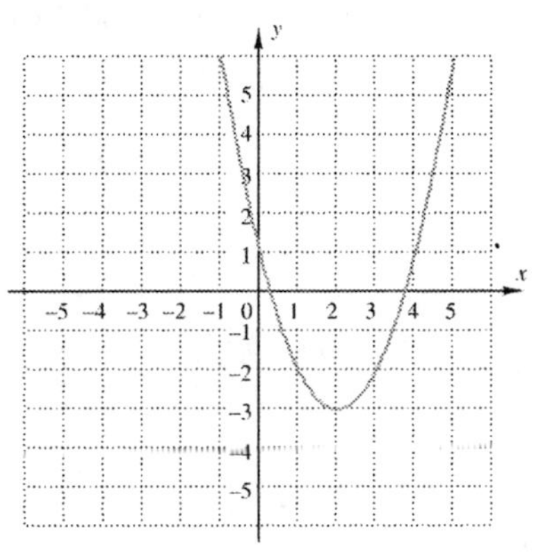

Find a formula for the inverse of the function, if the function is one-to-one. If not, state this.

3. $f(x) = x^3 + 6$

4. $f(x) = 2x - 4$

5. $f(x) = \dfrac{x}{8-x}$

6. $f(x) = x^2 - 4x + 4$

7. Use composition of functions to show that f^{-1} is as given:
$f(x) = \dfrac{1}{2}x - 3, \quad f^{-1}(x) = 2(x+3)$.

NAME______________________________

TEST FORM A

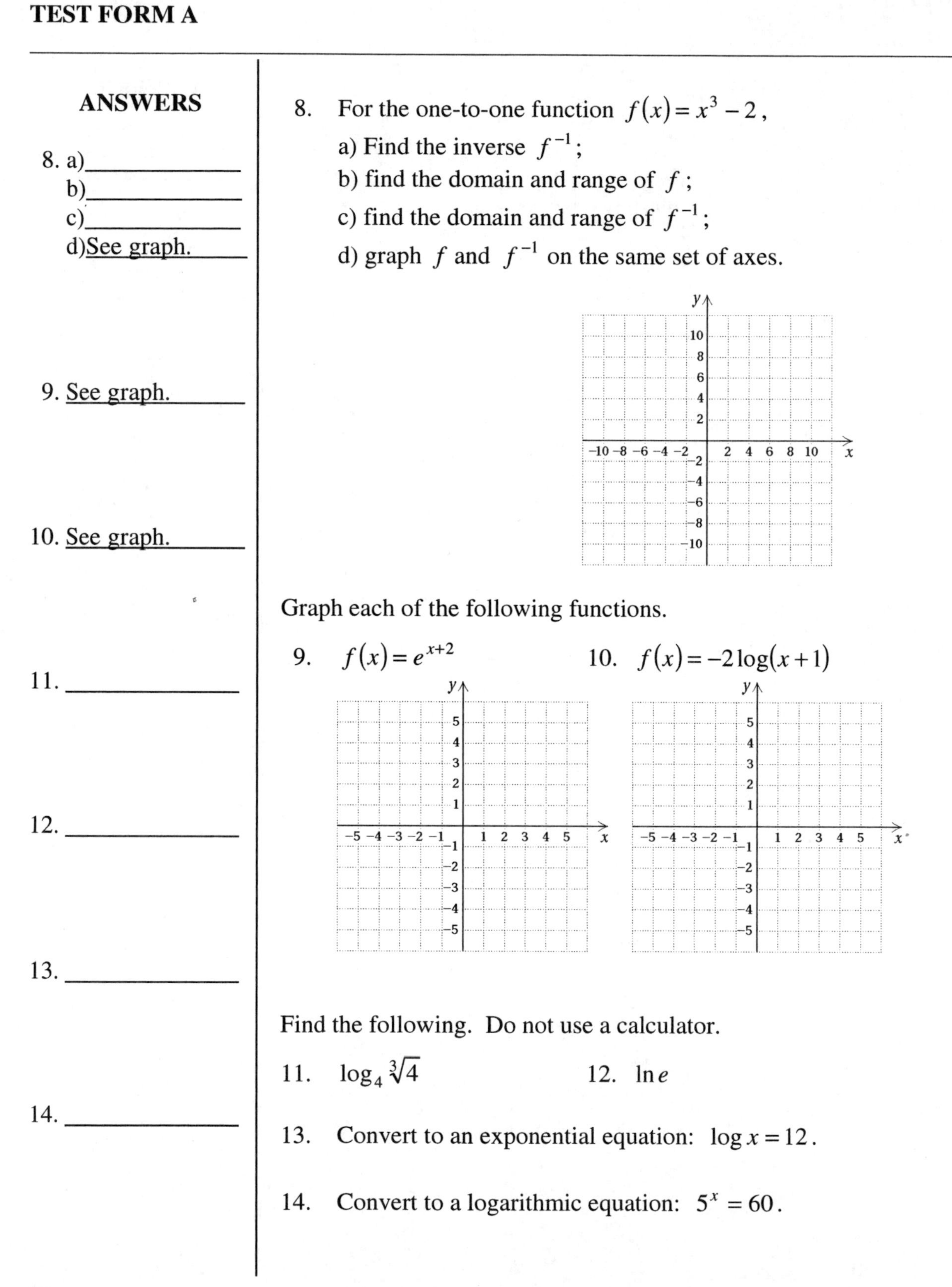

ANSWERS

8. a)____________
   b)____________
   c)____________
   d) See graph.

9. See graph.

10. See graph.

11. ____________

12. ____________

13. ____________

14. ____________

8. For the one-to-one function $f(x) = x^3 - 2$,

   a) Find the inverse f^{-1};

   b) find the domain and range of f;

   c) find the domain and range of f^{-1};

   d) graph f and f^{-1} on the same set of axes.

Graph each of the following functions.

9. $f(x) = e^{x+2}$

10. $f(x) = -2\log(x+1)$

Find the following. Do not use a calculator.

11. $\log_4 \sqrt[3]{4}$

12. $\ln e$

13. Convert to an exponential equation: $\log x = 12$.

14. Convert to a logarithmic equation: $5^x = 60$.

CHAPTER 4 **NAME**______________________

TEST FORM A

Find each of the following using a calculator. Round to four decimal places.

15. $\ln 0.8$

16. $\log \frac{1}{2}$

17. Find $\log_2 10$ using the change-of-base formula.

18. Express as a single logarithm: $\log_c \sqrt{x} + \log_c y - 2\log_c z$.

19. Express in terms of sums and differences of logarithms:
$\log \sqrt[3]{\frac{x^2}{y}}$.

20. Given that $\log_a 3 = 0.6826$ and $\log_a 4 = 0.8614$, find $\log_a 36$.

21. Simplify: $\ln e^{x+6}$.

Solve.

22. $\log_5 125 = x$

23. $\log_5 (x-2) + \log_5 (2x-9) = 2$

24. $3^{5+4x} = 9^x$

25. $e^{2x} = 10.4$

ANSWERS

15. ______________

16. ______________

17. ______________

18. ______________

19. ______________

20. ______________

21. ______________

22. ______________

23. ______________

24. ______________

25. ______________

CHAPTER 4 **NAME**__________________________

TEST FORM A

ANSWERS

26. ____________

27. a) ____________
b) ____________
c) ____________
d) ____________

28. ____________

26. The population of a country doubled in 30 yr. What was the exponential growth rate?

27. Suppose $\$5000$ is invested at interest rate k, compounded continuously, and grows to $\$6954.84$ in 6 yr.
a) Find the interest rate.
b) Find the exponential growth function.
c) Find the balance after 10 yr.
d) Find the doubling time.

---

28. Solve: $5\sqrt[4]{x} = 15$.

CHAPTER 4 NAME______________________

TEST FORM B CLASS_____ SCORE_____ GRADE_____

1. Find the inverse of the relation $\{(-3, 6), (4, 7), (0, 8), (-5, -2)\}$.

2. Determine whether the function shown below is one-to-one. Answer "yes" or "no."

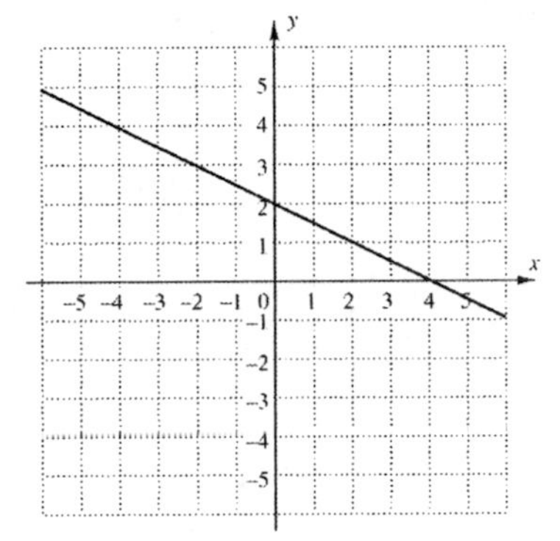

Find a formula for the inverse of the function, if the function is one-to-one. If not, state this.

3. $f(x) = x^3 - 8$

4. $f(x) = 3x + 2$

5. $f(x) = \dfrac{x}{5+x}$

6. $f(x) = x^2 - 2x + 1$

7. Use composition of functions to show that f^{-1} is as given:
$f(x) = \dfrac{1}{4}x + 6, \quad f^{-1}(x) = 4(x-6)$.

ANSWERS

1. ______________

2. ______________

3. ______________

4. ______________

5. ______________

6. ______________

7. ______________

NAME______________________________

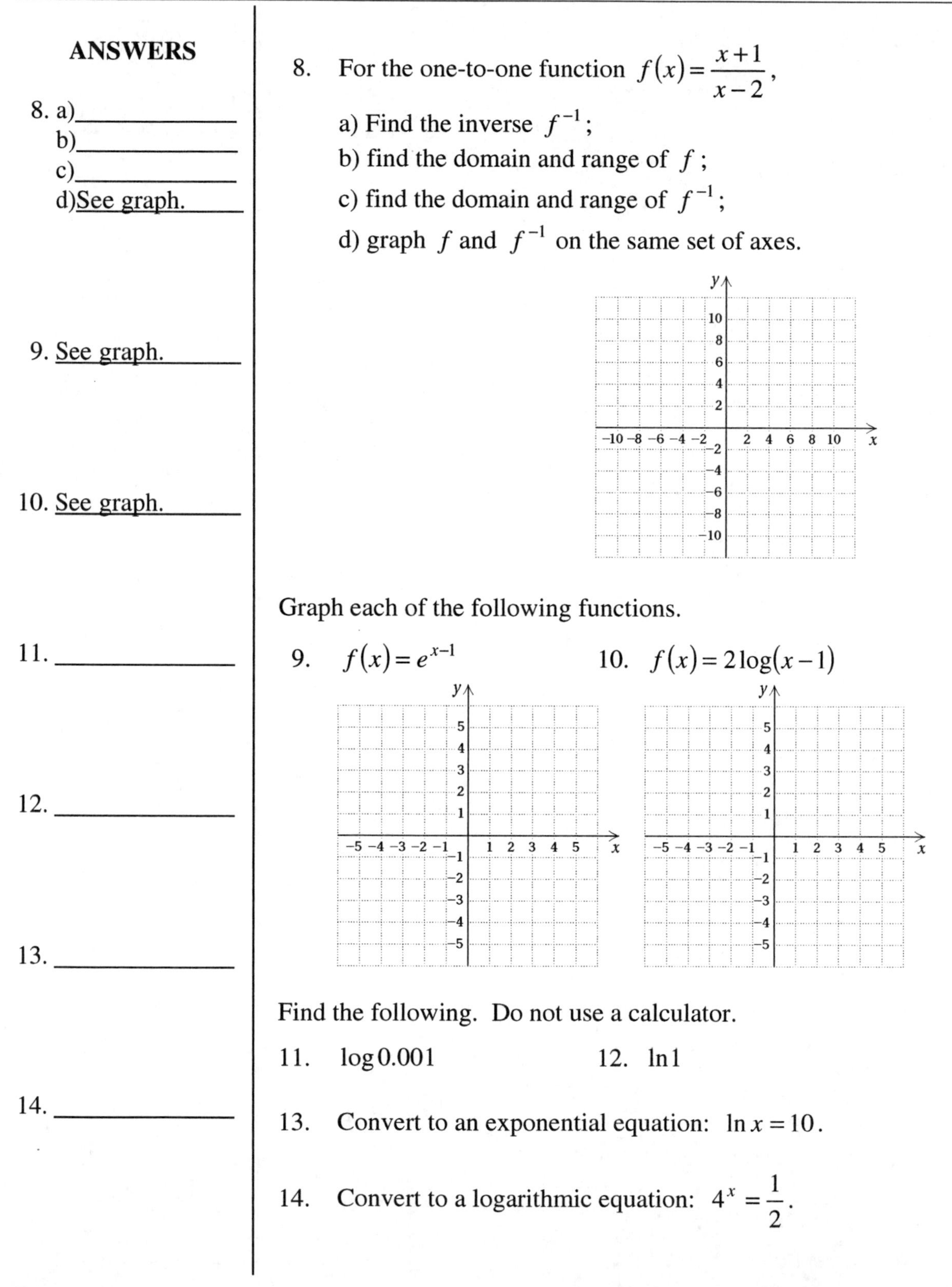

ANSWERS

8. a)____________
   b)____________
   c)____________
   d)See graph.

9. See graph.

10. See graph.

11. ____________

12. ____________

13. ____________

14. ____________

8. For the one-to-one function $f(x)=\dfrac{x+1}{x-2}$,

   a) Find the inverse f^{-1};

   b) find the domain and range of f;

   c) find the domain and range of f^{-1};

   d) graph f and f^{-1} on the same set of axes.

Graph each of the following functions.

9. $f(x)=e^{x-1}$

10. $f(x)=2\log(x-1)$

Find the following. Do not use a calculator.

11. $\log 0.001$

12. $\ln 1$

13. Convert to an exponential equation: $\ln x=10$.

14. Convert to a logarithmic equation: $4^x=\dfrac{1}{2}$.

CHAPTER 4 **NAME**____________________________

TEST FORM B

Find each of the following using a calculator. Round to four decimal places.

15. $\ln 100$

16. $\log 0.65$

17. Find $\log_3 12$ using the change-of-base formula.

18. Express as a single logarithm: $3\log_c x - \log_c \sqrt{y} + 2\log_c z$.

19. Express in terms of sums and differences of logarithms: $\log \sqrt[5]{y^3 z}$.

20. Given that $\log_a 5 = 0.8271$ and $\log_a 20 = 1.5395$, find $\log_a 4$.

21. Simplify: $\ln e^{4x-5}$.

Solve.

22. $\log_4 8 = x$

23. $\log_3(x-2) + \log_3(x+4) = 3$

24. $2^{5+x} = 32^{x-4}$

25. $e^{2x} = 6$

ANSWERS

15. ________________

16. ________________

17. ________________

18. ________________

19. ________________

20. ________________

21. ________________

22. ________________

23. ________________

24. ________________

25. ________________

CHAPTER 4 **NAME**______________________________

TEST FORM B

ANSWERS

26. ______________

27. a) ______________
b) ______________
c) ______________
d) ______________

28. ______________

26. The population of a country doubled in 25 yr. What was the exponential growth rate?

27. Suppose $8000 is invested at interest rate k, compounded continuously, and grows to $11,466.64 in 6 yr.
a) Find the interest rate.
b) Find the exponential growth function.
c) Find the balance after 10 yr.
d) Find the doubling time.

---

28. Solve: $4^{\sqrt{x}} = 64$.

CHAPTER 4 NAME________________

TEST FORM C CLASS_____ SCORE_____ GRADE_____

1. Find the inverse of the relation $\{(-6, 2), (5, 4), (0, 8), (3, -2)\}$.

2. Determine whether the function shown below is one-to-one. Answer "yes" or "no."

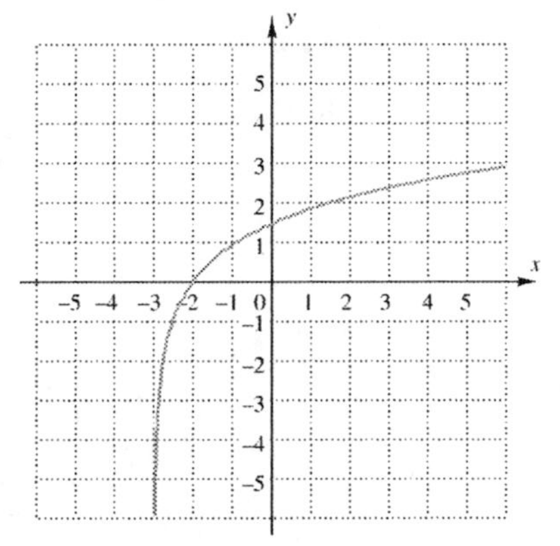

Find a formula for the inverse of the function, if the function is one-to-one. If it is not, state this.

3. $f(x) = x^3 + 1$

4. $f(x) = -2x + 1$

5. $f(x) = \dfrac{x}{3+x}$

6. $f(x) = x^2 - 2x - 3$

7. Use composition of functions to show that f^{-1} is as given: $f(x) = -\dfrac{2}{3}x,\ \ f^{-1}(x) = -\dfrac{3}{2}x$.

ANSWERS

1. ______________

2. ______________

3. ______________

4. ______________

5. ______________

6. ______________

7. ______________

ANSWERS

8. a)____________
   b)____________
   c)____________
   d)See graph.

9. See graph.

10. See graph.

11. ____________

12. ____________

13. ____________

14. ____________

8. For the one-to-one function $f(x)=\frac{2}{3-x}$,

   a) Find the inverse f^{-1};

   b) find the domain and range of f;

   c) find the domain and range of f^{-1};

   d) graph f and f^{-1} on the same set of axes.

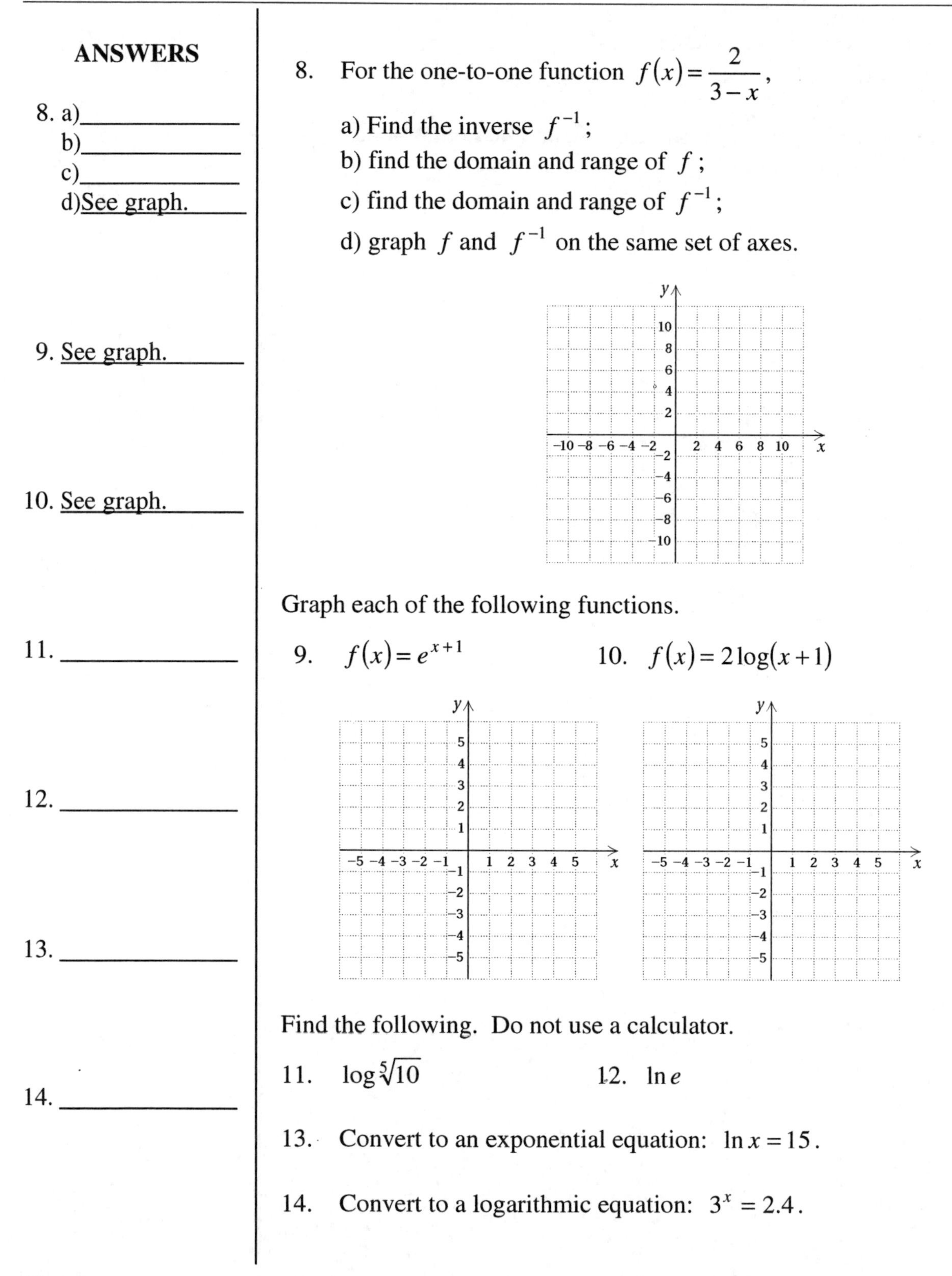

Graph each of the following functions.

9. $f(x)=e^{x+1}$

10. $f(x)=2\log(x+1)$

Find the following. Do not use a calculator.

11. $\log\sqrt[5]{10}$

12. $\ln e$

13. Convert to an exponential equation: $\ln x=15$.

14. Convert to a logarithmic equation: $3^x=2.4$.

CHAPTER 4 NAME____________________

TEST FORM C

Find each of the following using a calculator. Round to four decimal places.

15. $\ln 6.1$ 16. $\log 2.5$

17. Find $\log_4 24$ using the change-of-base formula.

18. Express as a single logarithm: $5\log_c x + \log_c y - 2\log_c z$.

19. Express in terms of sums and differences of logarithms: $\log \dfrac{\sqrt{x}y^2}{z}$.

20. Given that $\log_a 3 = 0.50000$ and $\log_a 2 = 0.3155$, find $\log_a 12$.

21. Simplify: $\ln e^{-x+2}$.

Solve.

22. $\log_2 64 = x$

23. $\log_2(x+4) + \log_2(x) = 5$

24. $4^{x-6} = 16^x$

25. $e^x = 6.3$

ANSWERS

15. ____________

16. ____________

17. ____________

18. ____________

19. ____________

20. ____________

21. ____________

22. ____________

23. ____________

24. ____________

25. ____________

CHAPTER 4 **NAME**____________________________

TEST FORM C

ANSWERS

26. ________________

27. a) ________________
b) ________________
c) ________________
d) ________________

28. ________________

26. The population of a country doubled in 70 yr. What was the exponential growth rate?

27. Suppose $4000 is invested at interest rate k, compounded continuously, and grows to $4934.71 in 6 yr.
a) Find the interest rate.
b) Find the exponential growth function.
c) Find the balance after 10 yr.
d) Find the doubling time.

---

28. Solve: $4\sqrt[3]{x^2} = 1$.

CHAPTER 4 NAME________________________________

TEST FORM D CLASS_____ SCORE_____ GRADE_____

---

1. Find the inverse of the relation $\{(-6,-8),(-3,5),(6,-2),(0,4)\}$.

2. Determine whether the graph shown below is one-to-one. Answer "yes" or "no."

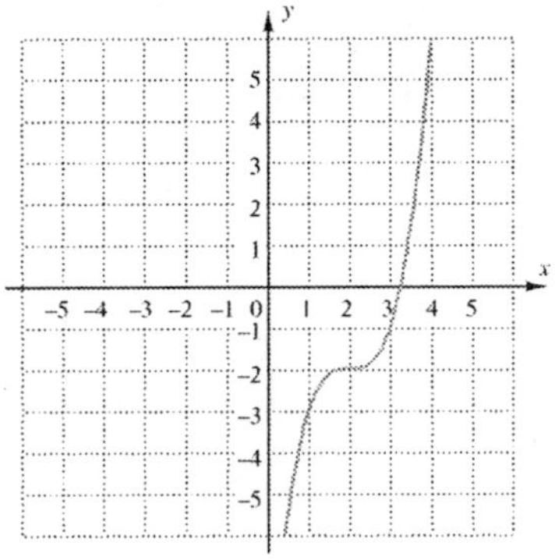

Find a formula for the inverse of the function, if the function is one-to-one. If it is not, state this.

3. $f(x)=x^3-2$

4. $f(x)=4-3x$

5. $f(x)=\dfrac{x}{x-1}$

6. $f(x)=x^2-2x$

7. Use composition of functions to show that f^{-1} is as given:

$f(x)=4x-5,\quad f^{-1}(x)=\dfrac{x+5}{4}$.

ANSWERS

1. ______________

2. ______________

3. ______________

4. ______________

5. ______________

6. ______________

7. ______________

CHAPTER 4 **NAME**__________________________

TEST FORM D

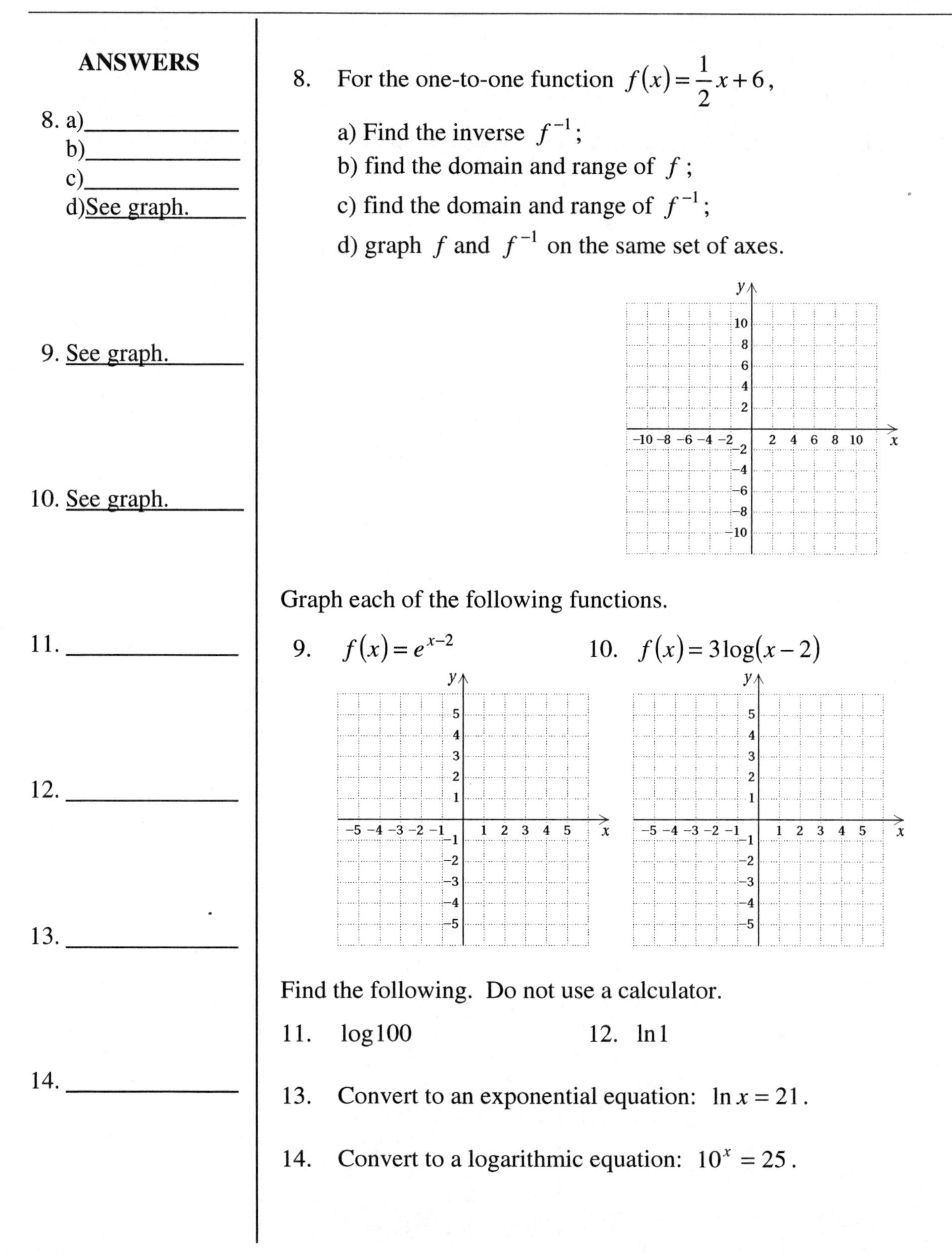

ANSWERS

8. a)____________
   b)____________
   c)____________
   d)See graph.

9. See graph.

10. See graph.

11. ____________

12. ____________

13. ____________

14. ____________

8. For the one-to-one function $f(x)=\frac{1}{2}x+6$,

   a) Find the inverse f^{-1};
   b) find the domain and range of f;
   c) find the domain and range of f^{-1};
   d) graph f and f^{-1} on the same set of axes.

Graph each of the following functions.

9. $f(x)=e^{x-2}$

10. $f(x)=3\log(x-2)$

Find the following. Do not use a calculator.

11. $\log 100$

12. $\ln 1$

13. Convert to an exponential equation: $\ln x = 21$.

14. Convert to a logarithmic equation: $10^{x} = 25$.

CHAPTER 4 **NAME**______________________________

TEST FORM D

Find each of the following using a calculator. Round to four decimal places.

15. $\ln 12$

16. $\log 25$

17. Find $\log_5 12$ using the change-of-base formula.

18. Express as a single logarithm: $2\log_c x + \log_c \sqrt{y} - \log_c z$.

19. Express in terms of sums and differences of logarithms:
$\log \frac{\sqrt{x^3 y^5}}{z^2}$.

20. Given that $\log_a 2 = 0.3333$ and $\log_a 12 = 1.1950$, find $\log_a 6$.

21. Simplify: $\ln e^{-3x+4}$.

Solve.

22. $\log_8 2 = x$

23. $\log_2(x+5) + \log_2(x-1) = 4$

24. $2^{3x+1} = 8^{4x}$

25. $e^x = 25$

ANSWERS

15. ____________

16. ____________

17. ____________

18. ____________

19. ____________

20. ____________

21. ____________

22. ____________

23. ____________

24. ____________

25. ____________

CHAPTER 4 **NAME**______________________

TEST FORM D

ANSWERS

26. ____________

27. a) ____________
    b) ____________
    c) ____________
    d) ____________

28. ____________

26. The population of a country doubled in 10 yr. What was the exponential growth rate?

27. Suppose $10,000 is invested at interest rate k, compounded continuously, and grows to $14,769.81 in 6 yr.
    a) Find the interest rate.
    b) Find the exponential growth function.
    c) Find the balance after 10 yr.
    d) Find the doubling time.

---

28. Solve: $3\sqrt[3]{x} = 20$.

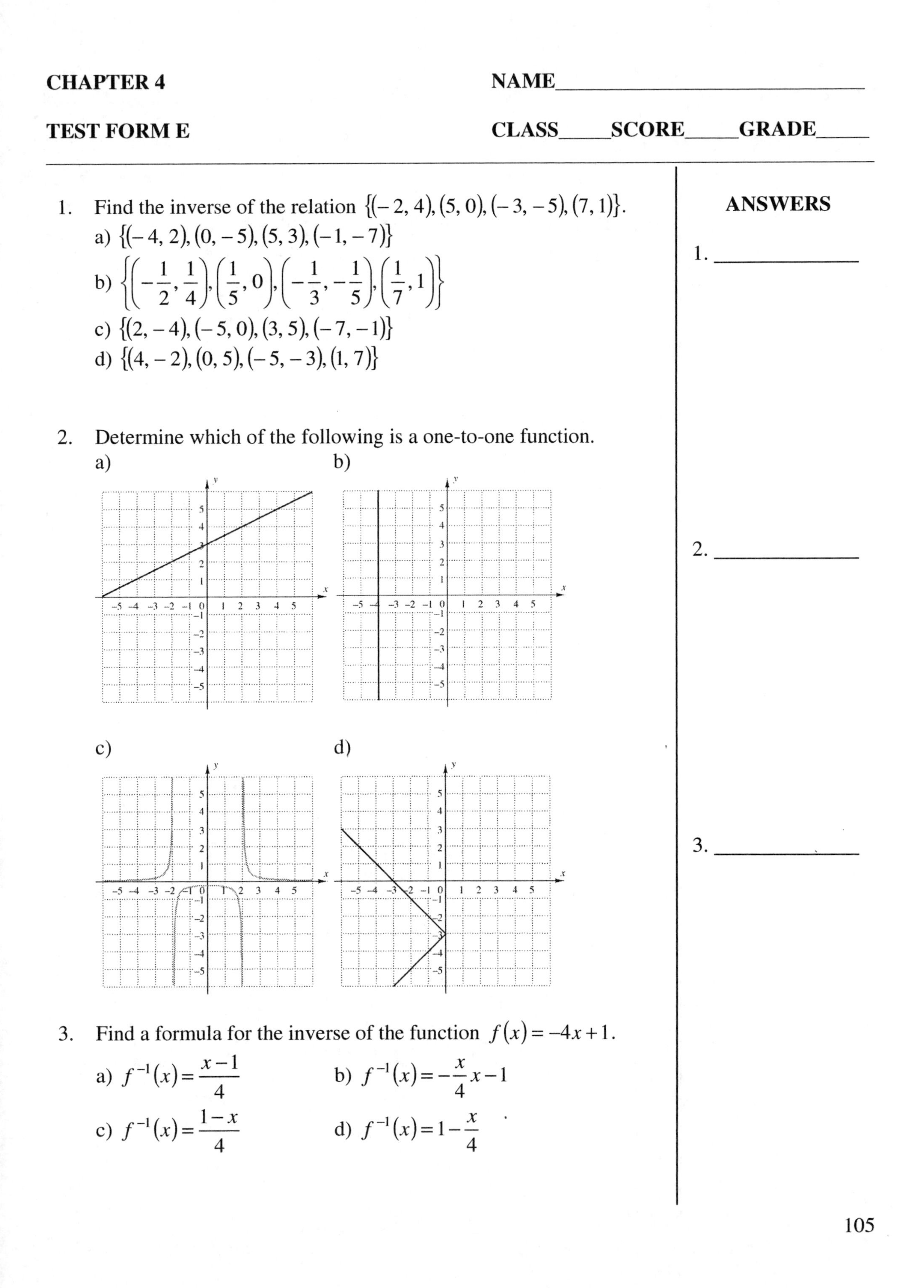

CHAPTER 4 NAME______________________________

TEST FORM E CLASS_____SCORE_____GRADE_____

ANSWERS

1. ______________

2. ______________

3. ______________

1. Find the inverse of the relation $\{(-2, 4), (5, 0), (-3, -5), (7, 1)\}$.

   a) $\{(-4, 2), (0, -5), (5, 3), (-1, -7)\}$

   b) $\left\{\left(-\frac{1}{2}, \frac{1}{4}\right), \left(\frac{1}{5}, 0\right), \left(-\frac{1}{3}, -\frac{1}{5}\right), \left(\frac{1}{7}, 1\right)\right\}$

   c) $\{(2, -4), (-5, 0), (3, 5), (-7, -1)\}$

   d) $\{(4, -2), (0, 5), (-5, -3), (1, 7)\}$

2. Determine which of the following is a one-to-one function.

   a) b)

   c) d)

3. Find a formula for the inverse of the function $f(x) = -4x + 1$.

   a) $f^{-1}(x) = \dfrac{x-1}{4}$ b) $f^{-1}(x) = -\dfrac{x}{4}x - 1$

   c) $f^{-1}(x) = \dfrac{1-x}{4}$ d) $f^{-1}(x) = 1 - \dfrac{x}{4}$

ANSWERS

4. ______________

5. ______________

4. Find a formula for the inverse of the function $f(x) = x^3 - 2$.

   a) $f^{-1}(x) = \sqrt[3]{x} + 2$ b) $f^{-1}(x) = \sqrt[3]{x+2}$

   c) $f^{-1}(x) = \sqrt[3]{x = 2}$ d) $f^{-1}(x) = x^3 + 2$

5. Which of the following graphs illustrates the graph of $g(x) = e^x - 3$?

   a) b)

   c) d)

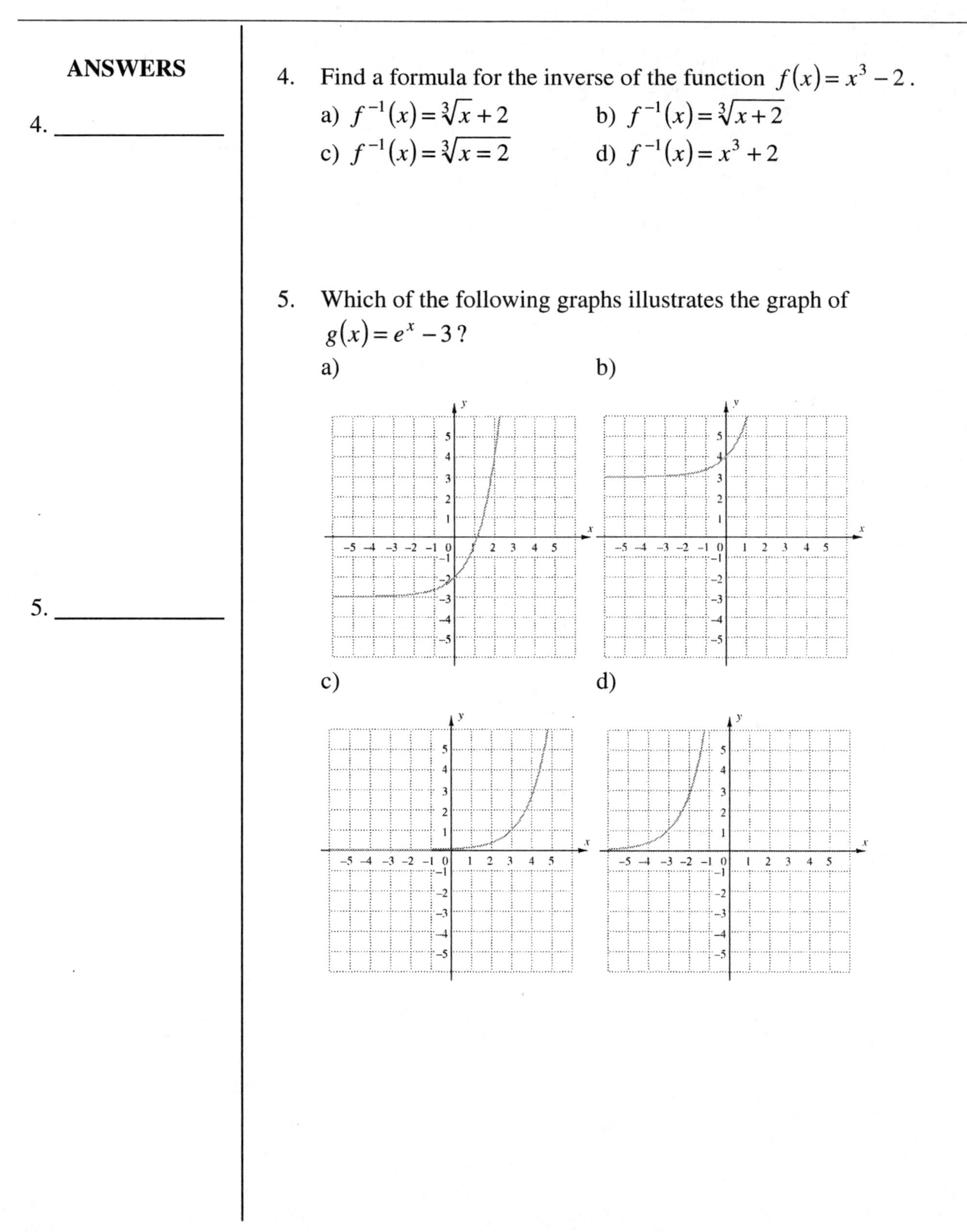

6. Which of the following graphs illustrates the graph of $f(x)=\log(x-2)$?

a) b) c) d)

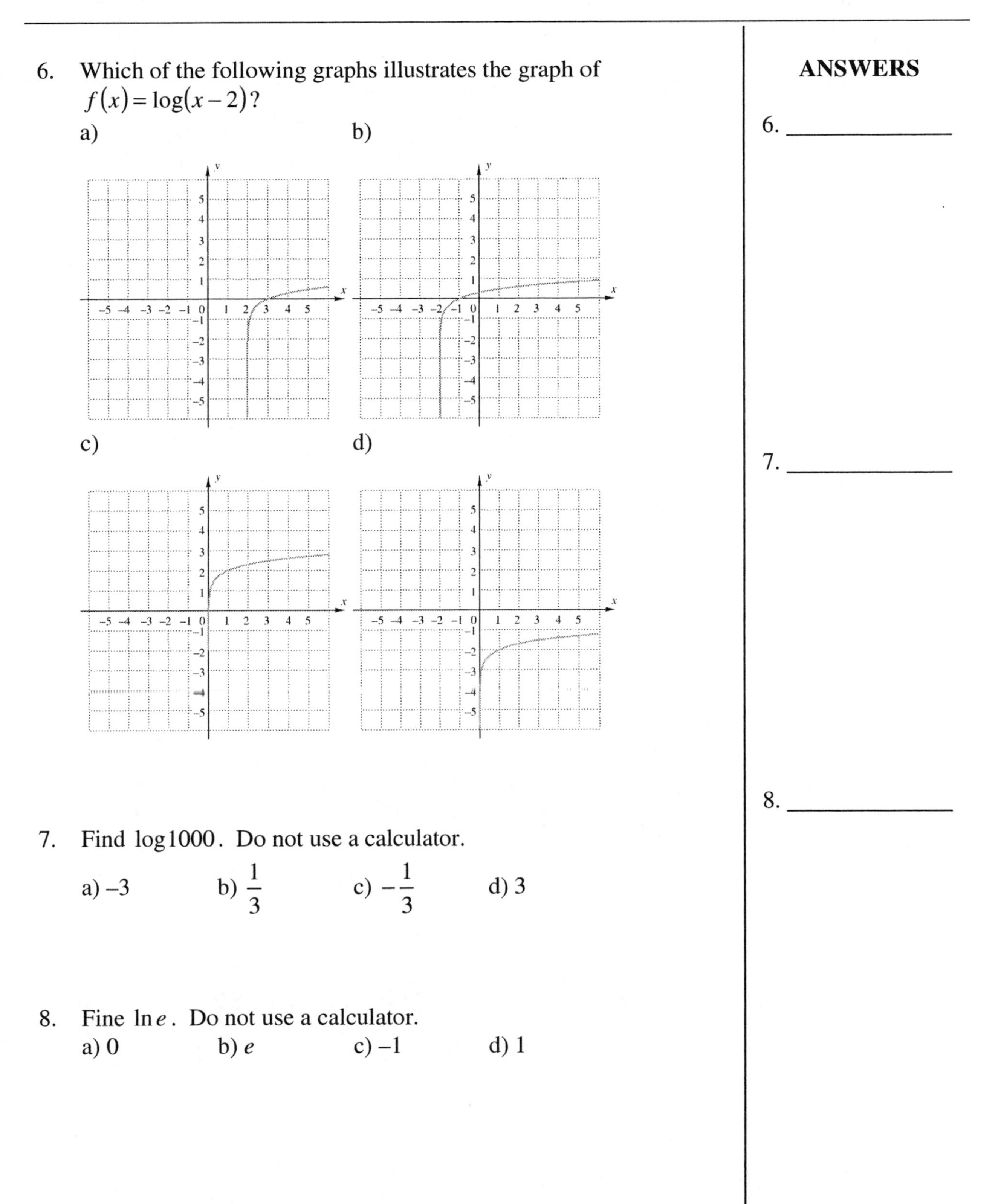

7. Find $\log 1000$. Do not use a calculator.

a) –3 b) $\frac{1}{3}$ c) $-\frac{1}{3}$ d) 3

8. Fine $\ln e$. Do not use a calculator.

a) 0 b) e c) –1 d) 1

ANSWERS

6. ______________

7. ______________

8. ______________

CHAPTER 4 NAME________________________________

TEST FORM E

ANSWERS

9. ______________

10. ______________

11. ______________

12. ______________

13. ______________

14. ______________

9. Convert to an exponential equation: $\log_3 x = 5$.

 a) $x = 5^3$ b) $x = 3^5$ c) $x^5 = 3$ d) $x^3 = 5$

10. Convert to a logarithmic equation: $4^x = 12.8$.

 a) $x = \log_4 12.8$ b) $x = \log_{12.8} 4$

 c) $\log_x 12.8 = 4$ d) $\log_x 4 = 12.8$

11. Find $\ln 2$ using a calculator. Round to four decimal places.

 a) 0.3010 b) 7.3891 c) 0.6931 d) 100

12. Find $\log_4 24$ using the change-of-base formula.

 a) 6 b) 0.7782 c) 2.2925 d) 1.7918

13. Express in terms of sums and differences of logarithms: $\log \sqrt[3]{xy^2}$.

 a) $\frac{1}{3}\log x + \frac{2}{3}\log y$ b) $-\frac{1}{3}\log x - \frac{2}{3}\log y$

 c) $3\log x + 6\log y$ d) $\frac{1}{3}\log x \cdot \frac{2}{3}\log y$

14. Given that $\log_a 16 = 1.7227$ and $\log_a 3 = 0.6826$, find $\log_a 48$.

 a) 1.1759 b) 2.4053 c) 1.6812 d) 1.5440

CHAPTER 4 NAME______________________________

TEST FORM E

ANSWERS

15. Simplify: $\ln e^{6t}$.

a) e^{-6t} b) te^6 c) $6t$ d) $-6t$

15. ____________

16. Solve: $\log_{100} 10 = x$.

a) $\frac{1}{10}$ b) 2 c) -2 d) $\frac{1}{2}$

16. ____________

17. Solve: $\log_2(x-3)+\log_2(2x-10)=4$.

a) 4 b) $\frac{29}{3}$ c) 7 d) No solution

17. ____________

18. Solve: $3^{x+2} = 27^{5x}$

a) $\frac{1}{7}$ b) $\frac{1}{22}$ c) $-\frac{1}{4}$ d) $-\frac{7}{4}$

18. ____________

19. $e^{-2x} = 0.3$

a) –0.2386 b) 0.6020 c) –1.2040 d) –0.6020

19. ____________

20. The population of a city doubled in 40 yr. What was the exponential growth rate?

a) 1.0% b) 1.8% c) 1.7% d) 3.0%

20. ____________

CHAPTER 4 NAME________________________

TEST FORM E

ANSWERS

21. ______________

22. ______________

23. ______________

24. ______________

21. Suppose $\$8000$ is invested at interest rate k, compounded continuously, and grows to $\$10{,}962.07$ in 5 yr. Find the interest rate.

a) 7.4 % b) 6.3 % c) 5.4 % d) 6.5 %

22. For the account described in Exercise 21, find the amount in the account after 10 yr.

a) $13,924.14 b) $14,259.22
c) $15,664.41 d) $15,020.88

23. For the account described in Exercise 21, find the doubling time.

a) 11.0 yr b) 10.7 yr c) 3.5 yr d) 4.6 yr

---

24. Find the domain: $f(x) = \ln(\log_2 x)$.

a) $(0, \infty)$ b) $(1, \infty)$ c) $[1, \infty)$ d) (e, ∞)

CHAPTER 4 NAME______________________________

TEST FORM F CLASS_____ SCORE_____ GRADE_____

ANSWERS

1. ______________

2. ______________

3. ______________

1. Find the inverse of the relation $\{(3,-2),(4,0),(-5,-1),(-1,6)\}$.
   a) $\{(-3,2),(-4,0),(5,1),(1,-6)\}$
   b) $\{(2,-3),(0,-4),(1,5),(-6,1)\}$
   c) $\{(-2,3),(0,4),(-1,-5),(6,-1)\}$
   d) $\left\{\left(\frac{1}{3},-\frac{1}{2}\right),\left(\frac{1}{4},0\right),\left(-\frac{1}{5},-1\right),\left(-1,\frac{1}{6}\right)\right\}$

2. Determine which of the following is a one-to-one function.

a) b) c) d)

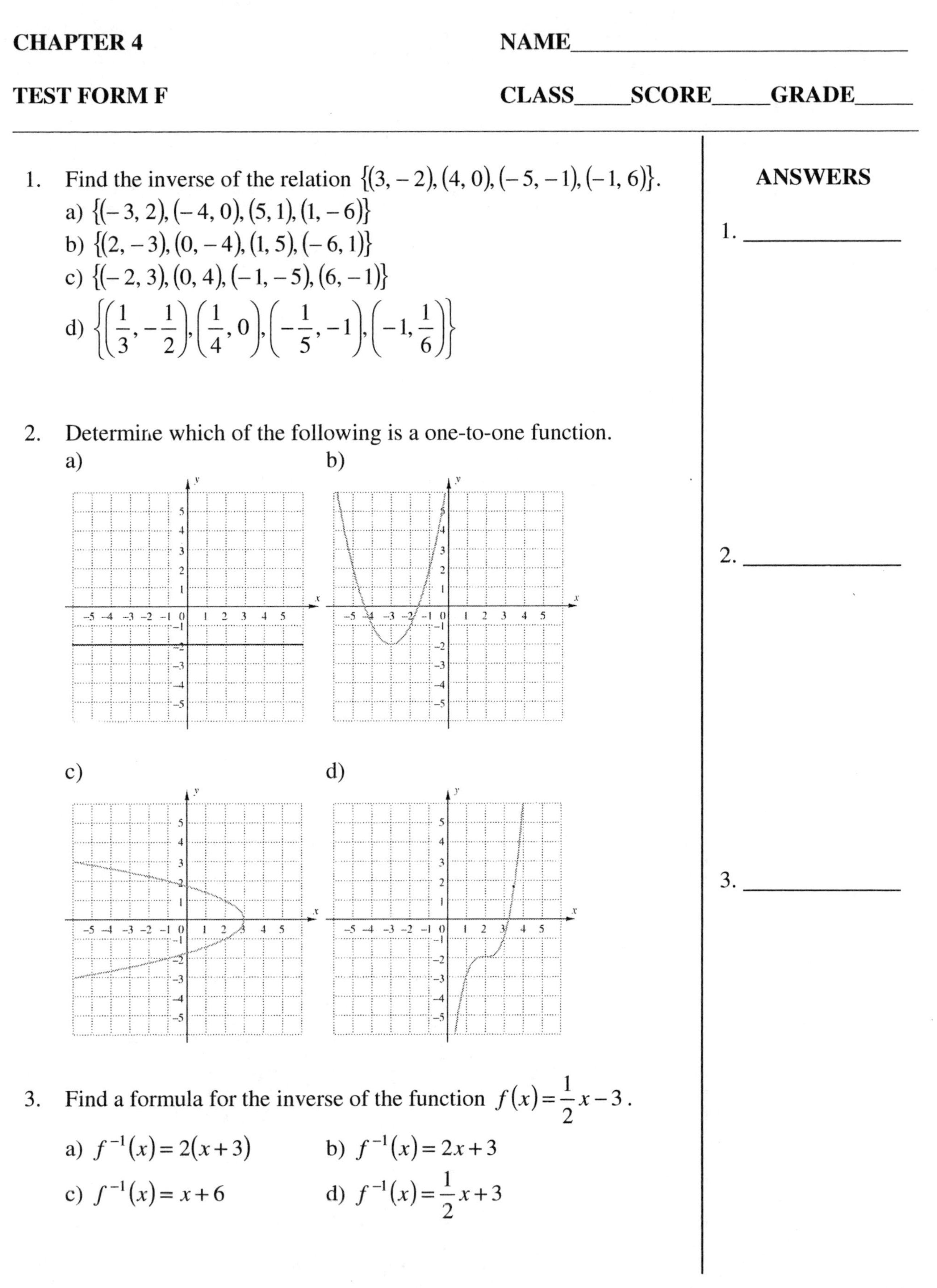

3. Find a formula for the inverse of the function $f(x)=\frac{1}{2}x-3$.

   a) $f^{-1}(x)=2(x+3)$ b) $f^{-1}(x)=2x+3$

   c) $f^{-1}(x)=x+6$ d) $f^{-1}(x)=\frac{1}{2}x+3$

CHAPTER 4 **NAME**____________________________

TEST FORM F

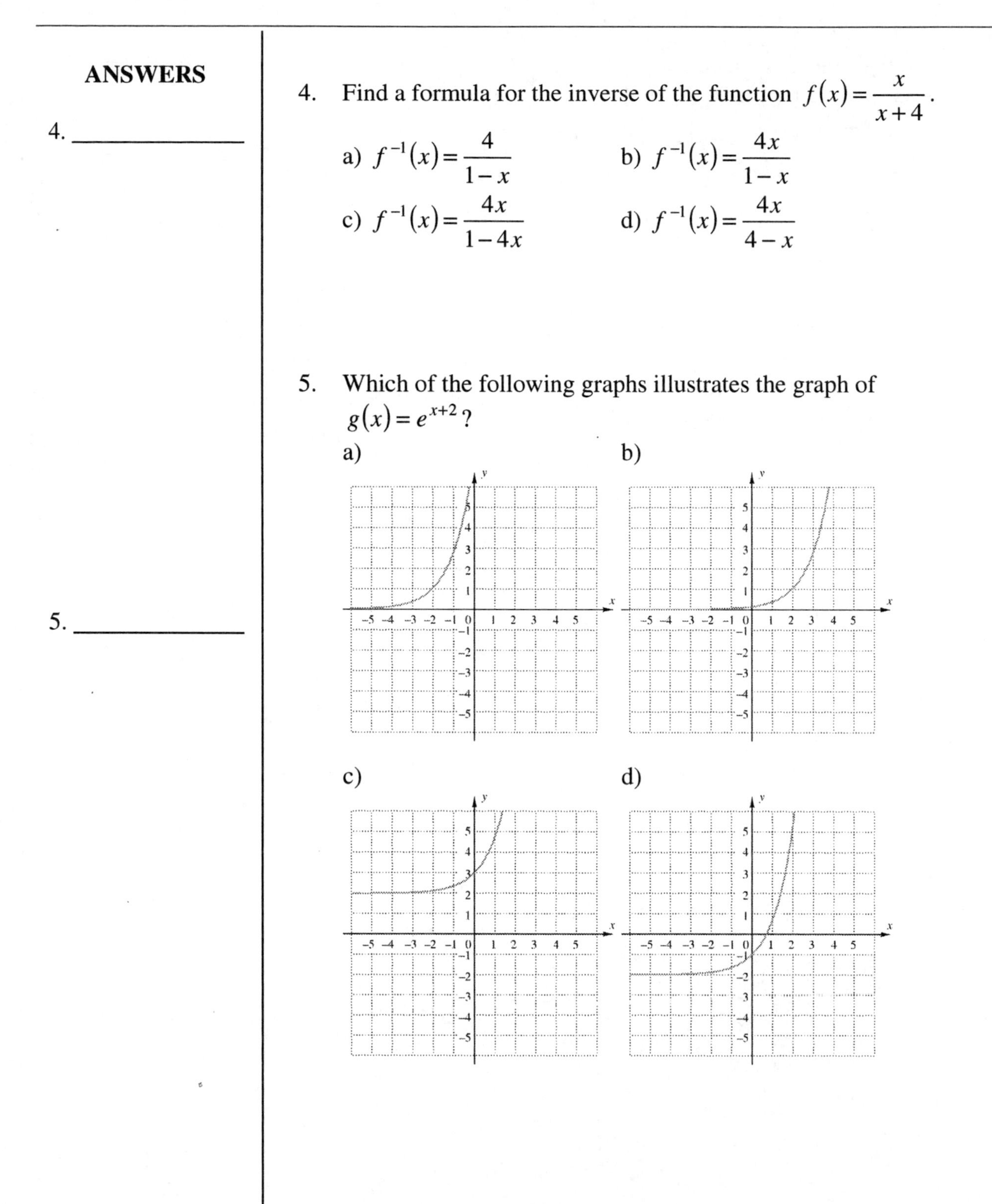

ANSWERS

4. ______________

5. ______________

4. Find a formula for the inverse of the function $f(x)=\dfrac{x}{x+4}$.

a) $f^{-1}(x)=\dfrac{4}{1-x}$ b) $f^{-1}(x)=\dfrac{4x}{1-x}$

c) $f^{-1}(x)=\dfrac{4x}{1-4x}$ d) $f^{-1}(x)=\dfrac{4x}{4-x}$

5. Which of the following graphs illustrates the graph of $g(x)=e^{x+2}$?

a) b)

c) d)

CHAPTER 4 **NAME**________________________

TEST FORM F

ANSWERS

6. ____________

7. ____________

8. ____________

6. Which of the following graphs illustrates the graph of $f(x) = \ln(x+4)$?

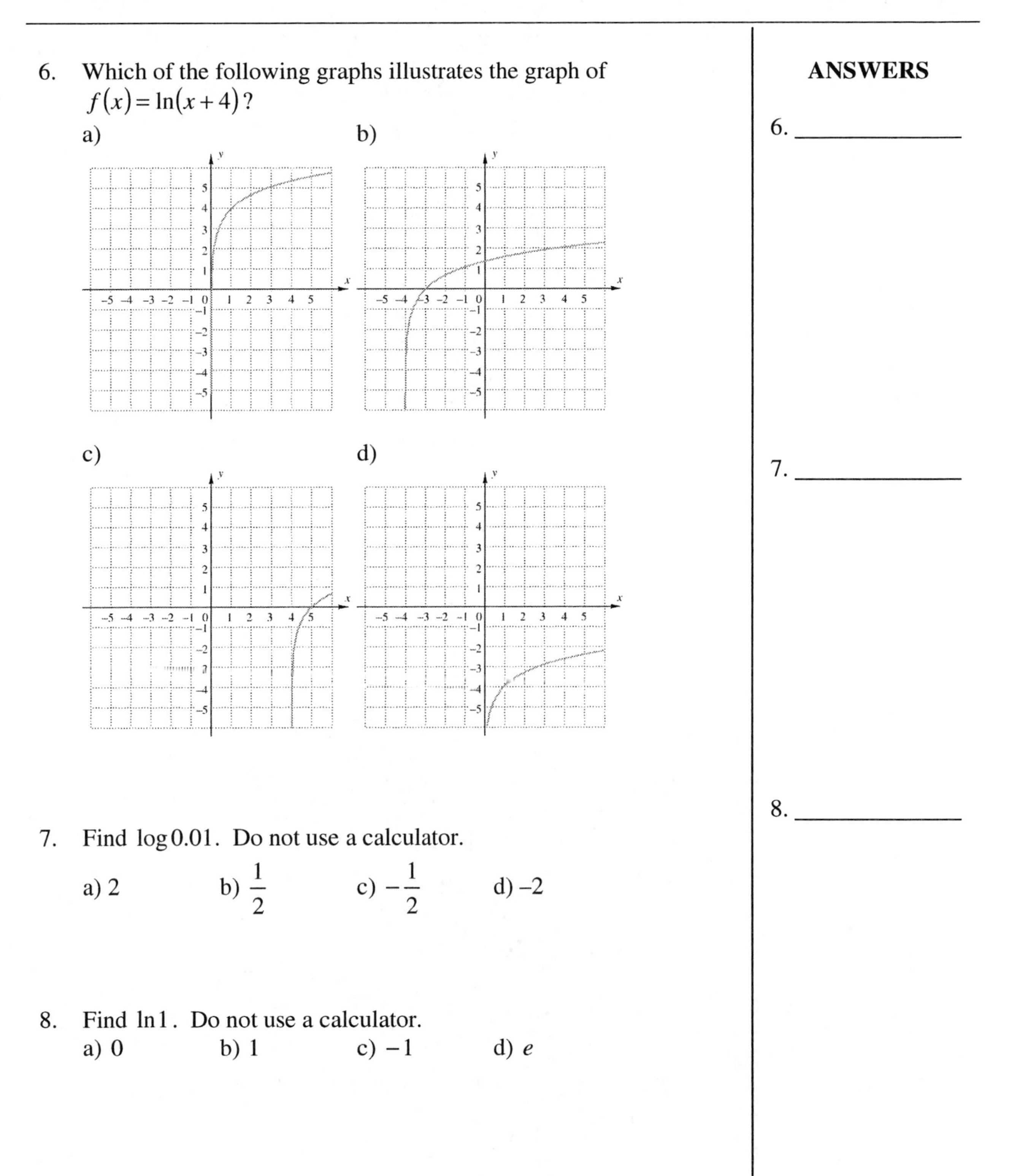

a) b) c) d)

7. Find $\log 0.01$. Do not use a calculator.

   a) 2 b) $\frac{1}{2}$ c) $-\frac{1}{2}$ d) –2

8. Find $\ln 1$. Do not use a calculator.

   a) 0 b) 1 c) -1 d) e

CHAPTER 4 **NAME**__________________________

TEST FORM F

ANSWERS

9. ____________

10. ____________

11. ____________

12. ____________

13. ____________

14. ____________

9. Convert to an exponential equation: $\log_5 x = 10$.

a) $x = 10^5$ b) $x^{10} = 5$ c) $10^x = 5$ d) $x = 5^{10}$

10. Convert to a logarithmic equation: $2^x = 20$.

a) $x = \log_2 20$ b) $x = \log 10$
c) $2 = \log_x 20$ d) $x = \log_{20} 2$

11. Find $\log 5.6$ using a calculator. Round to four decimal places.

a) 1.7228 b) 0.7482 c) 4.0254 d) 0.6990

12. Find $\log_2 10$ using the change-of-base formula.

a) 1 b) 0.3219 c) 3.3219 d) 0.6990

13. Express in terms of sums and differences of logarithms:

$\log\sqrt{\dfrac{x^4}{yz}}$.

a) $2\log x - \log y - \log z$

b) $\dfrac{1}{2}\log x - \log y - \log z$

c) $2\log x - \dfrac{1}{2}\log y + \dfrac{1}{2}\log z$

d) $2\log x - \dfrac{1}{2}\log y - \dfrac{1}{2}\log z$

14. Given that $\log_a 3 = 0.6131$ and $\log_a 12 = 1.3869$, find $\log_a 9$.

a) 1.2262 b) 0.7738 c) 1.8393 d) 2.2621

CHAPTER 4 **NAME**______________________________

TEST FORM F

ANSWERS

15. Simplify: $\ln e^{-4t}$.

a) $4t$ b) $-4t$ c) -4 d) e^{4t}

15. ______________

16. Solve: $\log_5 125 = x$.

a) 25 b) 3 c) –3 d) $\frac{1}{3}$

16. ______________

17. Solve: $\log_3(3x+6) - \log_3(x-6) = 2$.

a) 10 b) $-\frac{3}{2}$ c) 14 d) Does not exist

17. ______________

18. Solve: $4^{x+5} = 64^x$.

a) 5 b) $\frac{1}{3}$ c) $\frac{5}{2}$ d) No solution

18. ______________

19. Solve: $e^{2x} = 0.4$.

a) –1.6094 b) –0.9163 c) 0.7459 d) –0.4581

19. ______________

20. The population of a city doubled in 15 yr. What was the exponential growth rate?

a) 2.0% b) 4.6% c) 21.6% d) 3.9%

20. ______________

CHAPTER 4 NAME________________________

TEST FORM F

ANSWERS

21. ____________

22. ____________

23. ____________

24. ____________

21. Suppose $\$ 2000$ is invested at interest rate k, compounded continuously, and grows to $\$ 2473.53$ in 5 yr. Find the interest rate.

a) 7.89% b) 4.75% c) 4.25% d) 3.83%

22. For the account described in Exercise 21, find the amount in the account after 10 yr.

a) $3059.18 b) $4947.06
c) $2947.06 d) $3216.03

23. For the account described in Exercise 21, find the doubling time.

a) 21.1 yr b) 14.6 yr c) 7.1yr d) 16.3 yr

24. Solve: $|\log_2 x| = 6$.

a) –64, 64 b) $\frac{1}{64}$, 64 c) 64 d) $\frac{1}{36}$, 36

CHAPTER 5 NAME________________________

TEST FORM A CLASS____SCORE____GRADE____

Solve, if possible. Use any method. If there is no solution, state this.

1. $-5x + y = -4,$
   $-2y + 10x = 8$

2. $4x - 4y = 20,$
   $2x + 5y = -4$

3. $4x + 2y = 3,$
   $y = -2x - 1$

4. $x + 2y - 3z = 0,$
   $2x + 3y - 4z = 1,$
   $-4x + y - 2z = 3$

5. Classify the system in Exercise 1 as consistent or inconsistent and the equations as dependent or independent.

6. Classify the system in Exercise 4 as consistent or inconsistent and the equations as dependent or independent.

7. Peanuts which cost $3.50 per lb are to be mixed with almonds which cost $8 per lb to make a 20-lb blend that sells for $4.50 per lb. How many pounds of each should be used?

ANSWERS

1. ____________

2. ____________

3. ____________

4. ____________

5. ____________

6. ____________

7. ____________

CHAPTER 5 **NAME**________________________

TEST FORM A

ANSWERS

8. ______________

9. ______________

10. ______________

11. ______________

12. ______________

13. ______________

14. a) ______________

b) ______________

c) ______________

d) ______________

For Exercises 8 – 13, let

$$A = \begin{bmatrix} 6 & 4 \\ -3 & 2 \\ 1 & 0 \end{bmatrix}, B = \begin{bmatrix} 5 & 0 \\ -2 & 6 \end{bmatrix}, \text{ and } C = \begin{bmatrix} -1 & 2 \\ 4 & 7 \end{bmatrix}.$$

Find the following, if possible. If it is not possible, state this.

8. $B + C$

9. $C - A$

10. AC

11. BA

12. $2A$

13. B^{-1}

14. *Inventory Management.* The table below shows a school supply order to one vendor for four stores in a local chain. The order was placed the first week of August.

	Reams of Lined Paper	Spiral Notebooks	3-Ring Binders
Store 1	100	70	50
Store 2	120	80	60
Store 3	80	80	40
Store 4	60	100	30

a) Write the information in the table as a 4×3 matrix M.

b) In anticipation of a sale, the order was increased by 20 % for the second week of August. Write a matrix I that represents the increased order.

c) Find the sum $I + M$.

d) State what the entries of $I + M$ represent.

CHAPTER 5 NAME______________________

TEST FORM A

---

15. Write a matrix equation equivalent to the system of equations.
$5x + y + 6z = 8,$
$2x - y + z = -1,$
$4x - 2y + 3z = -4.$

Evaluate the determinant.

16. $\begin{vmatrix} 3 & 6 \\ -1 & 2 \end{vmatrix}$

17. $\begin{vmatrix} 5 & -1 & 3 \\ 0 & 4 & -2 \\ 2 & 6 & 1 \end{vmatrix}$

18. Solve using Cramer's rule. Show your work.
$3x - y = 6,$
$4x - 2y = 5$

19. Make a graph of $5x + y \leq -5$.

y
5
4
3
2
1
−5 −4 −3 −2 −1 1 2 3 4 5 x
−1
−2
−3
−4
−5

ANSWERS

15. ______________

16. ______________

17. ______________

18. ______________

19. See graph.

ANSWERS

20. ____________

21. ____________
____

22. ____________

23. ____________

20. Find the maximum and minimum values of $F = 2x - y$ subject to

$$x - y \geq 5$$
$$3x + 4y \leq 8$$
$$x \leq 6$$
$$y \geq -5.$$

21. *Maximizing Profit.* The Falls High student council sells hot dogs and popcorn during movie intermissions. They must sell at least 20 popcorns but cannot prepare more than 50. They must also sell at least 12 hot dogs but cannot cook more than 36. They cannot sell more than 60 items altogether. The profit on a hot dog is $\$1.00$ and on a popcorn is $\$0.75$. What is the maximum profit? How many hotdogs and popcorns must be sold to earn the maximum profit?

22. Decompose into partial fractions: $\dfrac{4x + 14}{x^2 - 3x - 4}$.

---

23. Three solutions of the equation $Ax + By = Cz - 14$ are $(-3, -3, 2)$, $(4, 1, -13)$,and $(6, -2, -9)$. Find *A*, *B*, and *C*.

CHAPTER 5 NAME____________________

TEST FORM B CLASS_____ SCORE_____ GRADE_____

Solve, if possible. Use any method. If there is no solution, state this.

1. $2x + 5y = 10$,
   $4x - 15 = -10y$

2. $3x + y = -6$,
   $-2x + 3y = 26$

3. $x - y = 5$,
   $2y = 2x - 10$

4. $2x + y - z = 9$,
   $3x - 4y + 2z = 25$,
   $x + y + 2z = -5$

5. Classify the system in Exercise 1 as consistent or inconsistent and the equations as dependent or independent.

6. Classify the system in Exercise 3 as consistent or inconsistent and the equations as dependent or independent.

7. Watermelon which costs \$0.80 per lb is to be mixed with honeydew melon which costs \$1.40 per lb to make 10 lb of mixed fruit that sells for \$1.00 per lb. How many pounds of each should be used?

ANSWERS

1. ____________

2. ____________

3. ____________

4. ____________

5. ____________

6. ____________

7. ____________

CHAPTER 5 NAME________________________

TEST FORM B

ANSWERS

8. ____________

9. ____________

10. ____________

11. ____________

12. ____________

13. ____________

14. a) ____________

b) ____________

c) ____________

d) ____________

For Exercises 8 – 13, let

$A=\begin{bmatrix} 8 & 1 & -2 \\ 0 & 4 & 3 \end{bmatrix}$, $B=\begin{bmatrix} -1 & 4 \\ 3 & 2 \end{bmatrix}$, and $C=\begin{bmatrix} 1 & -5 \\ 3 & 4 \end{bmatrix}$. Find the following, if possible. If it is not possible, state this.

8. $A+C$

9. $C-B$

10. AC

11. BC

12. $-2B$

13. B^{-1}

14. *Food Service Management.* A cafeteria manager is concerned about maintaining reasonable food costs. The table below shows the cost per serving, in dollars, for items on three daily specials.

Special	Entrée	Beverage	Dessert
Chef's Choice	6.25	1.20	1.00
Veggie Delight	3.00	1.20	2.25
House Special	5.50	1.20	1.50

On a particular day 19 'Chef's Choice' plates, 12 'Veggie Delight' plates, and 30 'House Special' plates were served.

a) Write the information in the table as a 3×3 matrix M.

b) Write a row matrix N that represents the number of each plate served.

c) Find the product NM.

d) State what the entries of NM represent.

CHAPTER 5 NAME________________________________

TEST FORM B

15. Write a matrix equation equivalent to the system of equations.
$2x + y - 5z = 10$,
$-3x - 4y + z = 1$,
$-x + 2y - 4z = 6$.

Evaluate the determinant.

16. $\begin{vmatrix} -2 & 4 \\ 7 & 8 \end{vmatrix}$

17. $\begin{vmatrix} 3 & 1 & -2 \\ 0 & 5 & -1 \\ -4 & 2 & 6 \end{vmatrix}$

18. Solve using Cramer's rule. Show your work.
$5x - 6y = 12$,
$-3x + 4y = 2$

19. Make a graph of $3x - y \leq 3$.

y
5
4
3
2
1
-5 -4 -3 -2 -1 1 2 3 4 5 x
-1
-2
-3
-4
-5

ANSWERS

15. ____________

16. ____________

17. ____________

18. ____________

19. See graph.

ANSWERS

20. ____________

21. ____________

22. ____________

23. ____________

20. Find the maximum and minimum values of $F = 3x + 2y$ subject to

$$\begin{aligned} x - y &\le 6 \\ -3x + 2y &\ge -16 \\ y &\le 0 \\ x &\ge 2. \end{aligned}$$

21. *Maximizing Income.* Amanda is planning to invest up to \$50,000 in corporate and municipal bonds. The least she is allowed to invest in corporate bonds is \$5000, and she does not want to invest more than \$25,000 in corporate bonds. She also does not want to invest more than \$30,000 in municipal bonds. The interest is 6 % on corporate bonds and 4 % on municipal bonds. This is simple interest for one year. How much should she invest in each type of bond to maximize her income? What is her maximum income?

22. Decompose into partial fractions: $\dfrac{x+13}{x^2 - 4x - 5}$.

23. Three solutions of the equation $Ax + By = Cz + 4$ are $(-2, -6, 9)$, $(-4, 8, -10)$, and $(4, 2, -9)$. Find A, B, and C.

CHAPTER 5 **NAME**______________________

TEST FORM C **CLASS**____ **SCORE**____ **GRADE**____

Solve, if possible. Use any method. If there is no solution, state this.

1. $4x + y = 11,$
   $5y - 4x = -17$

2. $3x - 2y = -8,$
   $-3x + 2y = 4$

3. $-2x + 5y = 13,$
   $4x + 26 = 10y$

4. $-3x + 3y - z = -8,$
   $4x + y + 3z = 4,$
   $2x - 5y + 2z = 21$

5. Classify the system in Exercise 1 as consistent or inconsistent and the equations as dependent or independent.

6. Classify the system in Exercise 3 as consistent or inconsistent and the equations as dependent or independent.

7. *Amusement Park Admission Prices.* Admission to the Upper Valley Amusement Park costs $6 more for adults than for children. Admission to the museum for 4 adults and 6 children costs $184. Find the cost of each adult's admission and each child's admission.

ANSWERS

1. ______________
2. ______________
3. ______________
4. ______________
5. ______________
6. ______________
7. ______________

CHAPTER 5 NAME______________________________

TEST FORM C

ANSWERS

8. ______________

9. ______________

10. ______________

11. ______________

12. ______________

13. ______________

14. a) ______________

b) ______________

c) ______________

d) ______________

For Exercises 8 – 13, let

$A = \begin{bmatrix} 1 & 0 & -3 \\ 2 & 4 & 6 \end{bmatrix}$, $B = \begin{bmatrix} 6 & -2 \\ 1 & 4 \end{bmatrix}$, and $C = \begin{bmatrix} 0 & -3 \\ 5 & 2 \end{bmatrix}$. Find the following, if possible. If it is not possible, state this.

8. $C - B$

9. $A + B$

10. AB

11. CB

12. $3A$

13. B^{-1}

14. *Production Management.* An elementary school sells three types of hot lunches during its two seatings. The following table shows the number of each type of lunch sold during each seating the second week in February.

	Pizza	Bagel	Baked Potato Bar
First Seating	30	45	25
Second Seating	50	20	55

It costs the lunch program \$2.00 for each pizza lunch, \$1.80 for each bagel lunch, and \$2.25 for each baked potato bar lunch.

a) Write the information in the table as a 2×3 matrix A.

b) Write a column matrix C that represents the cost of each type of lunch.

c) Find the product AC.

d) State what the entries in AC represent.

CHAPTER 5 NAME______________________________

TEST FORM C

15. Write a matrix equation equivalent to the system of equations.
$6x+4y+z=4$,
$-5x+2y+4z=6$,
$3x+y+2z=0$.

Evaluate the determinant.

16. $\begin{vmatrix} 5 & -4 \\ -2 & -1 \end{vmatrix}$

17. $\begin{vmatrix} 6 & -2 & 0 \\ 1 & 4 & 5 \\ 3 & -1 & 2 \end{vmatrix}$

18. Solve using Cramer's rule. Show your work.
$9x-3y=4$,
$-3x+7y=10$

19. Make a graph of $4x+y>4$.

ANSWERS

15. ______________

16. ______________

17. ______________

18. ______________

19. See graph.

CHAPTER 5 **NAME**______________________________

TEST FORM C

ANSWERS

20. ____________

21. ____________

22. ____________

23. ____________

20. Find the maximum and minimum values of $F = 5x - 2y$ subject to
$$\begin{aligned} x + 4y &\geq 4 \\ x - y &\leq 9 \\ x &\geq 5 \\ y &\leq 0. \end{aligned}$$

21. *Maximizing Profit.* Christine sells earrings and necklaces. She is able to display, at most, 400 pairs of earrings and 200 necklaces. Her insurance will not allow her to display more than 500 items for sale. Profit on each pair of earrings is \$12 and profit on each necklace is \$15. She must display at least 100 pairs of earrings and 100 necklaces in order to please her customers. How many of each type of jewelry should she have on display to maximize profit, assuming all items would sell?

22. Decompose into partial fractions: $\dfrac{7x+16}{x^2+2x-8}$.

---

23. The solutions of $Ax + By = Cz - 16$ are $(2, -1, 6)$, $(2, 5, 3)$, and $(-4, 8, -3)$. Find A, B, and C.

CHAPTER 5 **NAME**________________________

TEST FORM D **CLASS**____ **SCORE**____ **GRADE**____

Solve, if possible. Use any method. If there is no solution, state this.

1. $2x - 3y = -3,$
   $x + 2y = -12$

2. $3x - y = -2,$
   $2y - 4 = 6x$

3. $4x + 3y = -10,$
   $-6y = -20 + 8x$

4. $3x + 2y + z = 8,$
   $x - 4y + z = 22,$
   $x + y - 7z = -6$

5. Classify the system in Exercise 1 as consistent or inconsistent and the equations as dependent or independent.

6. Classify the system in Exercise 3 as dependent or independent and the equations as dependent or independent.

7. *Investment.* Liz inherited $8000 and invested it in two funds which pay 5.5% and 4% simple interest. The annual interest is $383. Find the amount invested at each rate.

ANSWERS

1. ____________

2. ____________

3. ____________

4. ____________

5. ____________

6. ____________

7. ____________

CHAPTER 5 NAME________________________________

TEST FORM D

ANSWERS

8. ______________

9. ______________

10. ______________

11. ______________

12. ______________

13. ______________

14. a) ______________

b) ______________

c) ______________

d) ______________

For Exercises 8 – 13, let

$$A = \begin{bmatrix} 0 & 8 \\ -2 & 4 \\ 3 & -1 \end{bmatrix}, B = \begin{bmatrix} 2 & 1 \\ 3 & -1 \end{bmatrix}, \text{ and } C = \begin{bmatrix} 6 & -2 \\ 0 & 7 \end{bmatrix}.$$ Find the following, if possible. If it is not possible, state this.

8. $C + A$

9. $B - C$

10. AB

11. CA

12. $-2A$

13. B^{-1}

14. *Snack Food Profit.* A concession service at a baseball game sells pretzels, peanuts, and cans of soda only. The table below shows the number of each item sold at three locations during one ball game.

	Home	Left Field	Right Field
Pretzels	30	40	50
Peanuts	40	50	70
Sodas	60	80	120

The concession service's profit on each pretzel is $\$0.80$, on each bag of peanuts is $\$0.60$, and on each soda is $\$1.00$.

a) Write the information in the table as a 3×3 matrix *M*.

b) Write a row matrix *N* that represents the profit per item.

c) Find the product *NM*.

d) State what the entries of *NM* represent.

CHAPTER 5 **NAME**______________________

TEST FORM D

ANSWERS

15. Write a matrix equation equivalent to the system of equations.

$x + 3y + z = 8$,
$3x - 4y + 3z = 2$,
$-x + +6y - 2z = 12$.

15. ______________

Evaluate the determinant.

16. $\begin{vmatrix} -1 & -6 \\ 3 & -4 \end{vmatrix}$

17. $\begin{vmatrix} 2 & 3 & -5 \\ 0 & 1 & 7 \\ -6 & -2 & 2 \end{vmatrix}$

16. ______________

17. ______________

18. Solve using Cramer's rule. Show your work.

$3x - 5y = 3$,
$-2x + 6y = 3$

18. ______________

19. Make a graph of $3x + 2y < -6$

19. See graph.

CHAPTER 5 NAME______________________________

TEST FORM D

ANSWERS

20. ______________

21. ______________
____

22. ______________

23. ______________

20. Find the maximum and minimum values of $F = 4x + 2y$ subject to
$$x + y \leq 5$$
$$x + 3y \geq 7$$
$$x \geq 2.$$

21. *Maximizing Profit.* Joanne's Bakery prepares pies and cakes. In a given week, a maximum of 120 pies and cakes can be prepared, of which 60 pies and 40 cakes are required by regular customers. The profit on a pie is $\$5$ and on a cake is $\$6$. How many of each item should the bakery make to maximize profit? What is the maximum profit?

22. Decompose into partial fractions: $\dfrac{9x+6}{x^2+2x-8}$.

---

23. Three solutions of the equation $Ax + By = Cz + 16$ are $(2, -1, 6)$, $(5, 4, 17)$, and $(3, -2, -1)$. Find *A*, *B*, and *C*.

CHAPTER 5 NAME________________________

TEST FORM E CLASS_____ SCORE_____ GRADE_____

ANSWERS

1. ____________
2. ____________
3. ____________
4. ____________
5. ____________
6. ____________

1. When solving $3x - 2y = 13,$ $4x + 3y = 6,$ find the y-coordinate.

   a) 3 b) –11 c) –2 d) –3

2. When solving $2x - y = 11,$ $6x + 5y = 9,$ find the x-coordinate.

   a) 4 b) –3 c) 12 d) $\frac{23}{2}$

3. When solving $6x + 5y = 8,$ $3x - 10y = -6,$ find the y-coordinate.

   a) $\frac{2}{3}$ b) $-\frac{4}{3}$ c) $-\frac{5}{4}$ d) $\frac{4}{5}$

4. Solve the system, if possible. $3x - 2y = 8,$ $y = \frac{3}{2}x - 4$

   a) $\left(\frac{8}{3} + \frac{2}{3}y,\ y\right)$ b) $(0, -4)$

   c) $(2, 1)$ d) No solution

5. When solving $3x + y - 2z = 5,$ $6x - 3y + 4z = -11,$ $-3x + 2y - 6z = 6,$ find the z-coordinate.

   a) $\frac{1}{3}$ b) $-\frac{29}{8}$ c) 5 d) $\frac{1}{2}$

6. *Snack Mixtures.* At Apple Tree Snacks a dried tropical fruit mixture worth \$7 per lb is mixed with mixed nuts worth \$10 per lb to get 30-lb of a mixture worth \$8.30 per lb. How much mixed nuts were used?

   a) 17 lb b) 13 lb c) 15 lb d) 14 lb

CHAPTER 5 **NAME**____________________

TEST FORM E

ANSWERS

7. ____________

8. ____________

9. ____________

10. ____________

11. ____________

For Exercises 7 – 11, let

$$A=\begin{bmatrix} 8 & -2 \\ -1 & 4 \\ 1 & 5 \end{bmatrix}, B=\begin{bmatrix} 4 & -1 \\ 0 & 3 \end{bmatrix}, \text{and } C=\begin{bmatrix} 5 & -4 \\ 3 & 2 \end{bmatrix}.$$

7. Find $B+C$.

a) $\begin{bmatrix} 17 & -18 \\ 9 & 6 \end{bmatrix}$ b) $\begin{bmatrix} 9 & -5 \\ 3 & 5 \end{bmatrix}$

c) $\begin{bmatrix} 4 & -1 & 5 & -4 \\ 0 & 3 & 3 & 2 \end{bmatrix}$ d) Not possible

8. Find $A-C$.

a) $\begin{bmatrix} -1 & 3 \\ -3 & -1 \end{bmatrix}$ b) $\begin{bmatrix} 3 & 2 \\ -4 & 2 \end{bmatrix}$ c) $\begin{bmatrix} 3 & 2 \\ -4 & 2 \\ 1 & 5 \end{bmatrix}$ d) Not possible

9. Find CB.

a) $\begin{bmatrix} 20 & -17 \\ 12 & 3 \end{bmatrix}$ b) $\begin{bmatrix} 17 & -18 \\ 9 & 6 \end{bmatrix}$

c) $\begin{bmatrix} 20 & 4 \\ 0 & 6 \end{bmatrix}$ d) Not possible

10. Find $-2B$.

a) $\begin{bmatrix} 2 & -3 \\ -2 & 1 \end{bmatrix}$ b) $\begin{bmatrix} -8 & 2 \\ 0 & -6 \end{bmatrix}$

c) $\begin{bmatrix} -8 & -1 \\ 0 & 3 \end{bmatrix}$ d) Not possible

11. Find C^{-1}.

a) $\begin{bmatrix} \frac{1}{5} & -\frac{1}{4} \\ \frac{1}{3} & \frac{1}{2} \end{bmatrix}$ b) $\begin{bmatrix} -5 & 4 \\ -3 & -2 \end{bmatrix}$ c) $\begin{bmatrix} \frac{1}{11} & \frac{2}{11} \\ -\frac{3}{22} & \frac{5}{22} \end{bmatrix}$ d) Not possible

CHAPTER 5 NAME______________________________

TEST FORM E

ANSWERS

12. ____________

13. ____________

14. ____________

12. *Inventory Management.* The table below shows an order to one bakery from two delis in a local chain. The order was placed the last week in July.

	Long Sub Rolls	Round Sub Rolls	Dinner Rolls
Eastside Deli	80	50	40
Westside Deli	100	60	40

The delis decreased the size of their orders by 10% the following week. Write a matrix which represents the orders for the following week.

a) $\begin{bmatrix} 72 & 45 & 36 \\ 90 & 54 & 36 \end{bmatrix}$ b) $\begin{bmatrix} 70 & 40 & 30 \\ 90 & 50 & 30 \end{bmatrix}$

c) $\begin{bmatrix} 88 & 55 & 44 \\ 110 & 66 & 44 \end{bmatrix}$ d) $\begin{bmatrix} 153 \\ 180 \end{bmatrix}$

13. Find the determinant.

$$\begin{vmatrix} 5 & 0 & -4 \\ 3 & 2 & 1 \\ -1 & 6 & -2 \end{vmatrix}$$

a) 104 b) 0 c) –24 d) –130

14. Find y using Cramer's rule.

$4x - y = -1,$

$-3x + 5y = 3$

a) $-\frac{2}{17}$ b) $\frac{9}{17}$ c) $\frac{15}{17}$ d) $\frac{17}{9}$

NAME______________________________

TEST FORM E

ANSWERS

15. ____________

16. ____________

17. ____________

18. ____________

15. Which of the following represents the graph of $-3x+4y \geq 12$?

a) b) c) d)

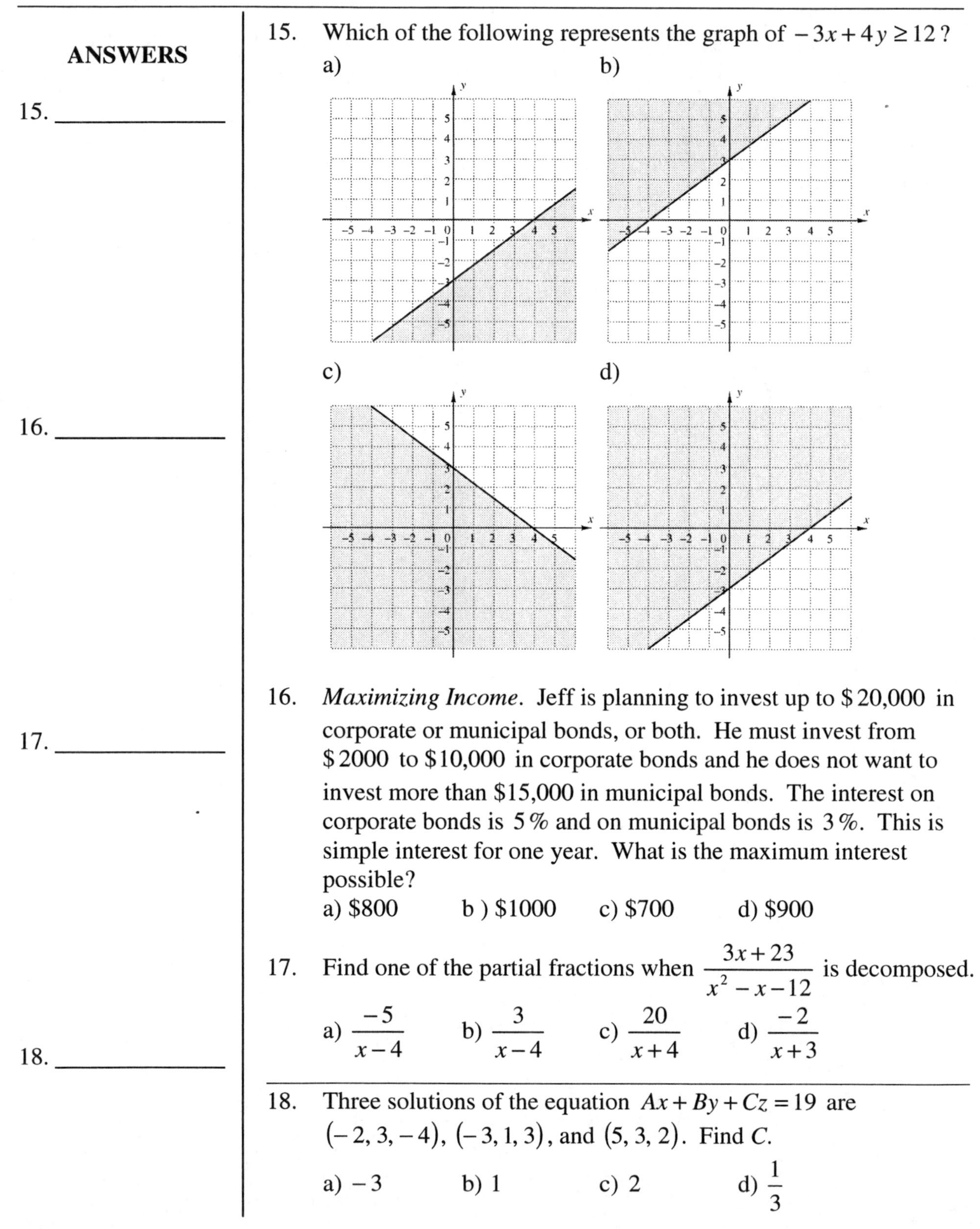

16. *Maximizing Income.* Jeff is planning to invest up to $\$20{,}000$ in corporate or municipal bonds, or both. He must invest from $\$2000$ to $\$10{,}000$ in corporate bonds and he does not want to invest more than $15,000 in municipal bonds. The interest on corporate bonds is 5% and on municipal bonds is 3%. This is simple interest for one year. What is the maximum interest possible?

a) $800 b) $1000 c) $700 d) $900

17. Find one of the partial fractions when $\dfrac{3x+23}{x^2-x-12}$ is decomposed.

a) $\dfrac{-5}{x-4}$ b) $\dfrac{3}{x-4}$ c) $\dfrac{20}{x+4}$ d) $\dfrac{-2}{x+3}$

---

18. Three solutions of the equation $Ax+By+Cz=19$ are $(-2,3,-4)$, $(-3,1,3)$, and $(5,3,2)$. Find C.

a) -3 b) 1 c) 2 d) $\dfrac{1}{3}$

CHAPTER 5 NAME________________________________

TEST FORM F CLASS_____ SCORE_____ GRADE_____

ANSWERS

1. When solving $6x+2y=-26$, $4x-5y=-11$, find the *y*-coordinate.

   a) –1 b) 4 c) –4 d) 1

2. When solving $5x-2y=-11$, $-4x+y=10$, find the *x*-coordinate.

   a) 3 b) –3 c) –2 d) $\frac{9}{13}$

3. When solving $x+2y=-1$, $2x+6y=2$, find the *y*-coordinate.

   a) -5 b) 5 c) 2 d) 0

4. Solve the system, if possible. $2x-y=8$, $2y-4x=-8$

   a) $\left(\frac{20}{3},\frac{16}{3}\right)$ b) $(3,-2)$ c) $(x,2x-8)$ d) No solution

5. When solving $2x+4y+z=0$, $-3x+2y+4z=-13$, $4x-6y-7z=24$, find the *z*-coordinate.

   a) 2 b) 5 c) –3 d) –22

6. *Ticket Prices*. One summer 1280 tickets were sold for the Westmore children's theatre production. Tickets cost \$22 for adults and \$15 for children. Total receipts were \$23,260. How many children's tickets were sold?

   a) 580 b) 300 c) 1080 d) 700

1. ____________
2. ____________
3. ____________
4. ____________
5. ____________
6. ____________

CHAPTER 5 **NAME**____________________________

TEST FORM F

ANSWERS

7. ____________

8. ____________

9. ____________

10. ____________

11. ____________

For Exercises 7 – 11, let

$$A = \begin{bmatrix} 4 & 2 & 3 \\ -1 & -5 & 1 \end{bmatrix}, B = \begin{bmatrix} 5 & -4 \\ 2 & -2 \end{bmatrix}, \text{and } C = \begin{bmatrix} 1 & -6 \\ 3 & 2 \end{bmatrix}.$$

7. Find $C + B$.

a) $\begin{bmatrix} -7 & 8 \\ 19 & -16 \end{bmatrix}$ b) $\begin{bmatrix} 6 & -10 \\ 5 & 0 \end{bmatrix}$

c) $\begin{bmatrix} 6 & -10 \\ 5 & -4 \end{bmatrix}$ d) Not possible

8. Find $C - A$.

a) $\begin{bmatrix} -3 & -8 & -3 \\ 4 & 7 & -1 \end{bmatrix}$ b) $\begin{bmatrix} -3 & -8 \\ 4 & 6 \end{bmatrix}$

c) $\begin{bmatrix} -4 & 12 \\ 3 & 10 \end{bmatrix}$ d) Not possible

9. Find CB.

a) $\begin{bmatrix} -7 & 8 \\ 19 & -16 \end{bmatrix}$ b) $\begin{bmatrix} -7 & -38 \\ -4 & -16 \end{bmatrix}$

c) $\begin{bmatrix} 5 & 24 \\ 6 & -4 \end{bmatrix}$ d) Not possible

10. Find $3A$.

a) $\begin{bmatrix} 7 & 5 & 6 \\ 2 & -2 & 4 \end{bmatrix}$ b) $\begin{bmatrix} 12 & 6 & 9 \\ -3 & -15 & 3 \end{bmatrix}$

c) $\begin{bmatrix} 12 & 2 & 3 \\ -3 & -5 & 1 \end{bmatrix}$ d) Not possible

11. Find C^{-1}.

a) $\begin{bmatrix} 1 & -\frac{1}{6} \\ \frac{1}{3} & \frac{1}{2} \end{bmatrix}$ b) $\begin{bmatrix} -1 & 6 \\ -3 & 2 \end{bmatrix}$ c) $\begin{bmatrix} \frac{1}{10} & \frac{3}{10} \\ -\frac{3}{20} & \frac{1}{20} \end{bmatrix}$ d) Not possible

CHAPTER 5 NAME________________________

TEST FORM F

ANSWERS

12. ____________

13. ____________

14. ____________

12. The table below shows expenses, in dollars, for two sales representatives for one term.

	Postage	Phone	Copies
J. Smith	150.00	80.00	120.00
M. Jones	50.00	200.00	75.00

Their budget calls for a 5 % increase in spending for the upcoming term. Which matrix represents their budget for the next term?

a) $\begin{bmatrix} 150.05 & 80.05 & 120.05 \\ 50.05 & 200.05 & 75.05 \end{bmatrix}$

b) $\begin{bmatrix} 155.00 & 85.00 & 125.00 \\ 55.00 & 205.00 & 80.00 \end{bmatrix}$

c) $\begin{bmatrix} 157.50 & 84.00 & 126.00 \\ 52.50 & 210.00 & 78.75 \end{bmatrix}$

d) $\begin{bmatrix} 7.50 & 4.00 & 6.00 \\ 2.50 & 10.00 & 3.75 \end{bmatrix}$

13. Evaluate the determinant.

$$\begin{vmatrix} -6 & 0 & 5 \\ 1 & -2 & 4 \\ 3 & -1 & 1 \end{vmatrix}$$

a) 13 b) 23 c) 1 d) –61

14. Find x using Cramer's rule.

$3x-4y=2,$

$5x+y=6$

a) $\frac{8}{23}$ b) $\frac{23}{26}$ c) $\frac{26}{23}$ d) $\frac{22}{17}$

CHAPTER 5 NAME______________________________

TEST FORM F

ANSWERS

15. ____________

16. ____________

17. ____________

18. ____________

15. Which of the following represents the graph of $2x+5y \le -10$?

a) b) c) d)

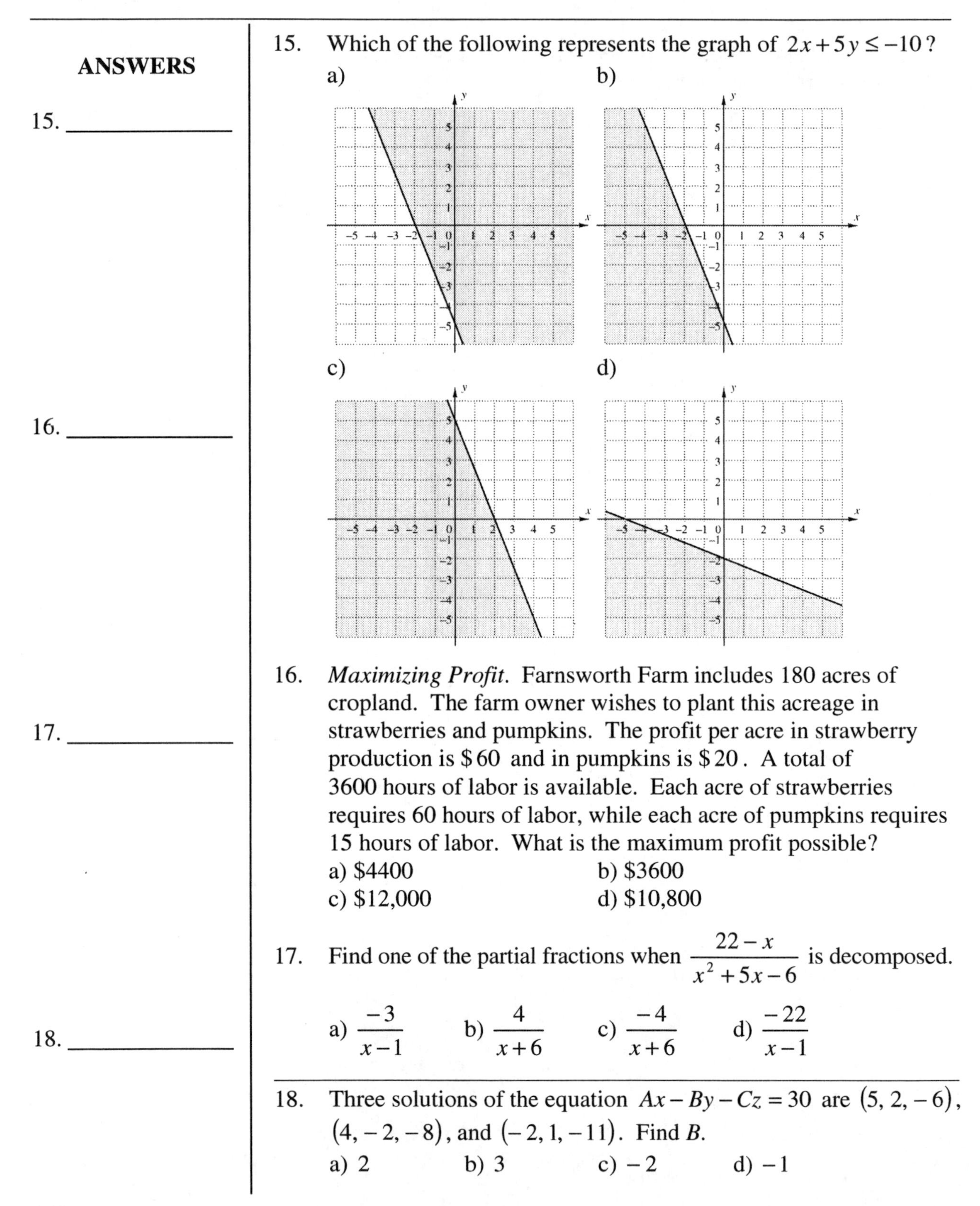

16. *Maximizing Profit.* Farnsworth Farm includes 180 acres of cropland. The farm owner wishes to plant this acreage in strawberries and pumpkins. The profit per acre in strawberry production is $\$60$ and in pumpkins is $\$20$. A total of 3600 hours of labor is available. Each acre of strawberries requires 60 hours of labor, while each acre of pumpkins requires 15 hours of labor. What is the maximum profit possible?

a) $4400 b) $3600
c) $12,000 d) $10,800

17. Find one of the partial fractions when $\dfrac{22-x}{x^2+5x-6}$ is decomposed.

a) $\dfrac{-3}{x-1}$ b) $\dfrac{4}{x+6}$ c) $\dfrac{-4}{x+6}$ d) $\dfrac{-22}{x-1}$

18. Three solutions of the equation $Ax - By - Cz = 30$ are $(5, 2, -6)$, $(4, -2, -8)$, and $(-2, 1, -11)$. Find *B*.

a) 2 b) 3 c) -2 d) -1

CHAPTER 6 NAME________________________

TEST FORM A CLASS_____SCORE_____GRADE_____

Match each of the following with its graph.

ANSWERS

1. $y^2 - 9x^2 = 9$ 1. ______________

2. $x^2 - 2x + y^2 + 6y - 15 = 0$ 2. ______________

3. $8x^2 + 3y^2 = 72$ 3. ______________

4. $x^2 + 8x - y = -10$ 4. ______________

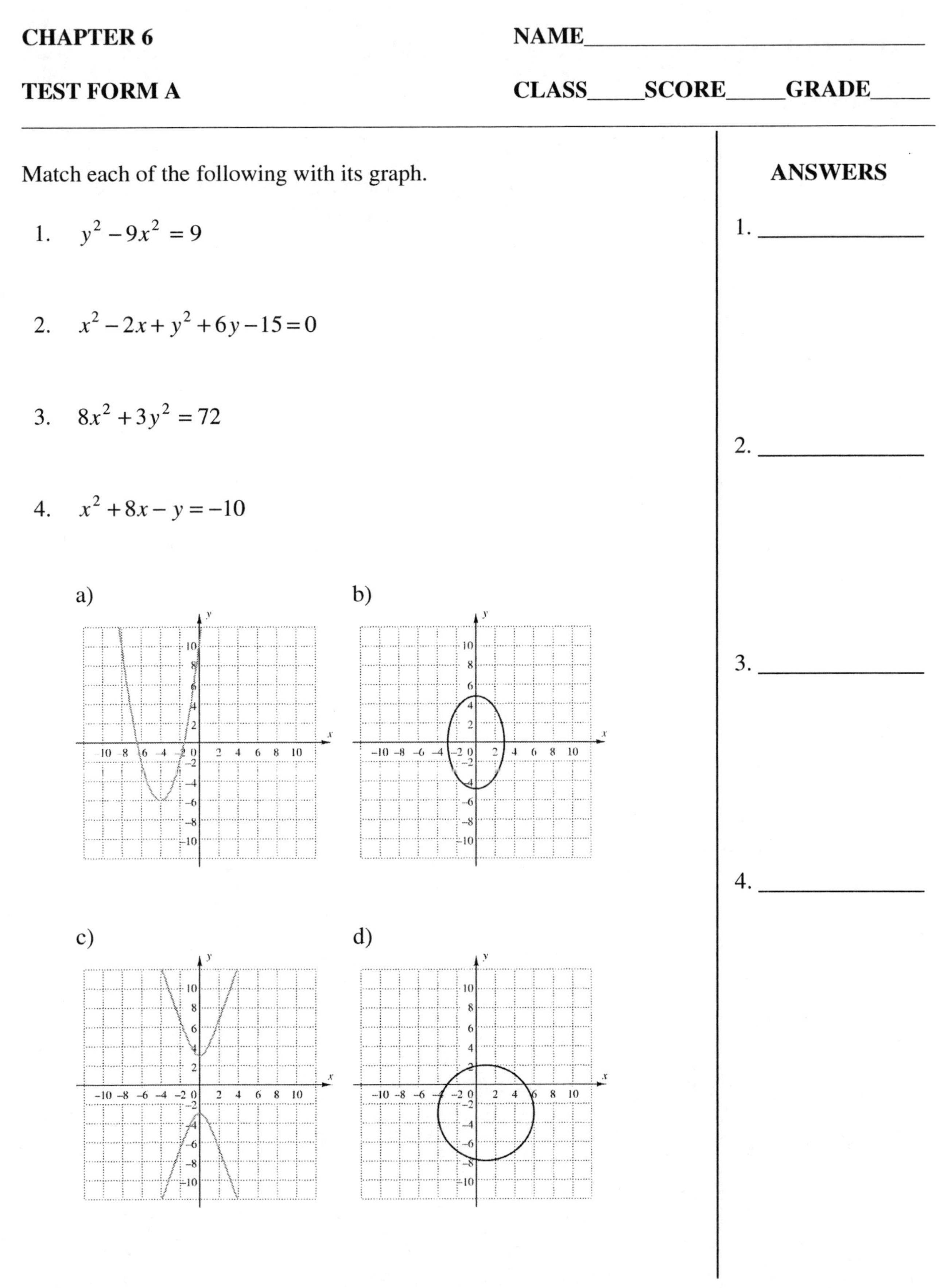

NAME______________________________

TEST FORM A

ANSWERS

5. Vertex: __________

Focus : __________

Directrix: __________

See graph. __________

6. ______________

7. Center: __________

Radius: __________

See graph. __________

8. Center: __________

Vertices: __________

Foci: __________

See graph. __________

5. Find the vertex, the focus, and the directrix of the parabola given by $x^2 + 2x + 8y - 47 = 0$. Then graph.

6. Find an equation of the parabola with focus $(0, -2)$ and directrix $y = 2$.

7. Find the center and the radius of the circle given by $x^2 + 4x + y^2 - 10y - 7 = 0$. Then graph.

8. Find the center, the vertices, and the foci of the ellipse given by $9x^2 + 16y^2 = 144$. Then graph.

CHAPTER 6 NAME______________________________

TEST FORM A

ANSWERS

9. Find an equation of the ellipse having vertices $(-5, 0)$ and $(5, 0)$ with minor axis of length 6.

9. ______________

10. Find the center, the vertices, the foci, and the asymptotes of the hyperbola given by $\frac{(y-3)^2}{9} - \frac{(x+2)^2}{4} = 1$. Then graph.

y
10
8
6
4
2
−10 −8 −6 −4 −2 2 4 6 8 10 x
−2
−4
−6
−8
−10

10. Center: ______________

Vertices: ______________

Foci: ______________

Asymptotes: ______________

See graph.

11. Find the asymptotes of the hyperbola given by $5x^2 - 3y^2 = 15$.

11. ______________

12. *Field Microphone.* A field microphone has a parabolic cross section. It is 20 in. wide at the opening and its focus is 2 in. from the vertex. How deep is the microphone at the vertex?

12. ______________

CHAPTER 6 NAME______________________________

TEST FORM A

ANSWERS

13. ______________

14. ______________

15. ______________

16. ______________

17. ______________

18. ______________

Solve.

13. $2x + y = -4,$
$2x^2 - y^2 = 14$

14. $-5x^2 + 2y^2 = 5,$
$3x^2 - 4y^2 = -73$

15. $x - y = 10,$
$xy = 24$

16. *Lot Dimensions.* A rectangular lot has a perimeter of 220 ft and an area of 3000 ft^2. Find its dimensions.

17. Graph the system of inequalities. Then find the coordinates of the points of intersection of the graphs.
$y < -x^2 + 4,$
$y \geq x - 2$

y
10
8
6
4
2
−10 −8 −6 −4 −2 2 4 6 8 10 x
−2
−4
−6
−8
−10

---

18. Find an equation of a circle for which the endpoints of a diameter are $(-2, 5)$ and $(-8, 13)$.

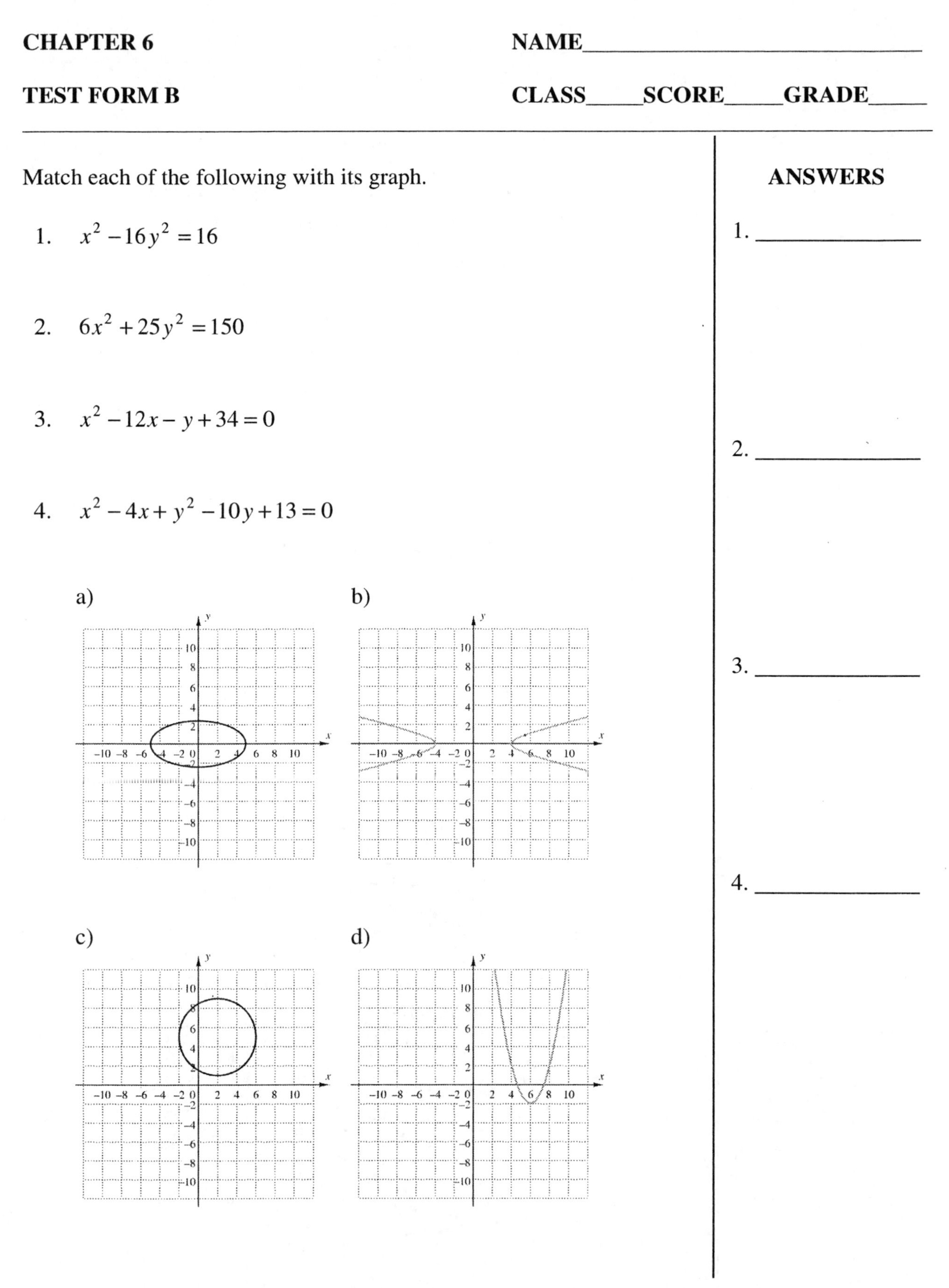

CHAPTER 6 **NAME**____________________________

TEST FORM B **CLASS**_____**SCORE**_____**GRADE**_____

Match each of the following with its graph.

1. $x^2 - 16y^2 = 16$

2. $6x^2 + 25y^2 = 150$

3. $x^2 - 12x - y + 34 = 0$

4. $x^2 - 4x + y^2 - 10y + 13 = 0$

a)

b)

c)

d)

ANSWERS

1. _______________

2. _______________

3. _______________

4. _______________

CHAPTER 6 **NAME**__________________________

TEST FORM B

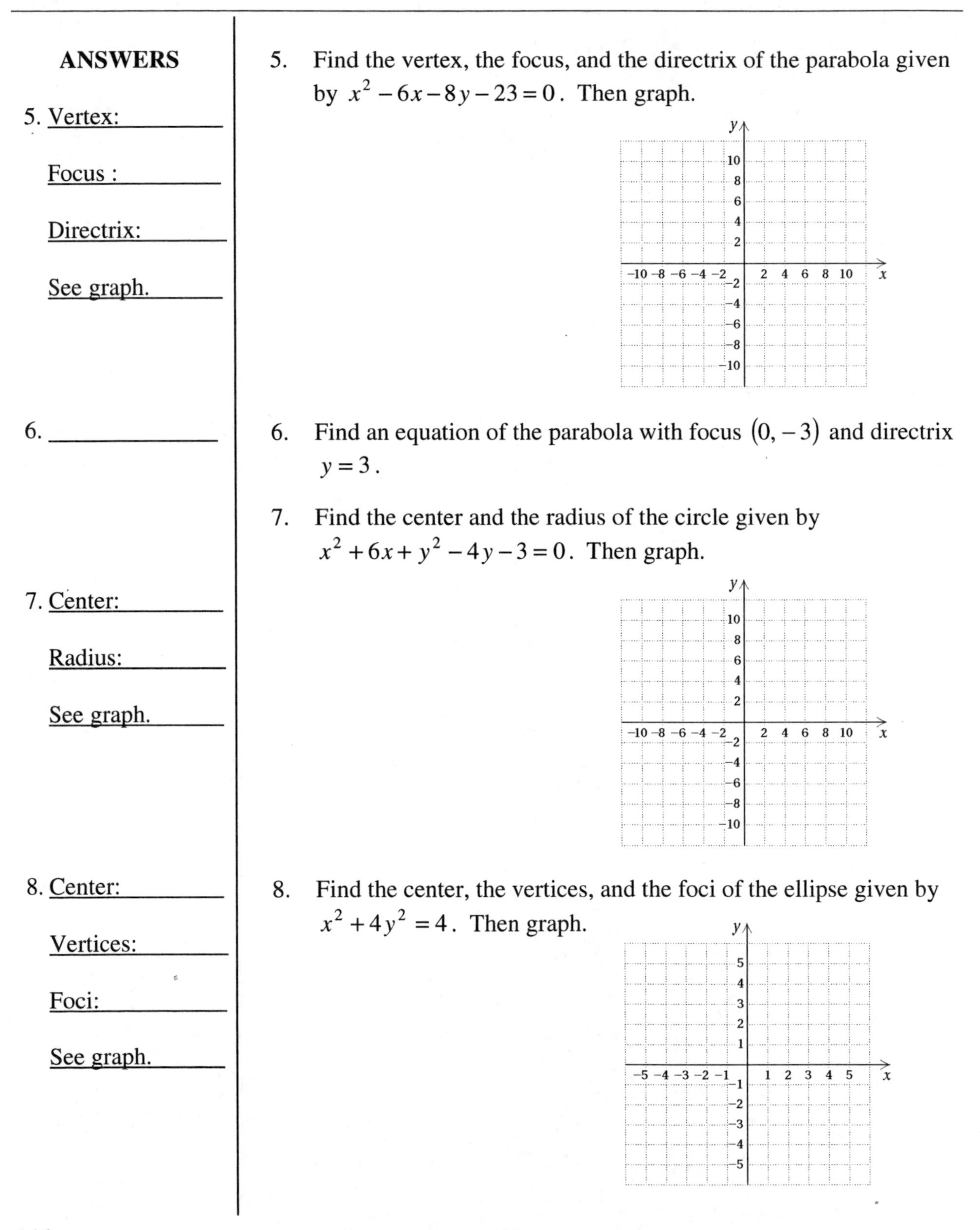

ANSWERS

5. Vertex: ________

Focus : ________

Directrix: ________

See graph.

6. __________

7. Center: ________

Radius: ________

See graph.

8. Center: ________

Vertices: ________

Foci: ________

See graph.

5. Find the vertex, the focus, and the directrix of the parabola given by $x^2 - 6x - 8y - 23 = 0$. Then graph.

6. Find an equation of the parabola with focus $(0, -3)$ and directrix $y = 3$.

7. Find the center and the radius of the circle given by $x^2 + 6x + y^2 - 4y - 3 = 0$. Then graph.

8. Find the center, the vertices, and the foci of the ellipse given by $x^2 + 4y^2 = 4$. Then graph.

CHAPTER 6 **NAME**______________________

TEST FORM B

---

9. Find an equation of the ellipse having vertices $(0, -3)$ and $(0, 3)$ with minor axis of length 2.

10. Find the center, the vertices, the foci, and the asymptotes of the hyperbola given by $\frac{(x-2)^2}{4} - \frac{(y-3)^2}{9} = 1$. Then graph.

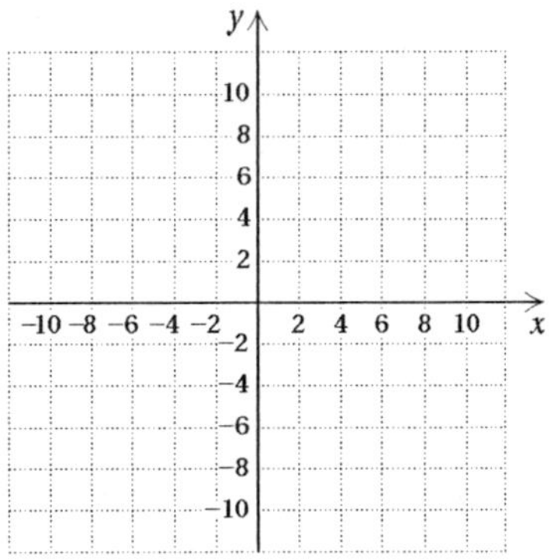

11. Find the asymptotes of the hyperbola given by $9x^2 - 2y^2 = 18$.

12. *Headlight mirror.* A car headlight has a parabolic cross section with a diameter of 6 in. Its bulb is placed at the focus, 1.5 in. from the vertex. Find its depth at the vertex.

ANSWERS

9. ______________

10. Center: ______________

Vertices: ______________

Foci: ______________

Asymptotes: ______________

See graph.

11. ______________

12. ______________

CHAPTER 6 **NAME**________________________

TEST FORM B

ANSWERS

13. ______________

14. ______________

15. ______________

16. ______________

17. ______________

18. ______________

Solve.

13. $x^2 + y^2 = 26$,
$x + y = 4$.

14. $7x^2 - 2y^2 = -11$,
$-10x^2 + 3y^2 = 17$

15. $3x + 2y = 1$,
$xy = -12$

16. *Sign Dimensions.* Orthographics Outdoor Advertising is building a rectangular sign with an area of 216 ft^2 and a perimeter of 60 ft. Find its dimensions.

17. Graph the system of inequalities. Then find the coordinates of the points of intersection of the graphs.
$y \geq x^2 - 3$,
$y < -x + 3$

y
10
8
6
4
2
−10 −8 −6 −4 −2 2 4 6 8 10 x
−2
−4
−6
−8
−10

---

18. Find an equation of the circle for which endpoints of the diameter are $(-2, 7)$ and $(8, 3)$.

CHAPTER 6 **NAME**______________________________

TEST FORM C **CLASS**_____**SCORE**_____**GRADE**_____

Match each of the following with its graph.

1. $5y^2 - x^2 = 20$

2. $y^2 - 10y - x + 27 = 0$

3. $4x^2 + 25y^2 = 100$

4. $x^2 + 10x + y^2 - 8y + 16 = 0$

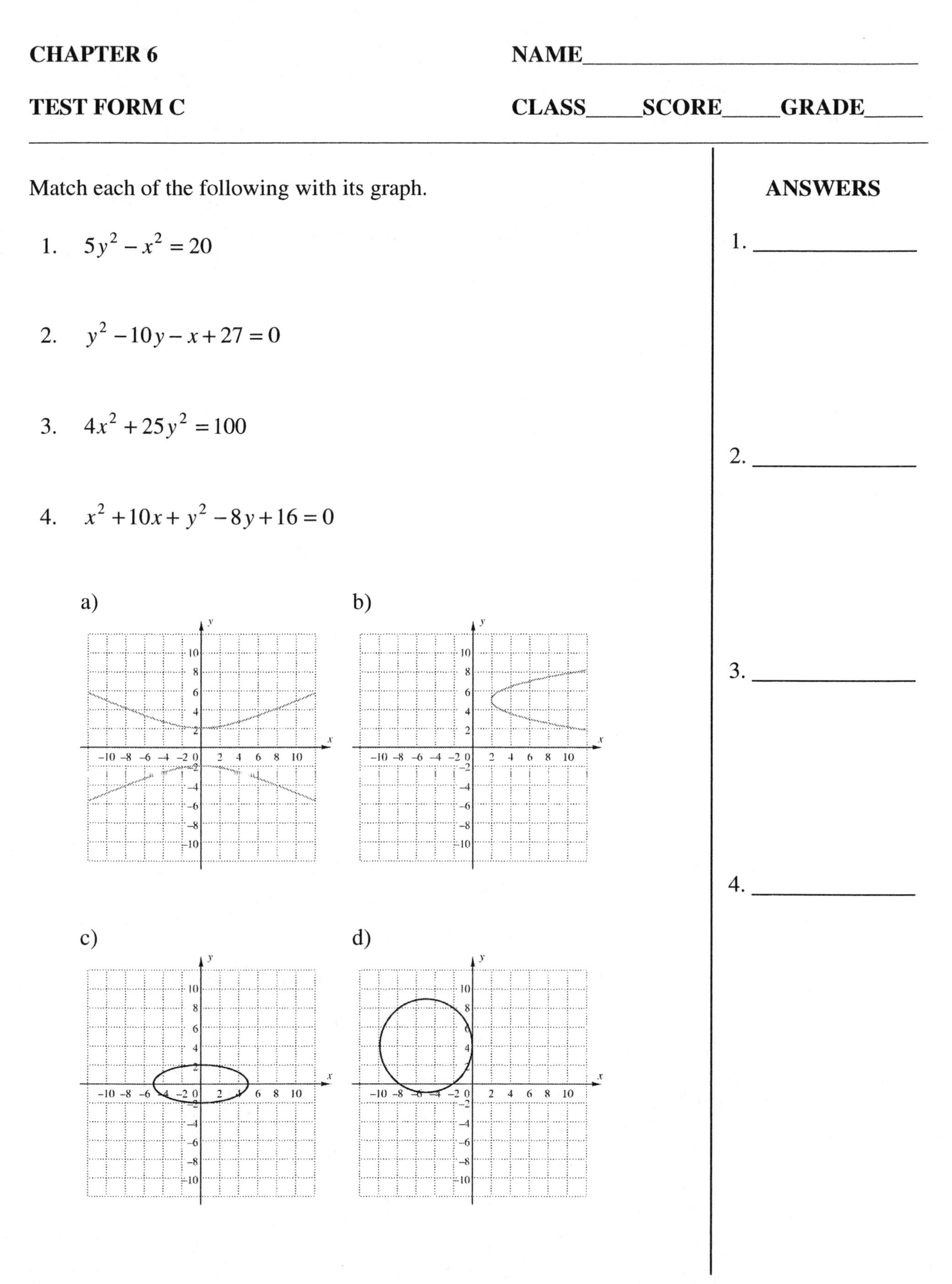

ANSWERS

1. ______________

2. ______________

3. ______________

4. ______________

CHAPTER 6 **NAME**____________________________

TEST FORM C

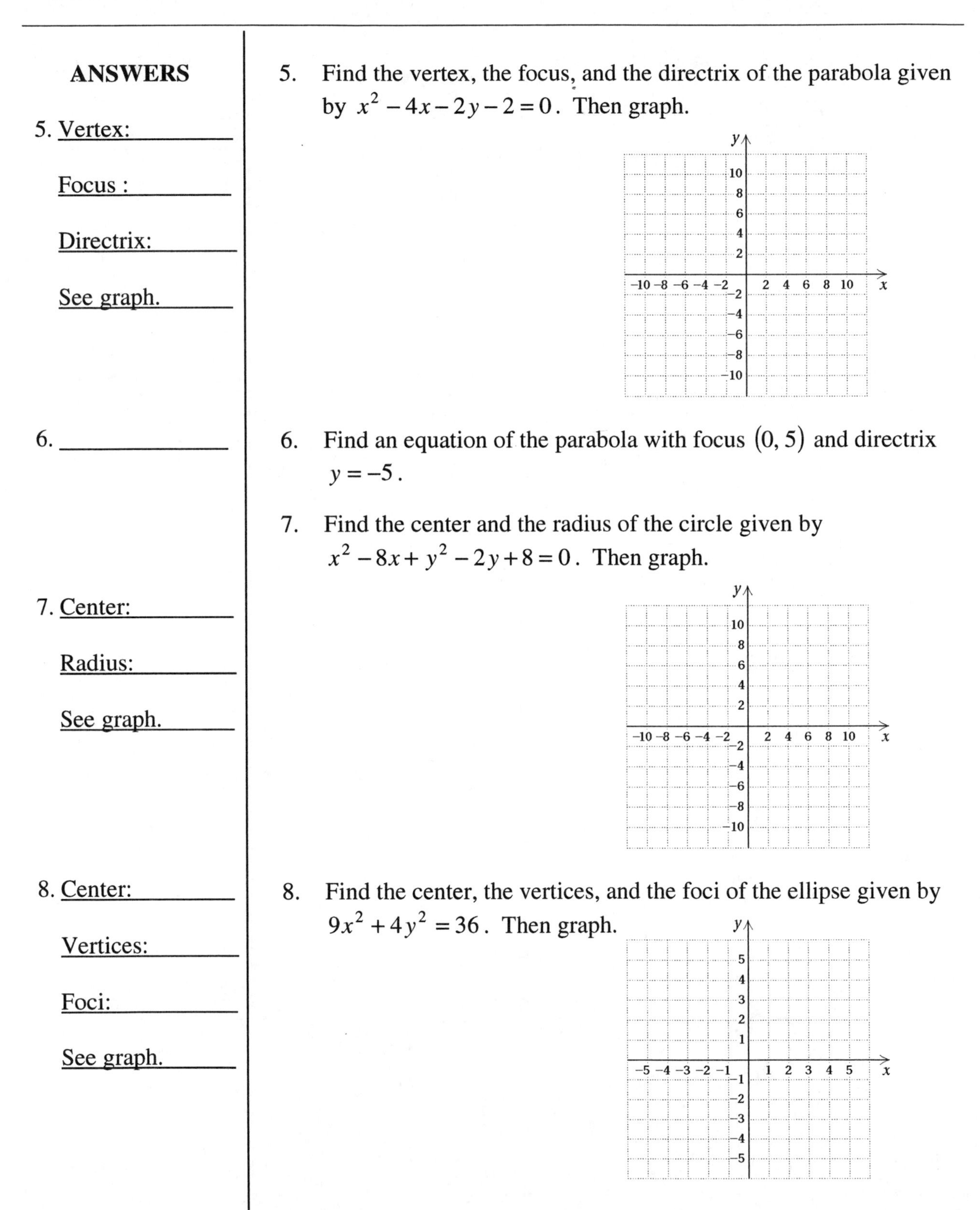

ANSWERS

5. Vertex: ________

Focus : ________

Directrix: ________

See graph.

6. ________

7. Center: ________

Radius: ________

See graph.

8. Center: ________

Vertices: ________

Foci: ________

See graph.

5. Find the vertex, the focus, and the directrix of the parabola given by $x^2 - 4x - 2y - 2 = 0$. Then graph.

6. Find an equation of the parabola with focus $(0, 5)$ and directrix $y = -5$.

7. Find the center and the radius of the circle given by $x^2 - 8x + y^2 - 2y + 8 = 0$. Then graph.

8. Find the center, the vertices, and the foci of the ellipse given by $9x^2 + 4y^2 = 36$. Then graph.

CHAPTER 6 NAME______________________

TEST FORM C

---

9. Find an equation of the ellipse having vertices $(-9, 0)$ and $(9, 0)$ with minor axis of length 6.

10. Find the center, the vertices, the foci, and the asymptotes of the hyperbola given by $\frac{(y-4)^2}{4} - \frac{(x-3)^2}{16} = 1$. Then graph.

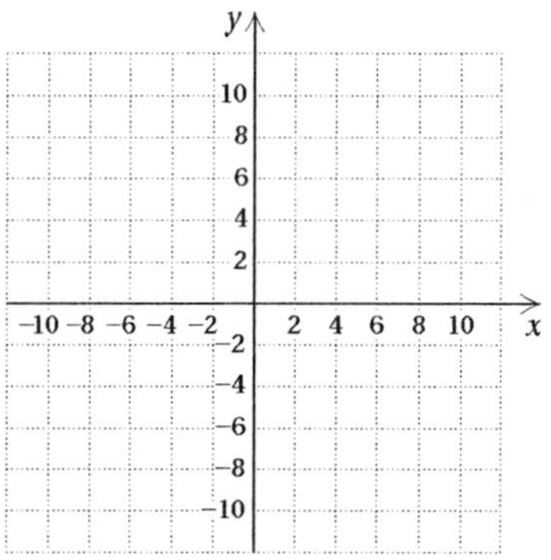

11. Find the asymptotes of the hyperbola given by $3y^2 - 10x^2 = 60$.

12. *Spotlight.* A spotlight has a parabolic cross-section that is 10 ft wide at the opening and 2 ft deep at the vertex. How far from the vertex is the focus?

ANSWERS

9. ____________

10. Center: ________

Vertices: ________

Foci: ________

Asymptotes: ________

See graph.

11. ____________

12. ____________

CHAPTER 6 **NAME**____________________________

TEST FORM C

ANSWERS

13. ________________

14. ________________

15. ________________

16. ________________

17. ________________

18. ________________

Solve.

13. $x^2 + y^2 = 41,$
    $x + y = -1.$

14. $2x^2 - y^2 = 14,$
    $3x^2 - 2y^2 = 19.$

15. $4x + 6y = 20,$
    $xy = -16$

16. *Lot Dimensions.* A rectangular lot has an area of 150,000 ft^2 and a perimeter of 1700 ft. Find its dimensions.

17. Graph the system of inequalities. Then find the coordinates of the points of intersection of the graphs.
    $y \geq x^2 - 5,$
    $y < 2x + 3$

y
10
8
6
4
2
−10 −8 −6 −4 −2 2 4 6 8 10 x
−2
−4
−6
−8
−10

---

18. Find an equation of the circle for which endpoints of the diameter are $(-6, -3)$ and $(4, 7)$.

CHAPTER 6 NAME______________________________

TEST FORM D CLASS_____SCORE_____GRADE_____

Match each of the following with its graph.

1. $y^2 + 10y - x + 21 = 0$

2. $32y^2 - 25x^2 = 200$

3. $4x^2 + 5y^2 = 20$

4. $x^2 + 2x + y^2 - 6y - 26 = 0$

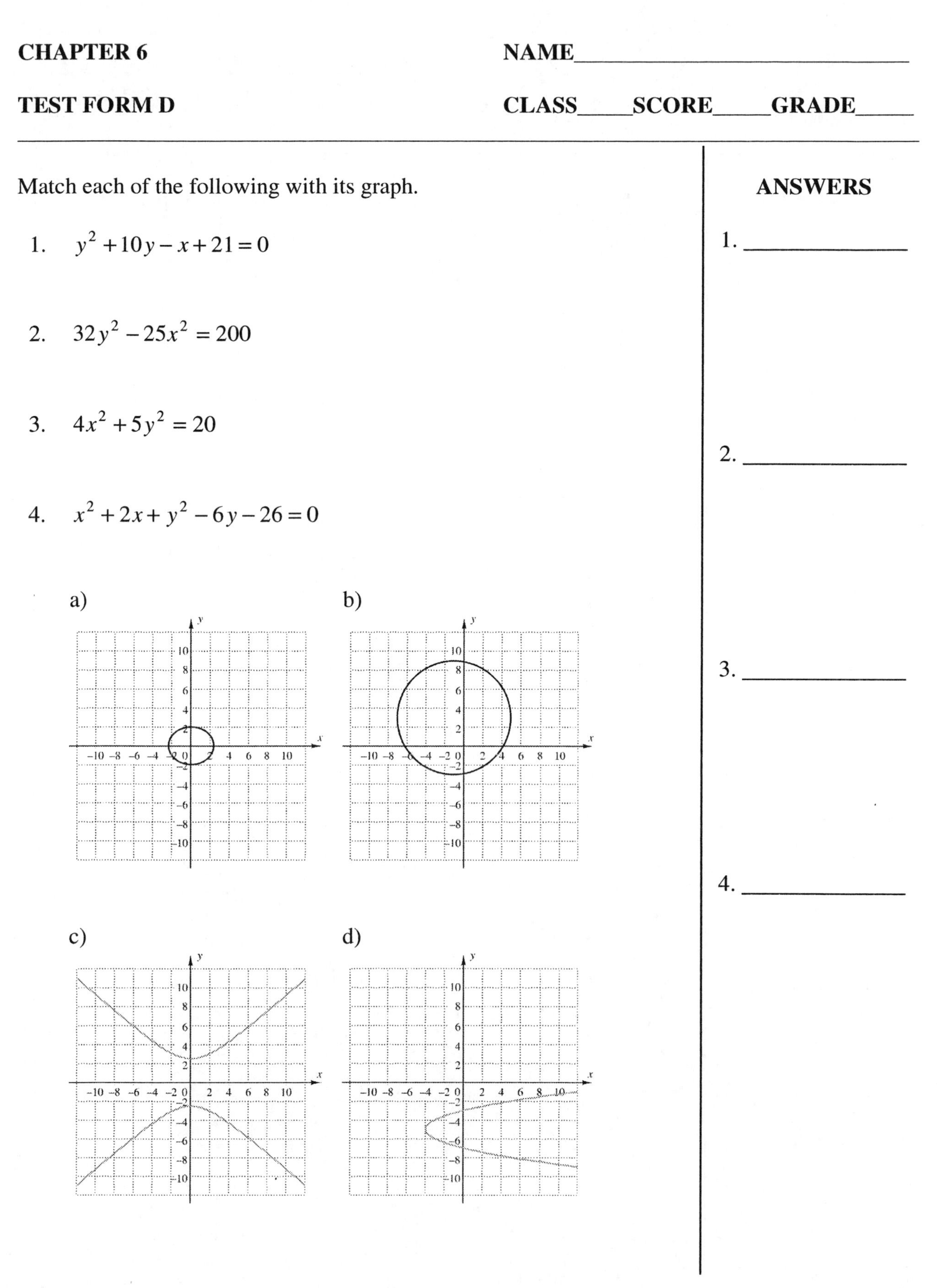

ANSWERS

1. ______________

2. ______________

3. ______________

4. ______________

CHAPTER 6 NAME______________________________

TEST FORM D

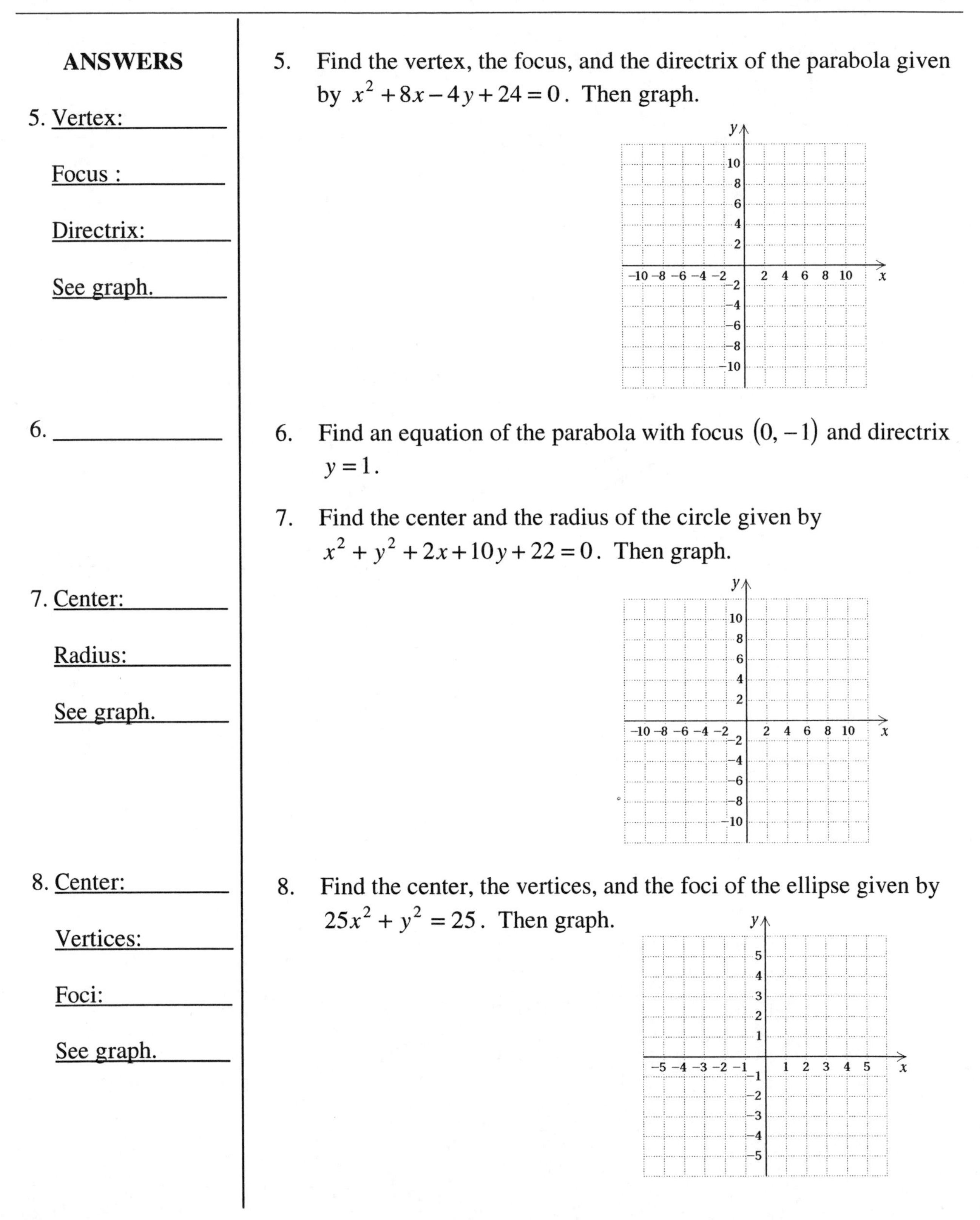

ANSWERS

5. Vertex: ____________

   Focus : ____________

   Directrix: ____________

   See graph.

6. ____________

7. Center: ____________

   Radius: ____________

   See graph.

8. Center: ____________

   Vertices: ____________

   Foci: ____________

   See graph.

5. Find the vertex, the focus, and the directrix of the parabola given by $x^2+8x-4y+24=0$. Then graph.

6. Find an equation of the parabola with focus $(0,-1)$ and directrix $y=1$.

7. Find the center and the radius of the circle given by $x^2+y^2+2x+10y+22=0$. Then graph.

8. Find the center, the vertices, and the foci of the ellipse given by $25x^2+y^2=25$. Then graph.

CHAPTER 6 NAME______________________________

TEST FORM D

---

9. Find an equation of the ellipse having vertices $(-10, 0)$ and $(10, 0)$ with minor axis of length 14.

10. Find the center, the vertices, the foci, and the asymptotes of the hyperbola given by $\frac{(y-1)^2}{9} - (x-4)^2 = 1$. Then graph.

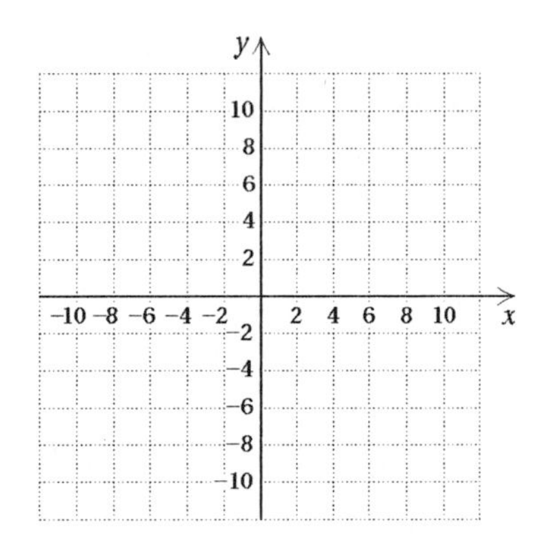

11. Find the asymptotes of the hyperbola given by $3x^2 - 8y^2 = 24$.

12. *Field Microphone.* A field microphone used at a football game has a parabolic cross-section and is 24 in. wide. The focus is 8 in. from the vertex. Find the depth of the microphone at the vertex. Round to the nearest tenth of an inch.

ANSWERS

9. ______________

10. Center: ________

Vertices: ________

Foci: ________

Asymptotes: ________

See graph.

11. ______________

12. ______________

CHAPTER 6 NAME______________________________

TEST FORM D

ANSWERS

13. ______________

14. ______________

15. ______________

16. ______________

17. ______________

18. ______________

Solve.

13. $3x + y = 13,$
$2x^2 - y^2 = -41$

14. $4x^2 + y^2 = 41,$
$5x^2 - 2y^2 = -30$

15. $6x + 8y = 14,$
$xy = -12$

16. *Storage Box Dimensions.* A-1 Carpentry is building an under-the-bed storage box. It is rectangular with a perimeter of 120 in. and a diagonal of $12\sqrt{13}$ in. Find the dimensions of the storage box.

17. Graph the system of inequalities. Then find the coordinates of the points of intersection of the graphs.
$y \le -2x^2 + 4,$
$y > x - 6$

18. Find the equation of a circle for which the endpoints of a diameter are $(6, 8)$ and $(-8, 2)$.

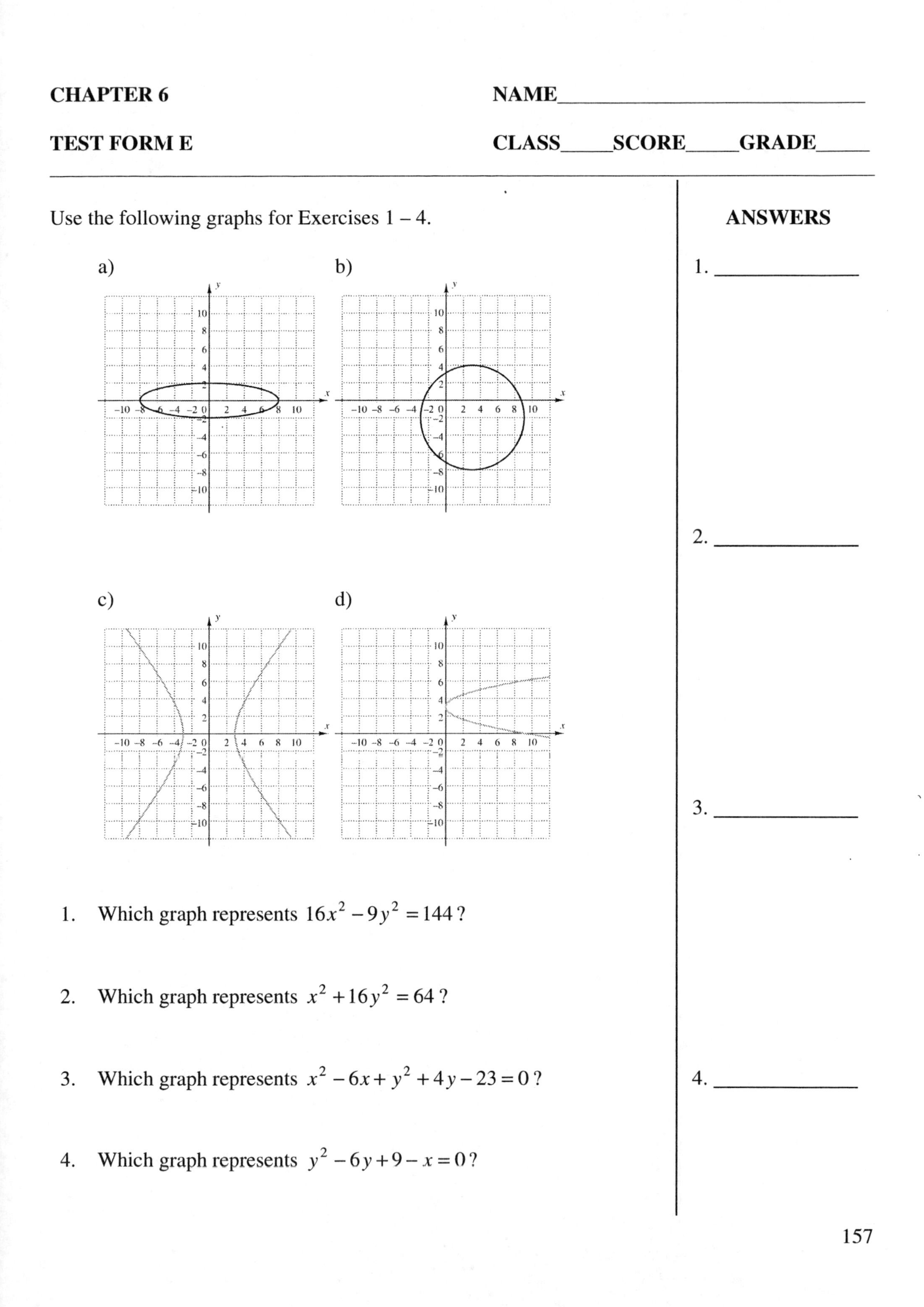

CHAPTER 6 NAME______________________________

TEST FORM E CLASS_____SCORE_____GRADE_____

Use the following graphs for Exercises 1 – 4.

a)

b)

c)

d)

1. Which graph represents $16x^2 - 9y^2 = 144$?

2. Which graph represents $x^2 + 16y^2 = 64$?

3. Which graph represents $x^2 - 6x + y^2 + 4y - 23 = 0$?

4. Which graph represents $y^2 - 6y + 9 - x = 0$?

ANSWERS

1. ______________

2. ______________

3. ______________

4. ______________

ANSWERS

5. ____________

6. ____________

7. ____________

8. ____________

9. ____________

5. Find an equation of the parabola with focus $(0,-4)$ and directrix $y=4$.

a) $x^2=16y$ b) $y^2=16x$

c) $x^2=y-4$ d) $x^2=-16y$

6. Find the vertex of the parabola given by $2x^2+12x-y+22=0$.

a) $(-3,4)$ b) $(3,-4)$ c) $(-3,-4)$ d) $(4,-3)$

7. Find the center and radius of the circle given by $x^2-4x+y^2+8y+11=0$.

a) $(2,4)$; 81 b) $(2,-4)$; 9

c) $(2,-4)$; 3 d) $(-2,4)$; 3

8. Find an equation of the ellipse having vertices $(0,-5)$ and $(0,5)$ with minor axis of length 6.

a) $\frac{x^2}{9}+\frac{y^2}{25}=1$ b) $\frac{x^2}{25}+\frac{y^2}{9}=1$

c) $\frac{y^2}{9}-\frac{x^2}{25}=1$ d) $\frac{x^2}{25}+\frac{y^2}{36}=1$

9. Find the foci of the ellipse given by $3x^2+4y^2=12$.

a) $(-2,0),(2,0)$ b) $(-1,0),(1,0)$

c) $(0,-1),(0,1)$ d) $(-\sqrt{7},0),(\sqrt{7},0)$

CHAPTER 6 **NAME**______________________________

TEST FORM E

ANSWERS

10. $\underline{\hspace{3cm}}$

11. $\underline{\hspace{3cm}}$

12. $\underline{\hspace{3cm}}$

10. Find an asymptote of the hyperbola given by $3x^2 - 4y^2 = 12$.

a) $y = \frac{2\sqrt{3}}{3}x$ b) $y = \frac{-4}{3}x$

c) $y = \frac{\sqrt{3}}{4}x$ d) $y = \frac{\sqrt{3}}{2}x$

11. Determine which graph represents the hyperbola given by $\frac{(x-5)^2}{9} - \frac{(y+2)^2}{4} = 1$.

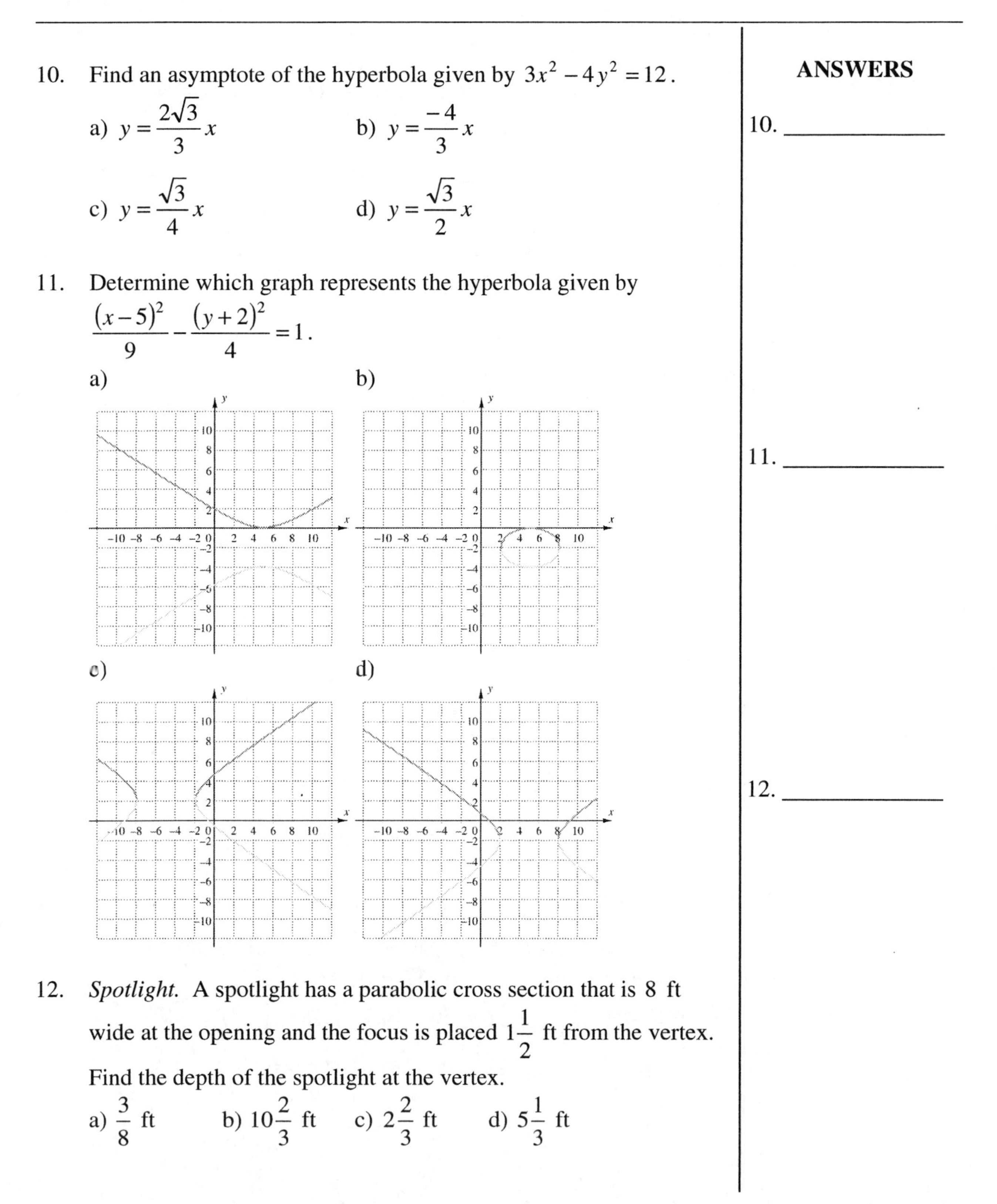

12. *Spotlight.* A spotlight has a parabolic cross section that is 8 ft wide at the opening and the focus is placed $1\frac{1}{2}$ ft from the vertex. Find the depth of the spotlight at the vertex.

a) $\frac{3}{8}$ ft b) $10\frac{2}{3}$ ft c) $2\frac{2}{3}$ ft d) $5\frac{1}{3}$ ft

CHAPTER 6 **NAME**________________________

TEST FORM E

ANSWERS

13. ____________

14. ____________

15. ____________

16. ____________

17. ____________

18. ____________

13. Find the *y*-coordinates of the solutions of $y^2 - 8x^2 = 17$,
$2x^2 + 3y^2 = 77$.

a) –1, 1 b) –5, 5 c) $-\frac{43}{19}, \frac{43}{19}$ d) $-\frac{291}{11}, \frac{291}{11}$

14. Find the sum of the *x*-coordinates of the solutions of
$5x + y = 17$,
$x^2 + y^2 = 13$.

a) 5 b) $\frac{17}{13}$ c) 3 d) $\frac{85}{13}$

15. Find the lesser of the *x*-coordinates of the solutions of
$3x - 5y = 8$,
$xy = 12$.

a) 2 b) $-\frac{18}{5}$ c) $-\frac{10}{3}$ d) –6

16. *Picture Dimensions*. A rectangular picture has an area of 192 in^2 and a diagonal of 20 in. Find its width.

a) 12 in. b) 6 in. c) 24 in. d) 18 in.

17. Find a point of intersection of the graphs in the system
$y \leq -x^2 + 1$,
$y > x - 5$.

a) $(-2, 3)$ b) $(-3, -5)$ c) $(-3, -2)$ d) $(-3, -8)$

---

18. Find an equation of the circle for which the endpoints of a diameter are $(-5, 3)$ and $(7, -1)$.

a) $(x-1)^2 + (y-1)^2 = 80$ b) $(x-1)^2 + (y-1)^2 = 40$

c) $(x+1)^2 + (y+1)^2 = 40$ d) $(x-1)^2 + (y-1)^2 = 2\sqrt{10}$

CHAPTER 6 NAME______________________________

TEST FORM F CLASS_____SCORE_____GRADE_____

Use the following graphs for Exercises 1 – 4.

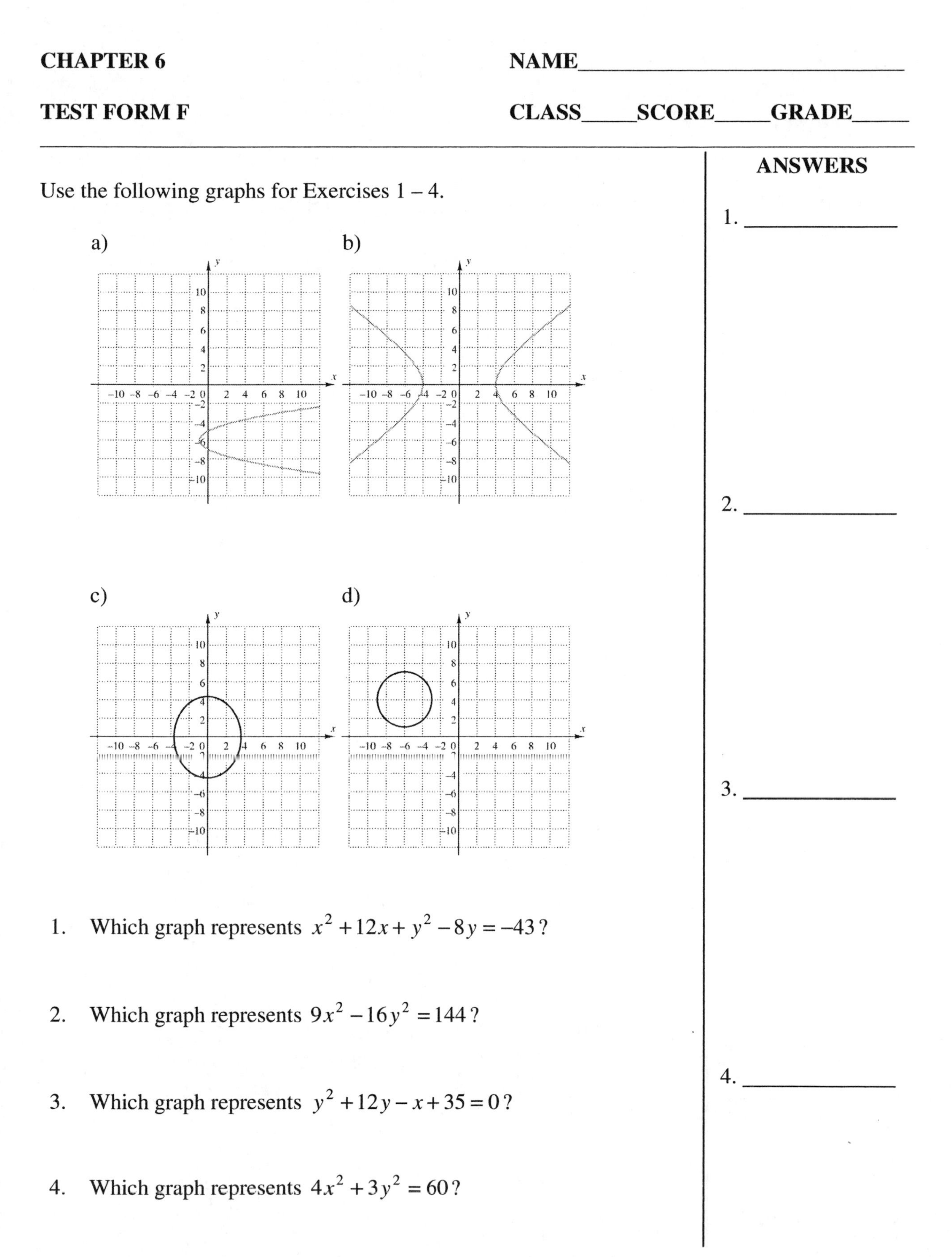

1. Which graph represents $x^2 + 12x + y^2 - 8y = -43$?

2. Which graph represents $9x^2 - 16y^2 = 144$?

3. Which graph represents $y^2 + 12y - x + 35 = 0$?

4. Which graph represents $4x^2 + 3y^2 = 60$?

ANSWERS

1. ______________

2. ______________

3. ______________

4. ______________

CHAPTER 6 **NAME**____________________________

TEST FORM F

ANSWERS

5. ____________

6. ____________

7. ____________

8. ____________

9. ____________

5. Find an equation of the parabola with focus $(0, 8)$ and directrix $y = -8$.

   a) $x^2 = 16y$ b) $x^2 = -32y$
   c) $x^2 = 32y$ d) $y^2 = 32x$

6. Find the vertex of the parabola given by $3x^2 + 12x - y + 16 = 0$.

   a) $(2, -4)$ b) $(4, -2)$ c) $(-2, -4)$ d) $(-2, 4)$

7. Find the center and radius of the circle given by $x^2 - 10x + y^2 + 6y + 18 = 0$.

   a) $(5, -3)$; 4 b) $(5, -3)$; 2
   c) $(-5, 3)$; 4 d) $(5, -3)$; 16

8. Find an equation of the ellipse having vertices $(-6, 0)$ and $(6, 0)$ with minor axis of length 6.

   a) $\frac{x^2}{36} + \frac{y^2}{36} = 1$ b) $\frac{x^2}{36} + \frac{y^2}{9} = 1$
   c) $\frac{x^2}{36} - \frac{y^2}{9} = 1$ d) $\frac{x^2}{144} + \frac{y^2}{36} = 1$

9. Find the foci of the ellipse given by $7x^2 + 8y^2 = 112$.

   a) $(0, -\sqrt{2}), (0, \sqrt{2})$ b) $(-2, 0), (2, 0)$
   c) $(-\sqrt{30}, 0), (\sqrt{30}, 0)$ d) $(-\sqrt{2}, 0), (\sqrt{2}, 0)$

CHAPTER 6 **NAME**______________________________

TEST FORM F

ANSWERS

10. Find an asymptote of the hyperbola given by $9y^2 - 2x^2 = 18$.

a) $y = -\frac{\sqrt{3}}{2}x$ b) $y = \frac{3\sqrt{2}}{2}x$

c) $y = -\frac{\sqrt{2}}{3}x$ d) $y = -\frac{4}{3}x$

10. ______________

11. Determine which graph represents the hyperbola given by $\frac{(y-4)^2}{9} - \frac{(x+2)^2}{4} = 1$.

a) b)

c) d)

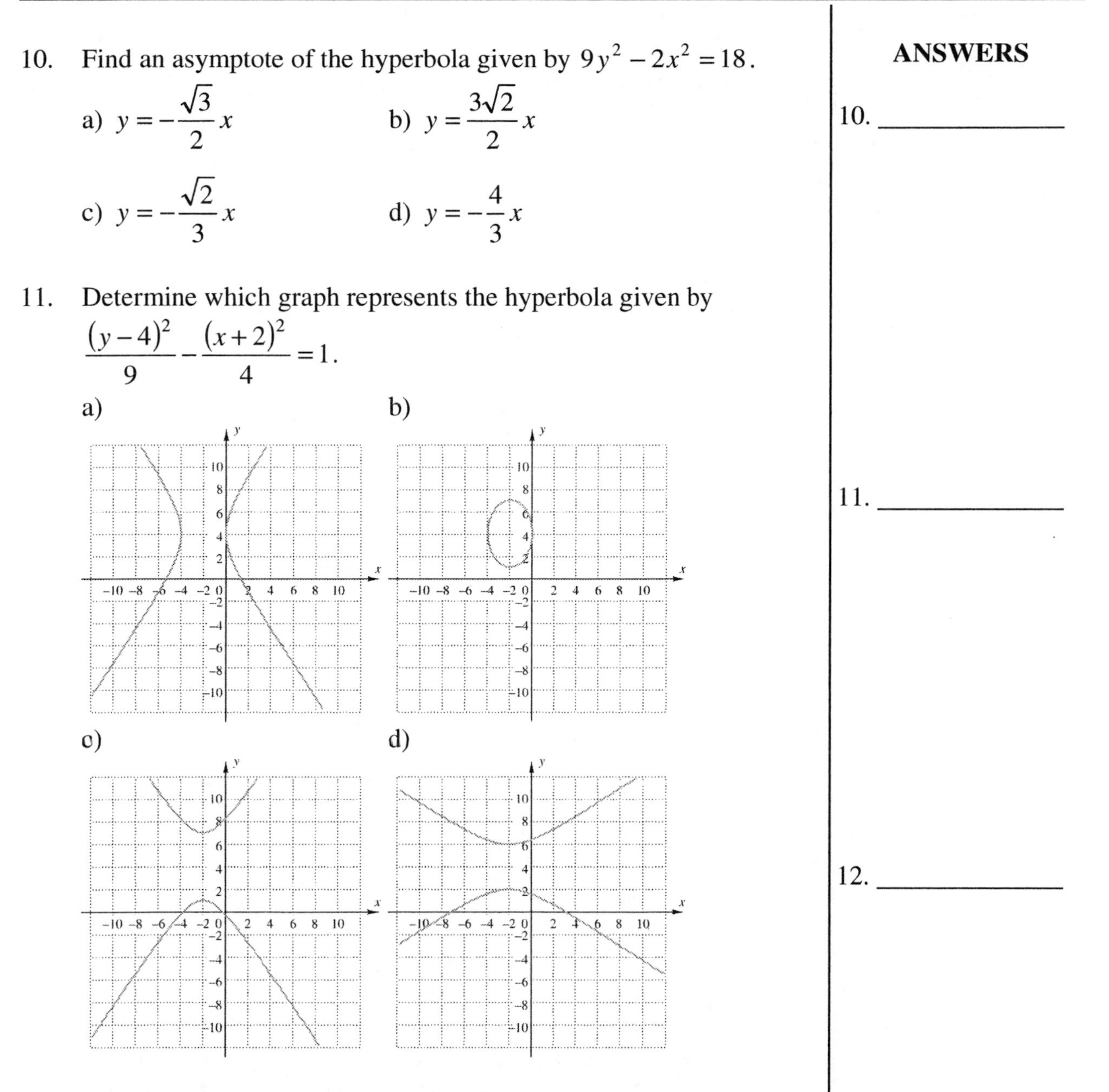

11. ______________

12. *Satellite Dish.* A satellite dish has a parabolic cross section. The dish is 10 ft wide at the opening and 2 ft deep at the vertex. How far from the vertex is the focus?

a) $3\frac{1}{8}$ ft b) $12\frac{1}{2}$ ft

c) $6\frac{1}{4}$ ft d) $4\frac{11}{16}$ ft

12. ______________

CHAPTER 6 NAME________________________

TEST FORM F

ANSWERS

13. ____________

14. ____________

15. ____________

16. ____________

17. ____________

18. ____________

13. Find the x-coordinates of the solutions of $x^2 + 3y^2 = 28$,
$-x^2 + 5y^2 = 4$.

a) –2, 2 b) –4, 4 c) –16, 16 d) –8, 8

14. Find the sum of the x-coordinates of the solutions of
$6x + y = -11$,
$2x^2 + y^2 = 9$.

a) –1 b) $-\dfrac{22}{19}$ c) –2 d) $-\dfrac{66}{19}$

15. Find the least of the coordinates of the solutions of
$3x + 4y = 14$,
$xy = -10$.

a) $-\dfrac{3}{2}$ b) –5 c) –2 d) $-\dfrac{20}{3}$

16. *Picture Dimensions.* A rectangular picture has an area of 60 in^2 and a diagonal of 13 in. Find its width.
a) 5 in. b) 10 in. c) 6 in. d) 8 in.

17. Find a point of intersection of the graphs in the system
$y \geq x^2 - 3$,
$y < 3x + 1$.
a) $(-2, -1)$ b) $(4, 13)$ c) $(-1, 2)$ d) $(2, 13)$

---

18. Find an equation of a circle for which the endpoints of a diameter are $(-2, -5)$ and $(-6, 3)$.

a) $(x-4)^2 + (y-1)^2 = 20$ b) $(x+4)^2 + (y+1)^2 = 40$

c) $(x+4)^2 + (y+1)^2 = 20$ d) $(x+4)^2 + (y+1)^2 = 400$

CHAPTER 7 **NAME**____________________________

TEST FORM A **CLASS**_____**SCORE**_____**GRADE**_____

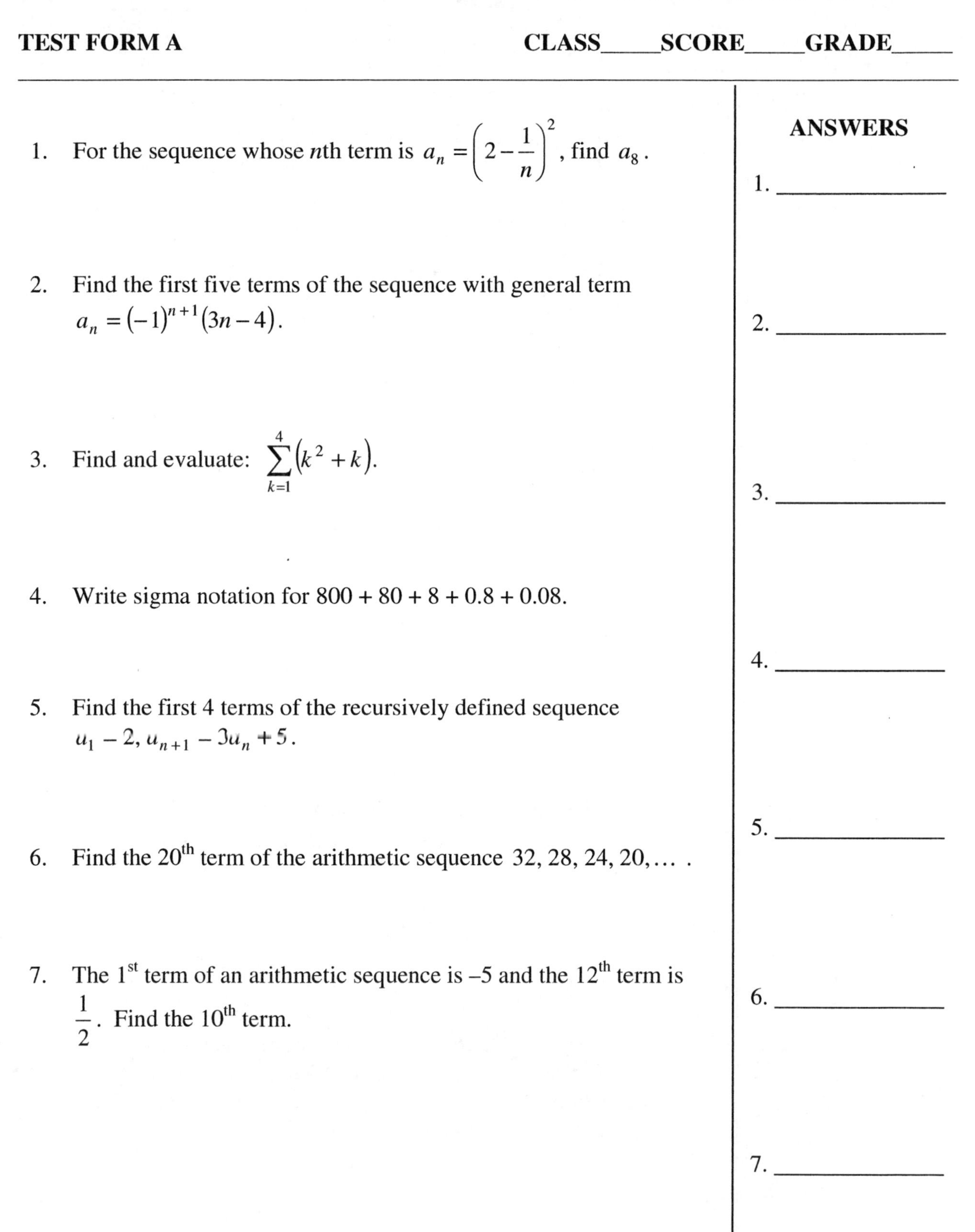

ANSWERS

1. For the sequence whose nth term is $a_n = \left(2 - \frac{1}{n}\right)^2$, find a_8.

2. Find the first five terms of the sequence with general term $a_n = (-1)^{n+1}(3n - 4)$.

3. Find and evaluate: $\sum_{k=1}^{4}(k^2 + k)$.

4. Write sigma notation for 800 + 80 + 8 + 0.8 + 0.08.

5. Find the first 4 terms of the recursively defined sequence $u_1 - 2,\ u_{n+1} - 3u_n + 5$.

6. Find the 20th term of the arithmetic sequence $32, 28, 24, 20, \ldots$.

7. The 1st term of an arithmetic sequence is –5 and the 12th term is $\frac{1}{2}$. Find the 10th term.

1. ______________

2. ______________

3. ______________

4. ______________

5. ______________

6. ______________

7. ______________

CHAPTER 7 **NAME**____________________________

TEST FORM A

ANSWERS

8. ____________

9. ____________

10. ____________

11. ____________

12. ____________

13. ____________

14. ____________

15. ____________

8. Find the sum of the first 20 terms of the series $2+12+22+\cdots$.

9. Find the sum $\sum_{k=1}^{24}(-2k-1)$.

10. Find the 7th term of the geometric sequence $3, 15, 75, \ldots$.

11. For a geometric sequence, $r = 2$ and $S_6 = 315$. Find a_1.

12. Find the sum $\sum_{k=1}^{10} 3(2)^k$.

13. Find the sum, if it exists: $100{,}000 + 80{,}000 + 64{,}000 + \cdots$.

14. Find fraction notation for $5.\overline{01}$.

15. *Amount of an Annuity.* To create a college fund, a parent makes a sequence of 15 yearly deposits of $\$1200$ each in a savings account on which interest is compounded annually at 3.5%. Find the amount of the annuity.

16. *Hourly Wage.* Jayden accepts a job with a starting hourly wage of $8.75, and is promised a raise of 20¢ per hour every month for two years. What will Jayden's hourly wage be at the end of the two-year period?

17. Use mathematical induction to prove that for every natural number n,

$$5+10+15+\cdots+5n=\frac{5n(n+1)}{2}.$$

Evaluate.

18. ${}_{12}P_3$

19. ${}_{13}C_7$

20. $\binom{n}{4}$

21. How many 4-letter code symbols can be formed with the letters P, R, O, D, U, C, and T without repetition?

22. How many 4-digit numbers can be formed using the digits 2, 4, 6, 8, and 0 if the digits can be repeated but the number must begin with 4?

ANSWERS

16. ______________

17. See work.

18. ______________

19. ______________

20. ______________

21. ______________

22. ______________

CHAPTER 7 NAME______________________________

TEST FORM A

ANSWERS

23. ______________

24. ______________

25. ______________

26. ______________

27. ______________

28. ______________

29. ______________

23. *Work crews.* There are 9 seniors and 6 juniors in a class. In how many ways can a clean-up crew of 3 seniors and 2 juniors be selected?

24. Expand $(x-a)^6$.

25. Find the 3rd term of the binomial expansion of $(2x+y)^5$.

26. Determine the number of subsets of a set containing 8 members.

27. *Chocolates.* Suppose we select, without looking or otherwise inspecting, a chocolate from a box that contains 14 cream-filled chocolates and 10 caramel-filled chocolates. What is the probability that we choose a cream-filled chocolate?

28. *Marbles.* Suppose Jay selects four marbles without looking from a bag containing 4 white marbles, 2 blue marbles, 8 red marbles, and 6 green marbles. What is the probability of getting 1 white marble and 3 red marbles?

---

29. Solve for n: ${}_nP_{10} = 3 \cdot {}_nP_9$.

CHAPTER 7 NAME______________________

TEST FORM B CLASS____ SCORE____ GRADE____

---

1. For the sequence whose nth term is $a_n = (-2)^{n-2}(n-1)$, find a_8.

2. Find the first five terms of the sequence with general term $a_n = \dfrac{(n-1)(n+2)}{3}$.

3. Find and evaluate: $\sum_{k=1}^{4} \dfrac{2^k}{k+1}$.

4. Write sigma notation for $-8 + (-3) + 2 + 7 + 12 + \cdots$.

5. Find the first 4 terms of the recursively defined sequence $a_1 = 4, a_{n+1} = 2a_n - 1$.

6. Find the 18th term of the arithmetic sequence $3, 7, 11, 15, \ldots$.

7. The 1st term of an arithmetic sequence is –8 and the 15th term is 34. Find the 7th term.

ANSWERS

1. ______________

2. ______________

3. ______________

4. ______________

5. ______________

6. ______________

7. ______________

CHAPTER 7 NAME______________________________

TEST FORM B

ANSWERS

8. ______________

9. ______________

10. ______________

11. ______________

12. ______________

13. ______________

14. ______________

15. ______________

8. Find the sum of the first 20 terms of the series $100+75+50+25+\cdots$.

9. Find the sum $\sum_{k=1}^{24}(3k-4)$.

10. Find the 6th term of the geometric sequence $50, 10, 2, \ldots$.

11. For a geometric sequence, $r=0.2$ and $S_5=4.9984$. Find a_1.

12. Find the sum $\sum_{k=1}^{7}4(-1)^k$.

13. Find the sum, if it exists: $2+\frac{5}{2}+\frac{28}{8}+\cdots$.

14. Find fraction notation for $3.\overline{15}$.

15. *The Economic Multiplier.* The government is making a $\$30{,}000$ expenditure for environmental education. If 35% of this is spent again, and so on, what is the total effect on the economy?

CHAPTER 7 **NAME**______________________________

TEST FORM B

---

16. *Hourly Wage.* Dakota accepts a job with a starting hourly wage of \$10.30. He is promised a raise of 30¢ per hour every two months for the next two years. What will his hourly wage be at the end of the two-year period?

17. Use mathematical induction to prove that for every natural number n,
$$5+9+13+\cdots+(4n+1)=n(2n+3).$$

Evaluate.

18. ${}_{13}P_5$

19. ${}_{10}C_7$

20. $\binom{n}{3}$

21. How many 5-letter code symbols can be formed with the letters F, A, C, T, O, and R without repetition?

22. How many 4-digit numbers can be formed using the digits 2, 4, 6, 8, and 0 if the digits can be repeated but the number must end with 6?

ANSWERS

16. ______________

17. See work.

18. ______________

19. ______________

20. ______________

21. ______________

22. ______________

CHAPTER 7 **NAME**________________________

TEST FORM B

ANSWERS

23. ____________

24. ____________

25. ____________

26. ____________

27. ____________

28. ____________

29. ____________

23. *Class Representatives.* A class of 75 must choose 3 representatives. How many ways can this be done?

24. Expand $(x-d)^5$.

25. Find the 4th term of the binomial expansion of $(p+q)^{10}$.

26. Determine the number of subsets of a set containing 5 members.

27. *Card drawing.* Suppose we draw a card from a well-shuffled deck of 52 cards. What is the probability of drawing a jack?

28. *Marbles.* Suppose Jay selects three marbles without looking from a bag containing 10 white marbles, 5 blue marbles, 3 red marbles, and 6 green marbles. What is the probability of getting 1 red marble, 1 white marble, and 1 blue marble?

---

29. Solve for n: $\binom{n}{6} = 2\binom{n-1}{5}$.

CHAPTER 7 **NAME**______________________________

TEST FORM C **CLASS**_____**SCORE**_____**GRADE**_____

1. For the sequence whose nth term is $a_n = (-1)^n(3n+2)$, find a_6.

2. Find the first five terms of the sequence with general term $a_n = \dfrac{2n-1}{n}$.

3. Find and evaluate: $\sum_{k=1}^{4} \dfrac{k^2}{2k}$.

4. Write sigma notation for $-3+6+(-12)+24+(-48)+\cdots$.

5. Find the first 4 terms of the recursively defined sequence $a_1 = 10, a_{n+1} = \dfrac{1}{2}a_n + 1$.

6. Find the 12th term of the arithmetic sequence $\dfrac{3}{4}, \dfrac{5}{4}, \dfrac{7}{4}, \ldots$.

7. The 1st term of an arithmetic sequence is 21 and the 12th term is 26.5. Find the 6th term.

ANSWERS

1. ______________

2. ______________

3. ______________

4. ______________

5. ______________

6. ______________

7. ______________

CHAPTER 7 **NAME**____________________________

TEST FORM C

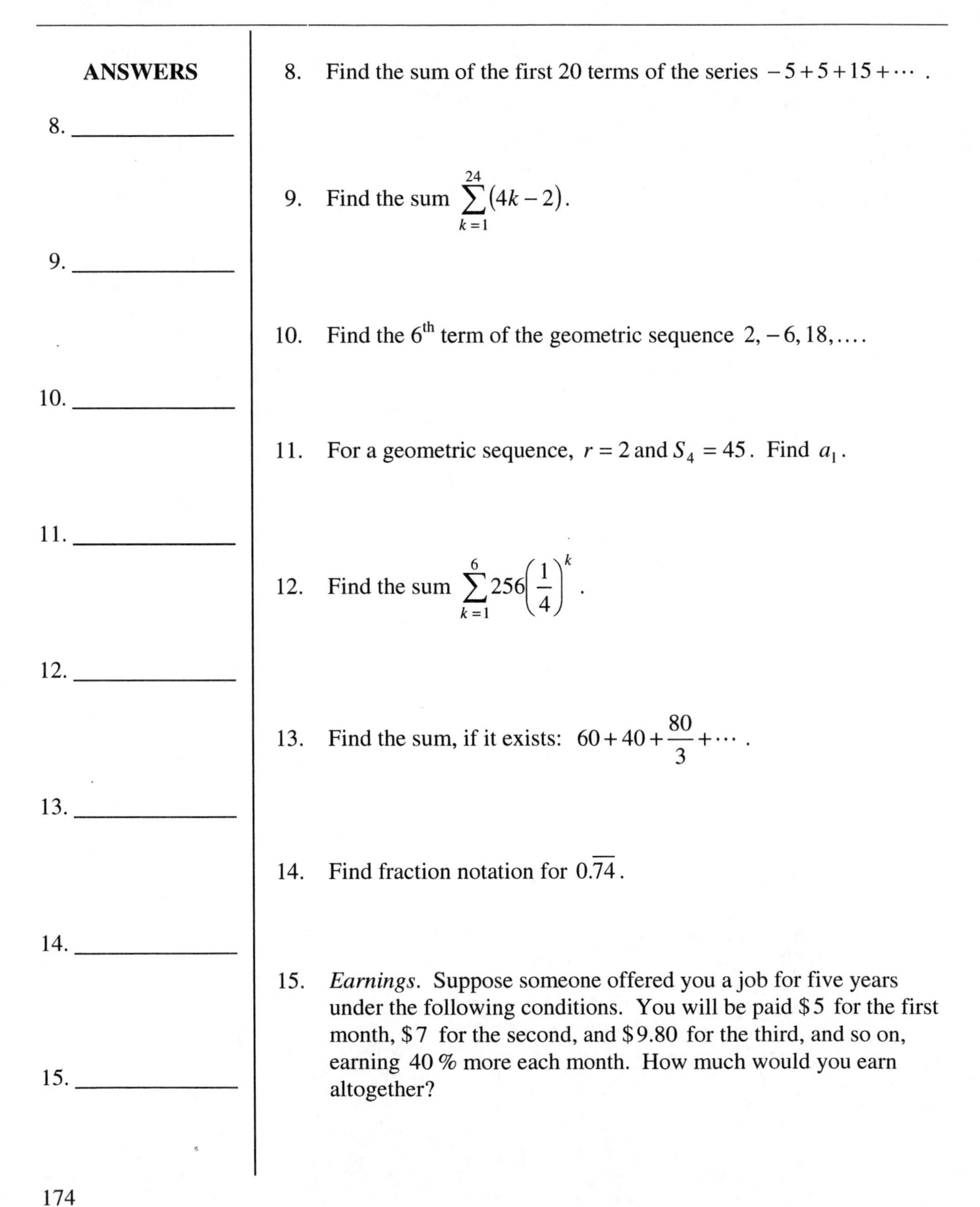

ANSWERS

8. ____________

9. ____________

10. ____________

11. ____________

12. ____________

13. ____________

14. ____________

15. ____________

8. Find the sum of the first 20 terms of the series $-5+5+15+\cdots$.

9. Find the sum $\sum_{k=1}^{24}(4k-2)$.

10. Find the 6th term of the geometric sequence $2, -6, 18, \ldots$.

11. For a geometric sequence, $r = 2$ and $S_4 = 45$. Find a_1.

12. Find the sum $\sum_{k=1}^{6} 256\left(\frac{1}{4}\right)^k$.

13. Find the sum, if it exists: $60+40+\frac{80}{3}+\cdots$.

14. Find fraction notation for $0.\overline{74}$.

15. *Earnings.* Suppose someone offered you a job for five years under the following conditions. You will be paid $\$5$ for the first month, $\$7$ for the second, and $\$9.80$ for the third, and so on, earning $40\,\%$ more each month. How much would you earn altogether?

CHAPTER 7 **NAME**______________________________

TEST FORM C

16. *Hourly Wage.* Barry accepts a job with a starting hourly wage of \$12.95. He is promised a raise of 60¢ per hour every 4 months for the next two years. What will his hourly wage be at the end of the two-year period?

17. Use mathematical induction to prove that for every natural number n,

$$1+2+2^2+\cdots+2^{n-1}=2^n-1.$$

Evaluate.

18. ${}_{13}P_9$

19. ${}_{20}C_9$

20. $\binom{n}{5}$

21. How many 4-letter code symbols can be formed with the letters E, X, P, A, N, and D without repetition?

22. How many 3-digit numbers can be formed using the digits 2, 4, 6, 8, and 0 if the digits can be repeated but the number must begin with 8?

ANSWERS

16. ______________

17. See work.

18. ______________

19. ______________

20. ______________

21. ______________

22. ______________

CHAPTER 7 **NAME**______________________________

TEST FORM C

ANSWERS

23. ______________

24. ______________

25. ______________

26. ______________

27. ______________

28. ______________

29. ______________

23. *School Committees*. Suppose a school community has 9 teachers and 100 students. How many committees can be formed consisting of 2 teachers and 5 students?

24. Expand $(x-2)^5$.

25. Find the 3rd term of the binomial expansion of $(s+t)^7$.

26. Determine the number of subsets of a set containing 6 members.

27. *Card drawing*. Suppose we draw a card from a well-shuffled deck of 52 cards. What is the probability of drawing a face card (jack, queen, or king)?

28. *Marbles*. Suppose Jay selects four marbles without looking from a bag containing 10 white marbles, 5 red marbles, 3 blue marbles, and 2 green marbles. What is the probability of getting 3 blue marbles and 1 red marble?

---

29. Solve for n: $\binom{n}{5}=\binom{n-1}{6}$.

CHAPTER 7 **NAME**____________________________

TEST FORM D **CLASS**_____**SCORE**_____**GRADE**_____

---

1. For the sequence whose *n*th term is $a_n = \frac{n}{2}(2n+1)$, find a_8.

2. Find the first five terms of the sequence with general term $a_n = \frac{(-1)^n(4n+3)}{n}$.

3. Find and evaluate: $\sum_{k=1}^{4} \frac{2k-1}{k^2}$.

4. Write sigma notation for $(-1)+2+(-3)+4+(-5)+6$.

5. Find the first 4 terms of the recursively defined sequence $a_1 = 0.5,\ a_{n+1} = 4+2a_n$.

6. Find the 17th term of the arithmetic sequence $12, 7, 2, -3, \ldots$.

7. The 1st term of an arithmetic sequence is -8 and the 15th term is -1. Find the 5th term.

ANSWERS

1. ______________

2. ______________

3. ______________

4. ______________

5. ______________

6. ______________

7. ______________

CHAPTER 7 NAME____________________________

TEST FORM D

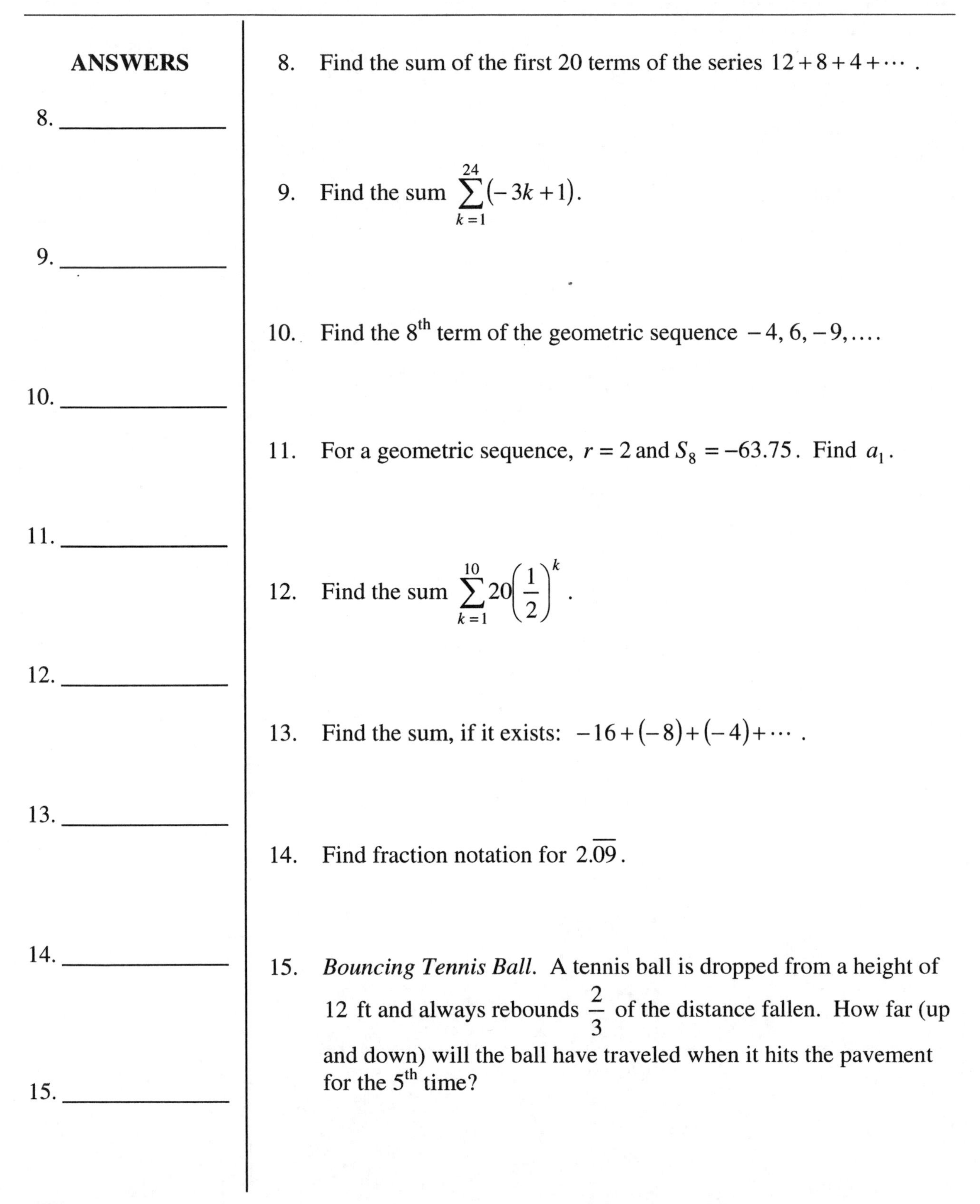

ANSWERS

8. ____________

9. ____________

10. ____________

11. ____________

12. ____________

13. ____________

14. ____________

15. ____________

8. Find the sum of the first 20 terms of the series $12+8+4+\cdots$.

9. Find the sum $\sum_{k=1}^{24}(-3k+1)$.

10. Find the 8th term of the geometric sequence $-4, 6, -9, \ldots$.

11. For a geometric sequence, $r=2$ and $S_8=-63.75$. Find a_1.

12. Find the sum $\sum_{k=1}^{10} 20\left(\frac{1}{2}\right)^k$.

13. Find the sum, if it exists: $-16+(-8)+(-4)+\cdots$.

14. Find fraction notation for $2.\overline{09}$.

15. *Bouncing Tennis Ball.* A tennis ball is dropped from a height of 12 ft and always rebounds $\frac{2}{3}$ of the distance fallen. How far (up and down) will the ball have traveled when it hits the pavement for the 5th time?

CHAPTER 7 NAME______________________________

TEST FORM D

---

16. *Hourly Wage.* Aidan accepts a job with a starting hourly wage of \$17.50. He is promised a raise of 80¢ per hour every three months for the next two years. What will his hourly wage be at the end of the two-year period?

17. Use mathematical induction to prove that for every natural number n,

$$1^2+2^2+3^2+\cdots+n^2=\frac{n(n+1)(2n+1)}{6}.$$

Evaluate.

18. ${}_{10}P_4$ 19. ${}_{12}C_2$ 20. $\binom{n}{3}$

21. How many 4-letter code symbols can be formed with the letters P, R, I, M, E, and S without repetition?

22. How many 5-digit numbers can be formed using the digits 2, 4, 6, 8, and 0 if the digits can be repeated but the number must begin with 6?

ANSWERS

16. ______________

17. See work.

18. ______________

19. ______________

20. ______________

21. ______________

22. ______________

CHAPTER 7 **NAME**____________________________

TEST FORM D

ANSWERS

23. ____________

24. ____________

25. ____________

26. ____________

27. ____________

28. ____________

29. ____________

23. *Dinner Specials.* For a particular special, a diner can choose one appetizer, one entrée, and one dessert. The restaurant offers choices from 4 appetizers, 3 entrees, and 2 desserts. In how many ways can a dinner special be formed?

24. Expand $(a-2)^5$.

25. Find the 4th term of the binomial expansion of $(3x+y)^4$.

26. Determine the number of subsets of a set containing 7 members.

27. *Socks.* Your sock drawer contains 8 black, 3 blue, 2 brown, and 2 white pairs of socks which are rolled into matching pairs. In the dark, you select a pair of socks. What is the probability that you select a pair that is white?

28. *Marbles.* Suppose Jay selects four marbles without looking from a bag containing 5 white marbles, 3 blue marbles, 8 red marbles, and 2 green marbles. What is the probability of getting 1 blue marble and 3 red marbles?

---

29. Solve for n: $\binom{n}{n-2}=15$.

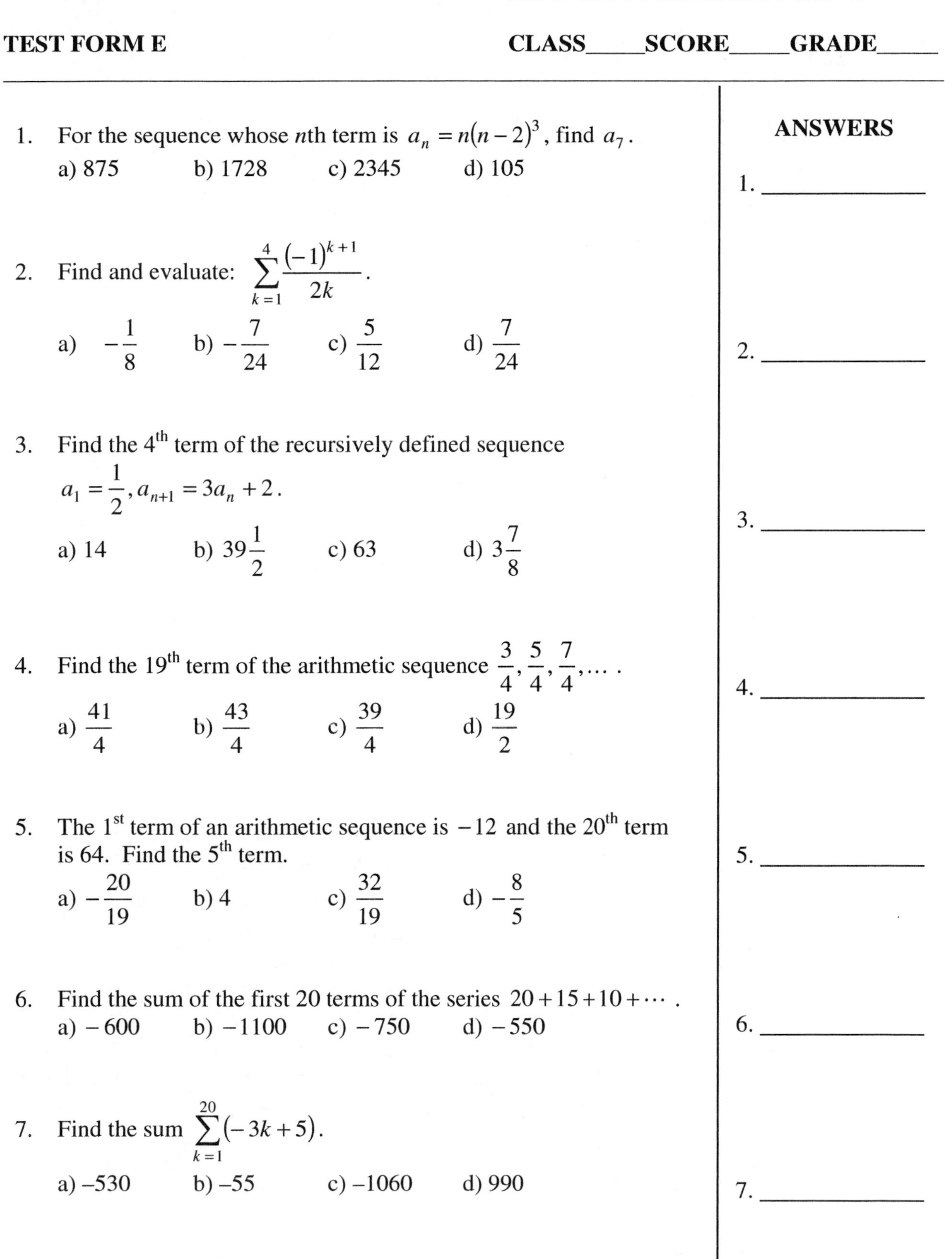

CHAPTER 7 **NAME**______________________________

TEST FORM E **CLASS**_____**SCORE**_____**GRADE**_____

ANSWERS

1. For the sequence whose nth term is $a_n = n(n-2)^3$, find a_7.
   a) 875 b) 1728 c) 2345 d) 105

   1. ____________

2. Find and evaluate: $\sum_{k=1}^{4} \frac{(-1)^{k+1}}{2k}$.

   a) $-\frac{1}{8}$ b) $-\frac{7}{24}$ c) $\frac{5}{12}$ d) $\frac{7}{24}$

   2. ____________

3. Find the 4th term of the recursively defined sequence
   $a_1 = \frac{1}{2}, a_{n+1} = 3a_n + 2$.

   a) 14 b) $39\frac{1}{2}$ c) 63 d) $3\frac{7}{8}$

   3. ____________

4. Find the 19th term of the arithmetic sequence $\frac{3}{4}, \frac{5}{4}, \frac{7}{4}, \ldots$.

   a) $\frac{41}{4}$ b) $\frac{43}{4}$ c) $\frac{39}{4}$ d) $\frac{19}{2}$

   4. ____________

5. The 1st term of an arithmetic sequence is -12 and the 20th term is 64. Find the 5th term.

   a) $-\frac{20}{19}$ b) 4 c) $\frac{32}{19}$ d) $-\frac{8}{5}$

   5. ____________

6. Find the sum of the first 20 terms of the series $20 + 15 + 10 + \cdots$.
   a) -600 b) -1100 c) -750 d) -550

   6. ____________

7. Find the sum $\sum_{k=1}^{20} (-3k + 5)$.

   a) –530 b) –55 c) –1060 d) 990

   7. ____________

CHAPTER 7 NAME______________________

TEST FORM E

ANSWERS

8. ______________

9. ______________

10. ______________

11. ______________

12. ______________

13. ______________

14. ______________

8. Find the 6th term of the geometric sequence 100, 80, 64, ...

a) $\frac{16{,}384}{625}$ b) $\frac{1024}{25}$ c) $\frac{4096}{125}$ d) $\frac{8192}{25}$

9. For a geometric sequence, $r = \frac{1}{4}$ and $S_4 = -2.65625$. Find a_1.

a) $-\frac{8}{3}$ b) -2 c) -8 d) $-\frac{85}{12}$

10. Find the sum $\sum_{k=1}^{8} (-1)^k 3^k$.

a) 4920 b) –9840 c) –1641 d) –4920

11. Find the sum, if it exists: $4 + 1 + \frac{1}{4} + \cdots$.

a) 16 b) $\frac{16}{3}$ c) 6 d) Does not exist

12. When $0.\overline{72}$ is expressed in simplified fraction notation, what is the denominator?

a) 72 b) 8 c) 11 d) 9

13. *The Economic Multiplier.* The government is making a \$3,200,000 expenditure for restoration of covered bridges. If 45 % of this is spent again, and so on, what is the total effect on the economy? Round to the nearest dollar.

a) \$7,111,111 b) \$1,760,000
c) \$4,640,000 d) \$5,818,182

14. A garden has 4 plants in the first row, 5 in the second row, 6 in the third row, and so on for 10 rows. How many plants are there altogether?

a) 14 b) 17 c) 85 d) 170

CHAPTER 7 **NAME**________________________

TEST FORM E

ANSWERS

15. Evaluate the statement:
$2n < n^2$, for $n = 1, 2, 3, \ldots$.

a) It is sometimes true. b) It is never true.
c) It is always true. d) It is not possible to evaluate.

15. ____________

16. Find S_{k+1}, the $(k+1)^{\text{st}}$ statement in the mathematical induction proof of $4+8+12+\cdots+4n = 2n(n+1)$ for $n = 1, 2, 3, \ldots$.

a) $4+4k = 2k(k+1)$
b) $4+8+12+\cdots+4k-2k(k+1) = 2(k+1)(k+2)$
c) $4+8+12+\cdots+4k = 2k(k+1)$
d) $4+8+12+\cdots+4(k+1) = 2(k+1)(k+2)$

16. ____________

17. ____________

17. Evaluate: ${}_8P_2$.
a) 28 b) 56 c) 20,160 d) 112

18. Evaluate: ${}_{12}C_5$.
a) 95,040 b) 3,991,680
c) 792 d) 5040

18. ____________

19. Evaluate: $\binom{n}{2}$.

a) $\dfrac{n!}{3!}$ b) $\dfrac{(n-2)!}{2!}$ c) $\dfrac{2!n!}{(n-2)!}$ d) $\dfrac{n!}{(n-2)!2!}$

19. ____________

20. *Test answers.* A true-false test contains 25 questions. How many possible answer sheets are there?
a) 33,554,432 b) 300
c) 625 d) 600

20. ____________

CHAPTER 7 **NAME**______________________________

TEST FORM E

ANSWERS

21. ______________

22. ______________

23. ______________

24. ______________

25. ______________

26. ______________

21. *Class Representatives.* A class has 100 members. How many different ways can it choose four representatives?
a) 3,921,225 b) 94,109,400
c) 25 d) 12,650

22. Expand $(x^2 - 1)^4$.
a) $x^8 - 1$
b) $x^8 - 4x^6 + 16x^4 - 4x^2 + 1$
c) $x^8 - 4x^6 + 6x^4 - 4x^2 + 1$
d) $x^8 + 4x^6 - 6x^4 + 4x^2 - 1$

23. Find the 3rd term of the binomial expansion of $(c + d)^8$.
a) $24c^6d^2$ b) $28c^6d^2$ c) $28c^4d^4$ d) $56c^4d^4$

24. Determine the number of subsets of a set containing 8 members.
a) 16 b) 128 c) 64 d) 256

25. *Card Drawing*. Suppose we draw a card from a well-shuffled deck of 52 cards. What is the probability of drawing a red king?
a) $\frac{1}{26}$ b) $\frac{2}{13}$ c) $\frac{1}{24}$ d) $\frac{1}{104}$

---

26. Solve for n: ${}_nP_5 = \frac{1}{42} \cdot {}_nP_7$.
a) 10 b) 14 c) 12 d) 11

CHAPTER 7 **NAME**____________________________

TEST FORM F **CLASS**_____**SCORE**_____**GRADE**_____

ANSWERS

1. For the sequence whose nth term is $a_n = 5(2n+1)^2$, find a_6.
   a) 845 b) 65 c) 725 d) 605

   1. ____________

2. Find and evaluate: $\sum_{k=1}^{3} \frac{k^2}{k+1}$.
   a) $\frac{9}{4}$ b) $\frac{23}{6}$ c) $\frac{181}{144}$ d) $\frac{49}{12}$

   2. ____________

3. Find the 4th term of the recursively defined sequence $a_1 = 3, a_{n+1} = 2a_n - 5$.
   a) -23 b) -9 c) -11 d) 3

   3. ____________

4. Find the 16th term of the arithmetic sequence 14, 8, 2,… .
   a) –82 b) 104 c) $\frac{38}{7}$ d) –76

   4. ____________

5. The 1st term of an arithmetic sequence is 7 and the 20th term is -50. Find the 5th term.
   a) –8 b) –5 c) $-\frac{22}{5}$ d) $-\frac{29}{4}$

   5. ____________

6. Find the sum of the first 20 terms of the series $\frac{1}{3}+\frac{4}{3}+\frac{7}{3}+\cdots$.
   a) $\frac{580}{3}$ b) $\frac{1180}{3}$ c) $\frac{590}{3}$ d) $\frac{640}{3}$

   6. ____________

7. Find the sum $\sum_{k=1}^{24} 4k+8$
   a) 104 b) 1392 c) 2784 d) 2496

   7. ____________

CHAPTER 7 **NAME**______________________

TEST FORM F

ANSWERS

8. ____________

9. ____________

10. ____________

11. ____________

12. ____________

13. ____________

14. ____________

8. Find the 8th term of the geometric sequence $10, 20, 40, \ldots$.

   a) 1280 b) 2560 c) 5120 d) 2550

9. For a geometric sequence, $r = 3$ and $S_5 = 12.1$. Find a_1.

   a) –0.5 b) –0.1 c) 0.3025 d) 0.1

10. Find the sum $\sum_{k=1}^{12} -3(2)^k$.

    a) –12,285 b) –24,570 c) –12,282 d) –12,288

11. Find the sum, if it exists: $0.2 + 0.4 + 0.8 + \cdots$.

    a) 2 b) 10 c) 250 d) Does not exist

12. When $1.\overline{38}$ is expressed in simplified fraction notation, what is the numerator?

    a) 99 b) 138 c) 137 d) 46

13. *Loan Repayment.* A family borrows \$20,000. The loan is to be repaid in 5 yr at 8 % interest, compounded annually. How much will be repaid at the end of 5 yr? Round to the nearest dollar.

    a) \$29,387 b) \$41,600
    c) \$21,600 d) \$29,549

14. A garden has 5 plants in the first row, 15 in the second row, 25 in the third row, 35 in the fourth row, and so on for 12 rows. How many plants are there altogether?

    a) 1320 b) 720 c) 780 d) 1440

CHAPTER 7 **NAME**______________________________

TEST FORM F

ANSWERS

15. Evaluate the statement:

$n^2 > (n-1)^2$, for $n = 1, 2, 3, \ldots$.

a) It is sometimes true. b) It is never true.
c) It is always true. d) It is not possible to evaluate.

16. Find and evaluate the third statement, S_3, in a mathematical induction proof of $2+5+8+\cdots+(3n-1)=\dfrac{n(3n+1)}{2}$, for n a natural number.

a) $2=\dfrac{1(3\cdot 1+1)}{2}$; True

b) $2+5+8=\dfrac{3(3\cdot 3+1)}{2}$; False

c) $2+5+8+\cdots+(3n-1)=\dfrac{n(3n+1)}{2}$; True

d) $2+5+8=\dfrac{3(3\cdot 3+1)}{2}$; True

17. Evaluate: ${}_{12}P_{10}$.

a) 66 b) 239,500,800
c) 132 d) 665,280

18. Evaluate: ${}_8C_3$.

a) 336 b) 6720 c) 56 d) 120

19. Evaluate: $\dbinom{n}{3}$.

a) $\dfrac{n!}{(n-3)!3!}$ b) $\dfrac{n!}{3!}$ c) $\dfrac{n!}{(n-3)!}$ d) $\dfrac{n!3!}{(n-3)!}$

20. *Test answers.* A multiple choice quiz contains 12 questions, each of which may be answered a, b, or c. How many possible answer sheets are there?

a) 531,441 b) 1728 c) 36 d) 1320

15. ____________

16. ____________

17. ____________

18. ____________

19. ____________

20. ____________

CHAPTER 7 **NAME**__________________________

TEST FORM F

ANSWERS

21. ____________

22. ____________

23. ____________

24. ____________

25. ____________

26. ____________

21. *Committee Members.* A club contains 20 members. How many different committees of 3 members are possible?
a) 6840 b) 3,486,784,401
c) 8000 d) 1140

22. Expand $(x+\sqrt{3})^4$.
a) x^4+9
b) $x^4+4\sqrt{3}x^3+18x^2+12\sqrt{3}x+9$
c) $x^4+12x^3+18x^2+36x+9$
d) $x^4+4\sqrt{3}x^3+48x^2+4\sqrt{3}x+9$

23. Find the 5th term of the binomial expansion of $(m+2)^5$.
a) $80m$ b) 32 c) $160m$ d) $32m$

24. Determine the number of subsets of a set containing 10 members.
a) 512 b) 100 c) 1024 d) 45

25. *Marbles.* Suppose we select, without looking, one marble from a bag containing 5 red marbles, 4 yellow marbles, and 7 blue marbles. What is the probability of selecting a red or yellow marble?
a) $\frac{9}{32}$ b) $\frac{9}{16}$ c) $\frac{5}{16}$ d) $\frac{3}{4}$

---

26. Solve for n: ${}_nP_6 = 6 \cdot {}_nP_4$.
a) 7 b) 8 c) 9 d) 10

ANSWER KEYS FOR ALTERNATE TEST FORMS A, B, C, D, E, AND F

Chapter R, Test Form A

1. a) 0; b) $\sqrt{18}; \sqrt[3]{7}$ 2. $\frac{3}{11}$ 3. $4x^2y$ 4. a) $[-3, 2)$; b)

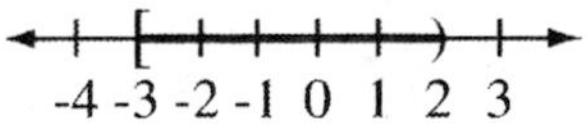

5. 5 6. 6 7. 0.000085 8. 6×10^{-15} 9. x^{-4} 10. $72a^4b^3$ 11. $-6a^2b^{-2}$

12. $2x^4+4x^3-6x$ 13. $4x^2-17x-15$ 14. $25n^2-30n+9$ 15. $-\frac{x+y}{3}$ 16. $6\sqrt{2}$

17. $2\sqrt[4]{2}$ 18. $16\sqrt{2}$ 19. $3\sqrt{10}$ 20. $38+3\sqrt{2}$ 21. $(4x+3)(x-5)$

22. $(m-4)(m^2+4m+16)$ 23. $5(m-3)(m+3)$ 24. $x(x-1)^2$ 25. $\frac{x+4}{x-9}$

26. $\frac{x-7}{(x+5)(x+7)}$ 27. $-8+4\sqrt{5}$ 28. $\sqrt[5]{x^4}$ 29. 5000 ft 30. 3 31. $\frac{21}{5}$

32. $-\frac{3}{4}, 5$ 33. $-\sqrt{13}, \sqrt{13}$ 34. $a^{4x}+2+a^{-4x}$

Chapter R, Test Form B

1. a) $-5, 0 6$; b) $-5, \frac{3}{4}, 0.6, 3\frac{1}{4}, -2.9$ 2. $\frac{5}{6}$ 3. $2ac$ 4. a) $[-2, 1)$; b)

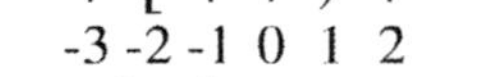

5. 9 6. 17 7. 5.2×10^{-3} 8. 1.47×10^{7} 9. y^8 10. $432x^2y^{12}$ 11. $-8a^5b^{-1}$

12. $-5x^3+5x^2+2x-10$ 13. $5x^2+4x-12$ 14. $4k^2-12k+9$ 15. $\frac{8-y}{8y}$ 16. $4\sqrt{5}$

17. $2\sqrt[3]{3}$ 18. $9\sqrt{3}$ 19. 20 20. $-5+2\sqrt{7}$ 21. $(2y+1)(y-5)$ 22. $(k-3)(k^2+3m+9)$

23. $7(x-5)(x+5)$ 24. $x(x-6)^2$ 25. $\frac{(x-1)(x+3)}{(x+4)^2}$ 26. $\frac{x-6}{(x+1)(x+3)}$ 27. $\frac{3-\sqrt{5}}{2}$

28. $\sqrt[3]{x^2}$ 29. 14.9 ft 30. $\frac{21}{4}$ 31. $\frac{2}{7}$ 32. $-\frac{5}{6}, 4$ 33. $-\sqrt{6}, \sqrt{6}$ 34. $x^{2a}-y^{2b}$

Chapter R, Test Form C

1. a) 0; b) $\frac{7}{6}, 0.53, 4\frac{1}{5}, -6.7$ 2. $\frac{2}{3}$ 3. $0.1x$ 4. a) $[-1, 3)$; b)

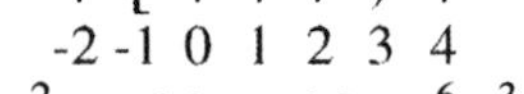

5. 15 6. 25 7. 0.000000596 8. 9×10^{-11} 9. x^2 10. $108x^6y^2$ 11. $-10m^{-6}n^3$

12. $-5x^4-3x^3+4x^2+6x$ 13. $3x^2+5x-12$ 14. $49n^2-28n+4$ 15. $\frac{16}{xy(x+y)}$

16. $3\sqrt{3}$ 17. $3\sqrt[3]{3}$ 18. $18\sqrt{3}$ 19. $5\sqrt{3}$ 20. $14-7\sqrt{2}$ 21. $(y-6)(3y+4)$

22. $(m+1)(m^2-m+1)$ 23. $5(n+8)(n-8)$ 24. $x(x-5)^2$ 25. $\frac{(x-5)(x+2)}{(x+5)(x-7)}$

Chapter R, Test Form C (continued)

26. $\frac{x+1}{(x-3)(x-1)}$ 27. $3-\sqrt{7}$ 28. $\sqrt[4]{y}$ 29. 23.9 ft 30. 2 31. $\frac{13}{3}$ 32. $-6, \frac{2}{3}$
33. $-2\sqrt{2}, 2\sqrt{2}$ 34. $x^{2a} - y^{-2a}$

Chapter R, Test Form D

1. a) 6; b) $\frac{2}{3}, 6.2, 4\frac{1}{2}, + -8.3$ 2. $\frac{3}{4}$ 3. $3xy^2$ 4. a) $(-3, 2]$, b) 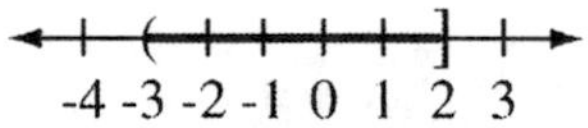

5. 13 6. 9 7. 2.34×10^7 8. 1.302×10^4 9. x^{-2} 10. $72x^{12}y^2$ 11. $-10a^{-2}b^{15}$
12. $-4x^4 - 2x^3 + 2x^2$ 13. $7x^2 - 61x - 18$ 14. $4m^2 - 20m + 25$ 15. $\frac{a^2+b^2}{ab(a+b)}$
16. $2\sqrt{30}$ 17. $5\sqrt[3]{2}$ 18. 0 19. $9\sqrt{10}$ 20. $11+\sqrt{5}$ 21. $(2y+5)(y-6)$
22. $(n-5)(n^2+5n+25)$ 23. $8(m-2)(m+2)$ 24. $x(x+8)^2$ 25. $\frac{x+5}{x+2}$
26. $\frac{x+6}{(x-2)(x+2)}$ 27. $\frac{15+3\sqrt{6}}{19}$ 28. $\sqrt[5]{x^4}$ 29. 19.9 ft 30. 8 31. 1 32. $-4, \frac{5}{4}$
33. $-\sqrt{5}, \sqrt{5}$ 34. $x^a(x^a-1)(x^{2a}+x^a+1)$

Chapter R, Test Form E

1. a 2. c 3. d 4. d 5. c 6. b 7. b 8. d 9. a 10. b 11. c 12. a 13. d
14. b 15. d 16. c 17. b 18. c 19. d 20. a 21. c 22. c 23. b 24. a 25. b
26. c 27. a 28. d

Chapter R, Test Form F

1. c 2. b 3. a 4. c 5. b 6. d 7. b 8. a 9. c 10. b 11. b 12. a 13. b
14. b 15. b 16. a 17. c 18. d 19. c 20. b 21. a 22. d 23. c 24. b 25. a
26. d 27. c 28. b

Chapter 1, Test Form A

1. 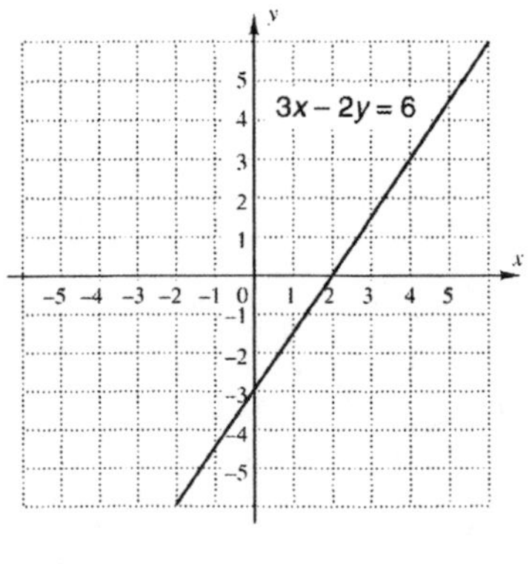

2. $\sqrt{125} \approx 11.180$ 3. (3, –4) 4. $(x+2)^2 + (y-3)^2 = 11$
5. (–6, 0); 3 6. a) Yes; b) $\{-5, -4, 1, 3\}$ 7. 9; $x^2 - 7$

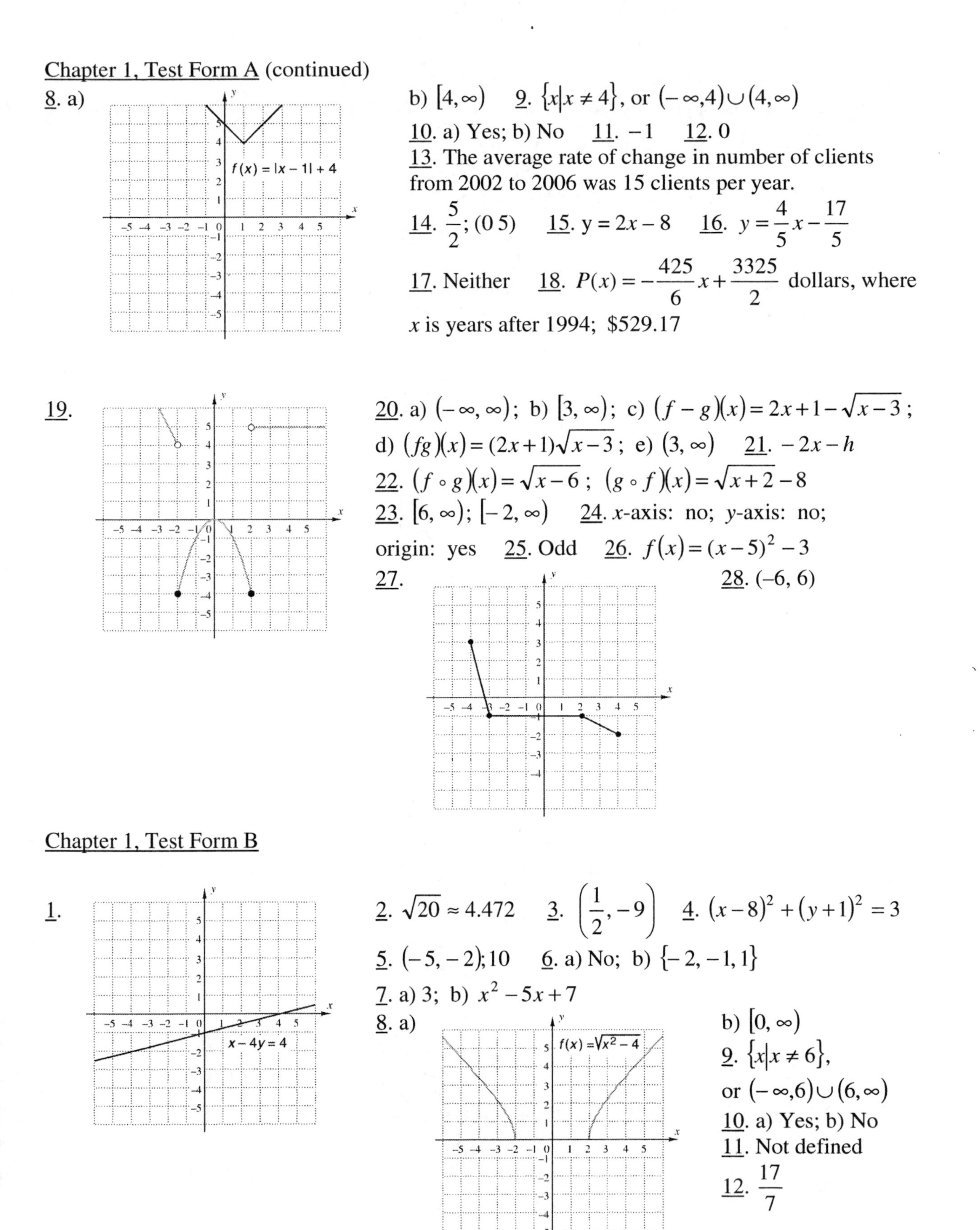

Chapter 1, Test Form A (continued)

8. a)

b) $[4, \infty)$ 9. $\{x \mid x \neq 4\}$, or $(-\infty, 4) \cup (4, \infty)$

10. a) Yes; b) No 11. -1 12. 0

13. The average rate of change in number of clients from 2002 to 2006 was 15 clients per year.

14. $\frac{5}{2}$; (0 5) 15. $y = 2x - 8$ 16. $y = \frac{4}{5}x - \frac{17}{5}$

17. Neither 18. $P(x) = -\frac{425}{6}x + \frac{3325}{2}$ dollars, where x is years after 1994; \$529.17

19.

20. a) $(-\infty, \infty)$; b) $[3, \infty)$; c) $(f-g)(x) = 2x + 1 - \sqrt{x-3}$; d) $(fg)(x) = (2x+1)\sqrt{x-3}$; e) $(3, \infty)$ 21. $-2x - h$

22. $(f \circ g)(x) = \sqrt{x-6}$; $(g \circ f)(x) = \sqrt{x+2} - 8$

23. $[6, \infty)$; $[-2, \infty)$ 24. x-axis: no; y-axis: no; origin: yes 25. Odd 26. $f(x) = (x-5)^2 - 3$

27.

28. (–6, 6)

Chapter 1, Test Form B

1.

2. $\sqrt{20} \approx 4.472$ 3. $\left(\frac{1}{2}, -9\right)$ 4. $(x-8)^2 + (y+1)^2 = 3$

5. $(-5, -2)$; 10 6. a) No; b) $\{-2, -1, 1\}$

7. a) 3; b) $x^2 - 5x + 7$

8. a)

b) $[0, \infty)$

9. $\{x \mid x \neq 6\}$, or $(-\infty, 6) \cup (6, \infty)$

10. a) Yes; b) No

11. Not defined

12. $\frac{17}{7}$

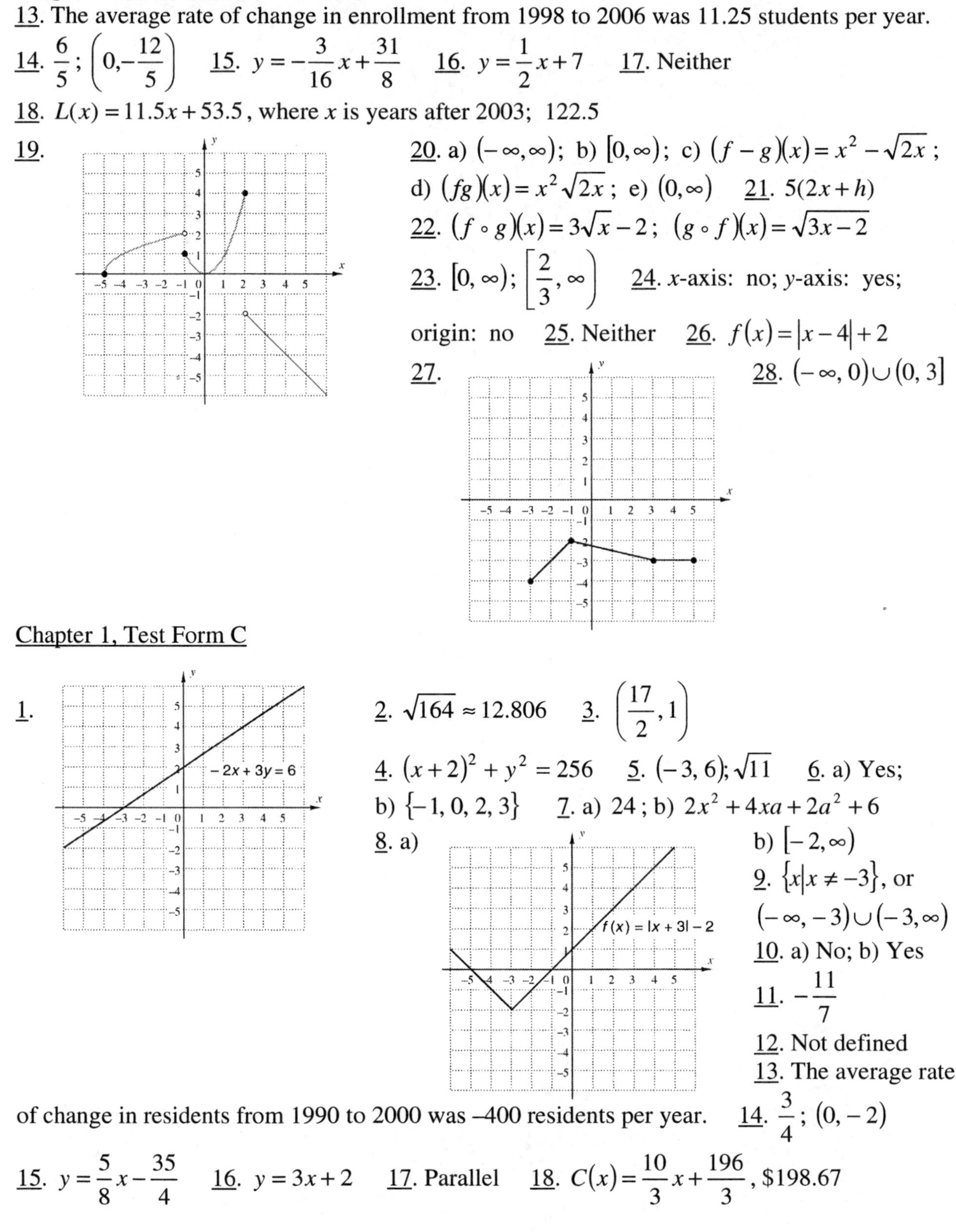

Chapter 1, Test Form B (continued)

13. The average rate of change in enrollment from 1998 to 2006 was 11.25 students per year.

14. $\frac{6}{5}$; $\left(0, -\frac{12}{5}\right)$ 15. $y = -\frac{3}{16}x + \frac{31}{8}$ 16. $y = \frac{1}{2}x + 7$ 17. Neither

18. $L(x) = 11.5x + 53.5$, where x is years after 2003; 122.5

19.

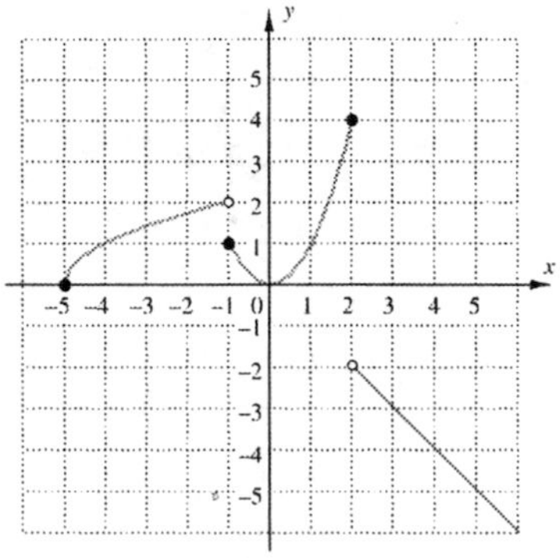

20. a) $(-\infty, \infty)$; b) $[0, \infty)$; c) $(f - g)(x) = x^2 - \sqrt{2x}$; d) $(fg)(x) = x^2\sqrt{2x}$; e) $(0, \infty)$ 21. $5(2x + h)$

22. $(f \circ g)(x) = 3\sqrt{x} - 2$; $(g \circ f)(x) = \sqrt{3x - 2}$

23. $[0, \infty)$; $\left[\frac{2}{3}, \infty\right)$ 24. x-axis: no; y-axis: yes; origin: no 25. Neither 26. $f(x) = |x - 4| + 2$

27.

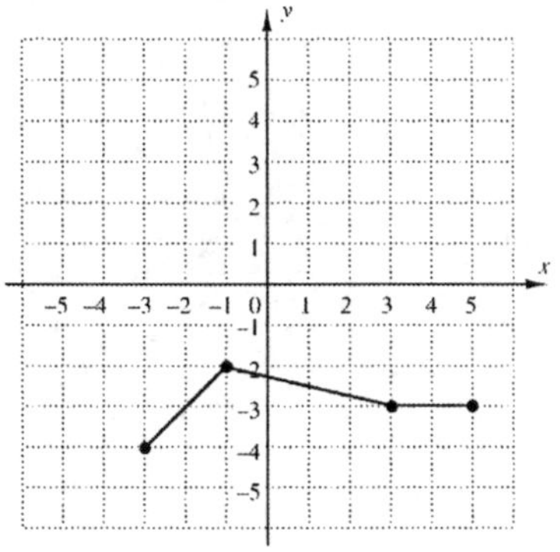

28. $(-\infty, 0) \cup (0, 3]$

Chapter 1, Test Form C

1.

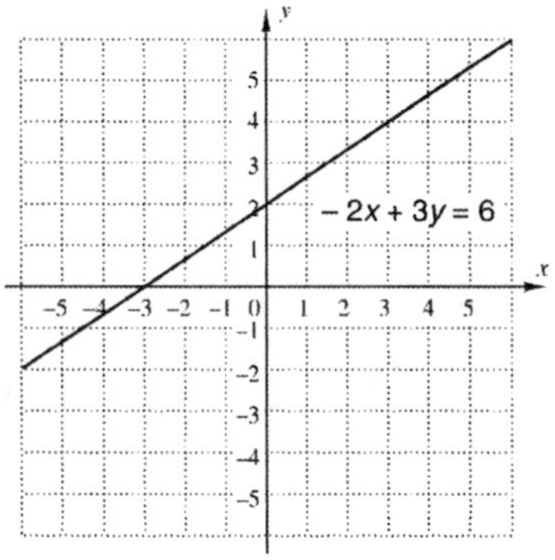

2. $\sqrt{164} \approx 12.806$ 3. $\left(\frac{17}{2}, 1\right)$

4. $(x + 2)^2 + y^2 = 256$ 5. $(-3, 6)$; $\sqrt{11}$ 6. a) Yes; b) $\{-1, 0, 2, 3\}$ 7. a) 24; b) $2x^2 + 4xa + 2a^2 + 6$

8. a)

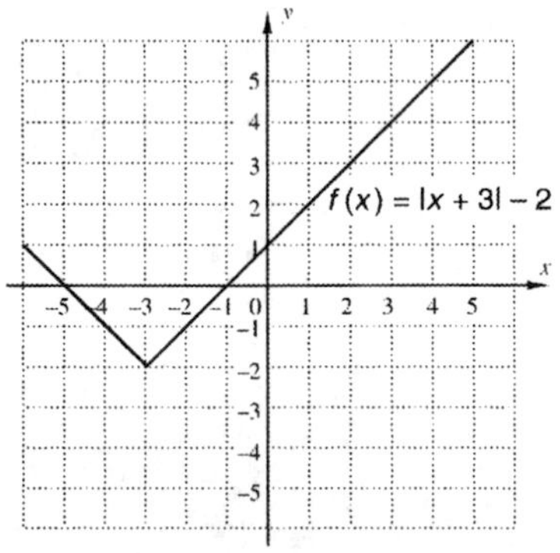

b) $[-2, \infty)$

9. $\{x | x \neq -3\}$, or $(-\infty, -3) \cup (-3, \infty)$

10. a) No; b) Yes

11. $-\frac{11}{7}$

12. Not defined

13. The average rate of change in residents from 1990 to 2000 was –400 residents per year. 14. $\frac{3}{4}$; $(0, -2)$

15. $y = \frac{5}{8}x - \frac{35}{4}$ 16. $y = 3x + 2$ 17. Parallel 18. $C(x) = \frac{10}{3}x + \frac{196}{3}$, \$198.67

Chapter 1, Test Form C (continued)

19.

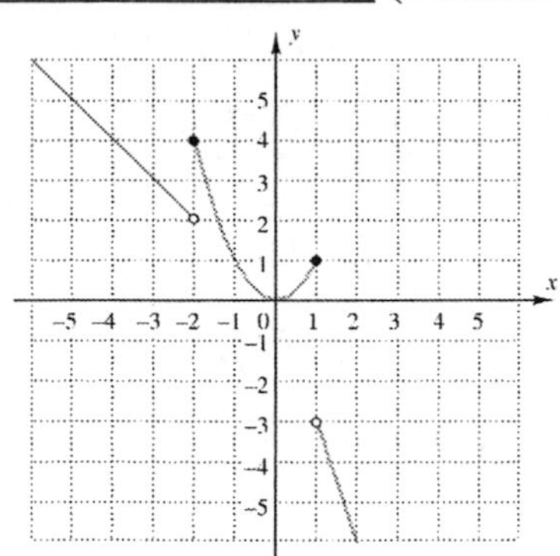

20. a) $(-\infty, \infty)$; b) $(-\infty, 0) \cup (0, \infty)$;

c) $(f - g)(x) = -2x + 4 - \frac{1}{x}$; d) $(fg)(x) = -2 + \frac{4}{x}$;

e) $(-\infty, 0) \cup (0, \infty)$ 21. $3x^2 + 3xh + h^2 - 1$

22. $(f \circ g)(x) = x^2 - 6x + 9$; $(g \circ f)(x) = x^2 - 3$

23. $(-\infty, \infty)$; $(-\infty, \infty)$ 24. x-axis: no; y-axis: yes; origin: no 25. Neither 26. $f(x) = (x+4)^3 + 6$

27.

28. $(-\infty, 0) \cup (0, 16)$

Chapter 1, Test Form D

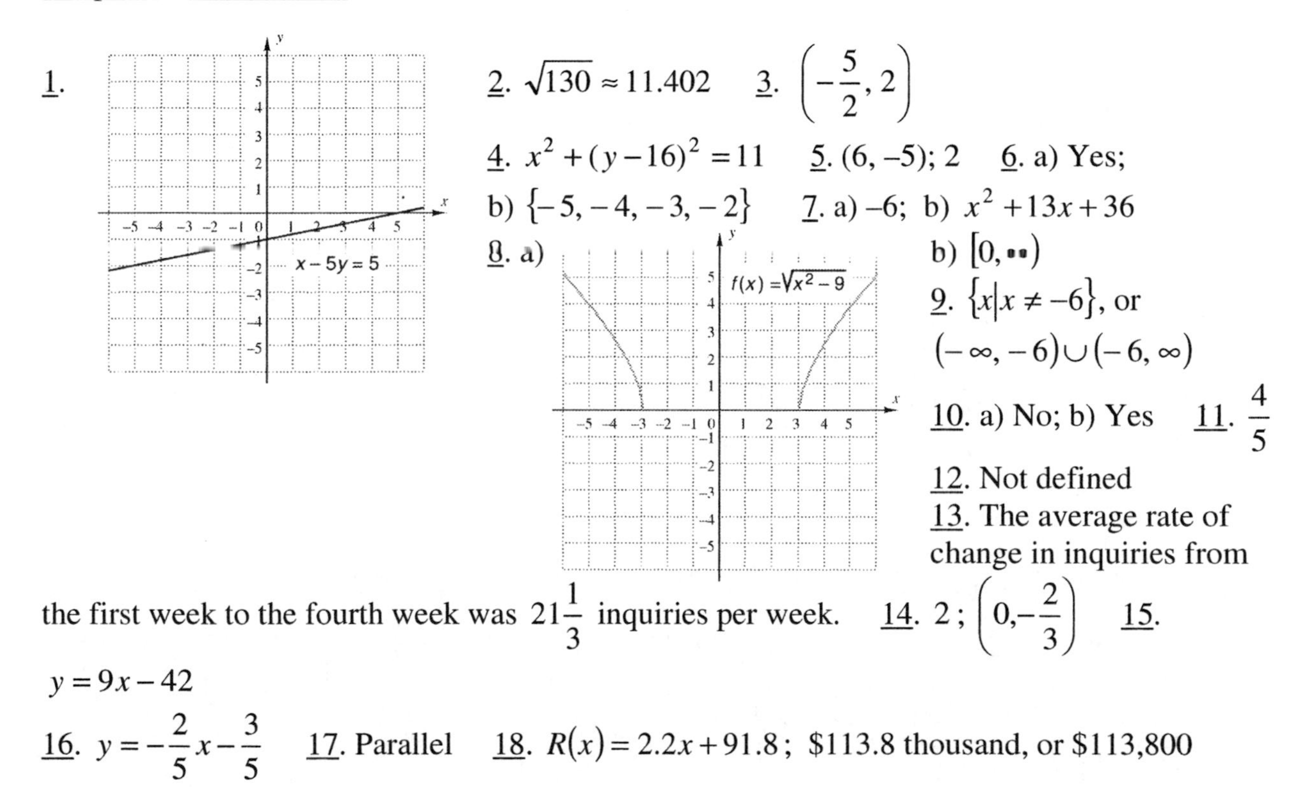

1.

2. $\sqrt{130} \approx 11.402$ 3. $\left(-\frac{5}{2}, 2\right)$

4. $x^2 + (y - 16)^2 = 11$ 5. (6, –5); 2 6. a) Yes; b) $\{-5, -4, -3, -2\}$ 7. a) –6; b) $x^2 + 13x + 36$

8. a)

b) $[0, \infty)$

9. $\{x | x \neq -6\}$, or $(-\infty, -6) \cup (-6, \infty)$

10. a) No; b) Yes 11. $\frac{4}{5}$

12. Not defined

13. The average rate of change in inquiries from the first week to the fourth week was $21\frac{1}{3}$ inquiries per week. 14. 2; $\left(0, -\frac{2}{3}\right)$ 15. $y = 9x - 42$

16. $y = -\frac{2}{5}x - \frac{3}{5}$ 17. Parallel 18. $R(x) = 2.2x + 91.8$; \$113.8 thousand, or \$113,800

Chapter 1, Test Form D (continued)

19.

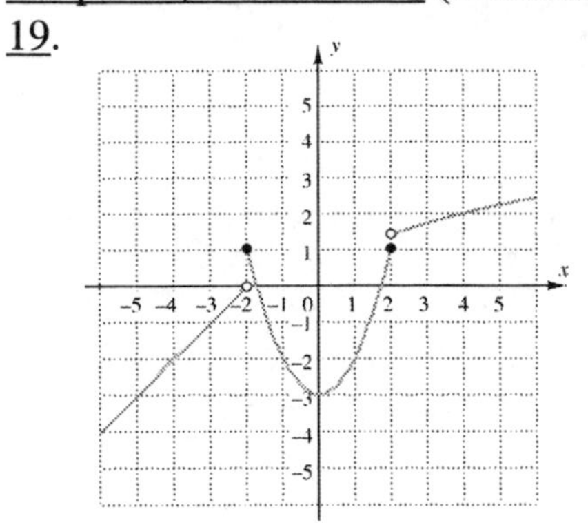

20. a) $(-\infty, 0)\cup(0, \infty)$; b) $(-\infty, \infty)$;
c) $(f-g)(x)=\frac{1}{x^2}-x-4$; d) $(fg)(x)=\frac{x+4}{x^2}$;
e) $(-\infty,-4)\cup(-4, 0)\cup(0, \infty)$ 21. $4x+2h$
22. $(f\circ g)(x)=\sqrt{x-3}$; $(g\circ f)(x)=\sqrt{x-5}+2$
23. $[3, \infty)$; $[5, \infty)$
24. x-axis: no; y-axis: no; origin: yes 25. Neither
26. $f(x)=\sqrt{x+5}-3$
27.

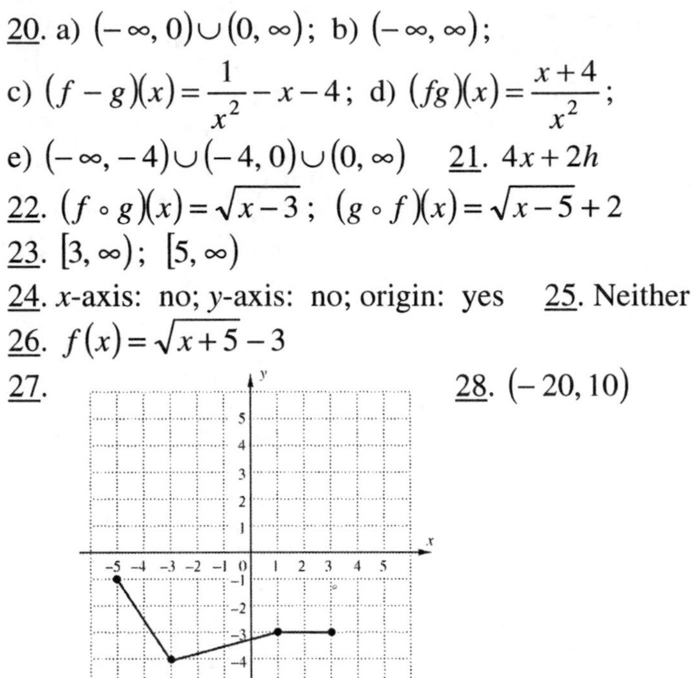

28. $(-20, 10)$

Chapter 1, Test Form E

1. b 2. a 3. c 4. d 5. a 6. a 7. c 8. b 9. c 10. a 11. d 12. b 13. d
14. d 15. d 16. a 17. c 18. b 19. a 20. c 21. b 22. c 23. a 24. a 25. d
26. a 27. b

Chapter 1, Test Form F

1. a 2. b 3. c 4. b 5. a 6. c 7. c 8. d 9. b 10. d 11. a 12. c 13. b
14. d 15. a 16. c 17. b 18. a 19. d 20. b 21. c 22. d 23. d 24. b
25. a 26. c 27. a

Chapter 2, Test Form A

1. $-\frac{13}{3}$ 2. 32 3. $-8, \frac{5}{2}$ 4. –4, 4 5. $-5i, 5i$ 6. –8, 3 7. $\frac{1\pm\sqrt{19}}{3}$ 8. $-\frac{1}{5}\pm\frac{3}{5}i$
9. 64 10. –7, 3 11. 5 12. 5, 9 13. $-\frac{17}{5}, \frac{9}{5}$ 14. $\left(\frac{4}{3}, \frac{13}{3}\right]$ 15. $\left(-\infty, -\frac{1}{3}\right]\cup\left[\frac{1}{4}, \infty\right)$
16. (–13, 3) 17. $(-\infty, -16]\cup[4, \infty)$ 18. $w=\frac{P-2l}{2}$ 19. $b=\frac{a}{8a-1}$ 20. $\frac{3\pm\sqrt{57}}{2}$
21. 4 mph 22. 115 ft by 135 ft 23. $\sqrt{13}\,i$ 24. $-11i$ 25. $-1-5i$ 26. $46+3i$
27. $\frac{19}{50}-\frac{17}{50}i$ 28. –1 29. $-\frac{1}{3}$ 30. $-9, \frac{2}{3}$ 31. $-3\pm2\sqrt{6}$

Chapter 2, Test Form A (continued)

32. a) $(3,-5)$; b) $x=3$; c) minimum $=-5$; d) $[-5,\infty)$; e)

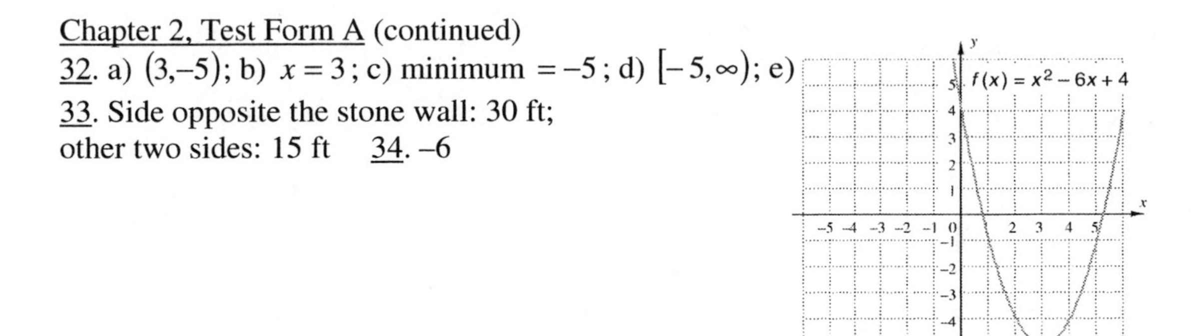

33. Side opposite the stone wall: 30 ft; other two sides: 15 ft 34. –6

Chapter 2, Test Form B

1. $\frac{27}{8}$ 2. 5 3. $-\frac{5}{4}, 9$ 4. $-\sqrt{3}, \sqrt{3}$ 5. $-7i, 7i$ 6. 2, 6 7. $\frac{1}{4}, 2$ 8. $\frac{1}{2} \pm \frac{\sqrt{19}}{2}i$

9. 9 10. $-4, \frac{5}{2}$ 11. -3 12. 6 13. $-\frac{13}{3}, 3$ 14. $\left[-\frac{5}{3}, 2\right)$ 15. $\left(-\infty, -\frac{7}{5}\right) \cup \left[\frac{1}{3}, \infty\right)$

16. $(-7, 13)$ 17. $(-\infty, 2] \cup [6, \infty)$ 18. $t = \frac{A-P}{Pr}$ 19. $m = \frac{3}{6+2n}$ 20. $2 \pm \sqrt{6}$

21. 8 mph 22. 25 ft; 60 ft 23. $\sqrt{6}i$ 24. $-10i$ 25. $-4-5i$ 26. $25-2i$

27. $\frac{21}{26} + \frac{27}{26}i$ 28. –1 29. $-\frac{1}{2}$ 30. $-3, \frac{5}{6}$ 31. $\frac{3 \pm \sqrt{69}}{10}$

32. a) $(3,2)$; b) $x=3$; c) minimum $=2$; d) $[2,\infty)$; e)

33. Parties under 25 people 34. 18

Chapter 2, Test Form C

1. $\frac{7}{2}$ 2. -32 3. $-\frac{1}{2}, \frac{3}{4}$ 4. –2, 2 5. $-4i, 4i$ 6. –2, 4 7. $-3, -\frac{2}{5}$ 8. $2 \pm \sqrt{2}i$

9. 16, 36 10. $\frac{1}{2}, 6$ 11. 4 12. 30 13. $-\frac{1}{2}, \frac{5}{4}$ 14. $\left[-\frac{3}{2}, 4\right)$ 15. $(-\infty, 1] \cup \left[\frac{9}{2}, \infty\right)$

16. (3, 9) 17. $(-\infty, -8] \cup [4, \infty)$ 18. $h = \frac{2A}{b}$ 19. $n = \frac{4A^2}{25}$ 20. $3 \pm \sqrt{17}$ 21. 120 mi

22. $\frac{25 - 5\sqrt{19}}{2} \approx 1.6$ ft 23. $\sqrt{11}i$ 24. $2\sqrt{3}i$ 25. $-3-7i$ 26. $14+5i$ 27. $\frac{17}{26} - \frac{19}{26}i$

Chapter 2, Test Form C (continued)

28. $-i$ 29. 2 30. $-2, -\frac{3}{4}$ 31. $\frac{-1 \pm \sqrt{41}}{4}$ 32. a) $(3,1)$; b) $x = 3$; c) maximum $= 1$; d) $(-\infty, 1]$; e)

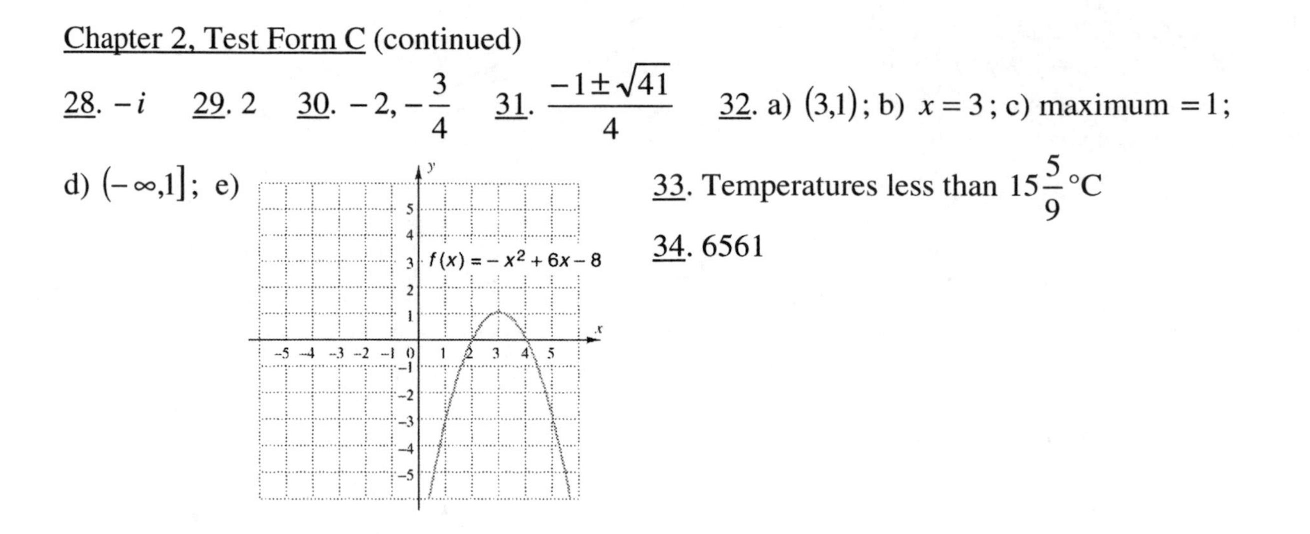

33. Temperatures less than $15\frac{5}{9}$ °C

34. 6561

Chapter 2, Test Form D

1. $\frac{9}{5}$ 2. 7 3. $-\frac{3}{5}, \frac{5}{2}$ 4. –3, 3 5. $-6i, 6i$ 6. 5, 7 7. $3 \pm \sqrt{6}$ 8. $\frac{3}{2} \pm \frac{\sqrt{19}}{2}i$ 9. 4

10. –4, 9 11. 3 12. 2 13. $-3, 13$ 14. $\left[-1, \frac{8}{5}\right)$ 15. $\left(-\infty, \frac{1}{2}\right] \cup \left(\frac{2}{3}, \infty\right)$

16. $(-\infty, -6] \cup [2, \infty)$ 17. (–9, 19) 18. $r = \frac{PV}{nt}$ 19. $k = \frac{T^2}{12.5}$ 20. $-2 \pm \sqrt{13}$

21. \$28.18 22. 100 km/h 23. $5i$ 24. $-7i$ 25. $13 - 10i$ 26. 25 27. $\frac{1}{2} - \frac{1}{2}i$

28. $-i$ 29. $\frac{5}{4}$ 30. $\frac{1}{2}, 6$ 31. $4 \pm \sqrt{11}$ 32. a) $(-2,4)$; b) $x = -2$; c) maximum $= 4$; d) $(-\infty, 4]$; e)

33. 36 in. 34. –3, 10

Chapter 2, Test Form E

1. b 2. d 3. c 4. d 5. a 6. c 7. b 8. a 9. a 10. c 11. d 12. b 13. d 14. a 15. a 16. b 17. d 18. d 19. a 20. c 21. a

Chapter 2, Test Form F

1. d 2. c 3. a 4. d 5. b 6. c 7. a 8. b 9. d 10. d 11. a 12. b 13. c 14. d 15. b 16. a 17. a 18. d 19. a 20. c 21. c

Chapter 3, Test Form A

1. a) cubic; b) $6x^3$; c) 6; d) 3 2. 0 has multiplicity 2; $-\frac{2}{3}$ has multiplicity 1; 6 has multiplicity 3

3. 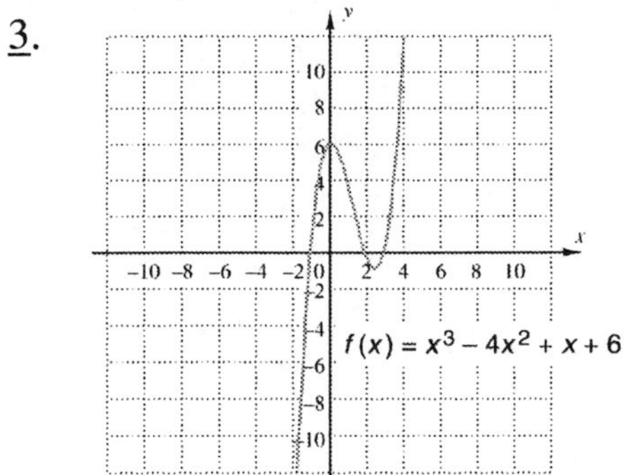

4. Not possible
5. $P(x) = (x+3)(x^3 - 5x^2 + 15x - 44) + 126$
6. $5x^3 - 13x^2 + 26x - 51$, R 100 7. –56 8. No
9. $f(x) = x^4 + x^3 - 8x^2 - 12x$ 10. $-\sqrt{3}, 7+2i$
11. $f(x) = x^3 - 5x^2 - 7x + 35$ 12. a) $\pm\frac{1}{5}, \pm\frac{2}{5}, \pm 1, \pm 2$
13. a) –3, –1, 2; b) $P(x) = (x+3)(x+1)(x-2)^2$
14. a) 2 or 0; b) 3 or 1

15. 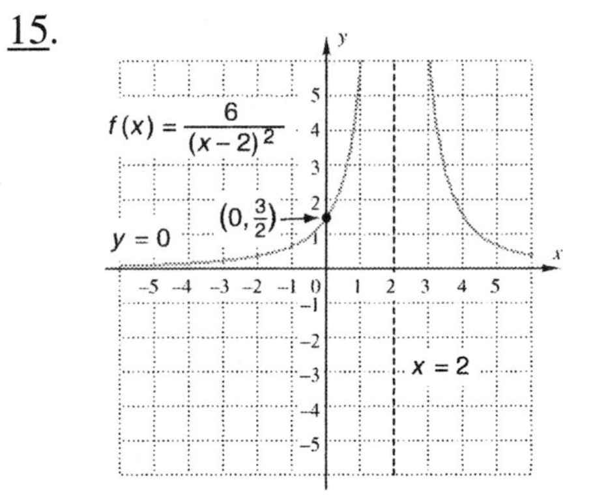

domain: $(-\infty, 2) \cup (2, \infty)$
x-intercept: none

16. $f(x) = \frac{x+3}{(x+2)(x-6)}$ 17. $\left(\frac{2}{3}, 5\right)$ 18. $\left(-\infty, -\frac{5}{2}\right] \cup (-1, \infty)$ 19. 2 sec

20. $[0, 0.31) \cup (14.69, \infty)$ days 21. $y = \frac{90}{x}$ 22. 56.4 in^3 23. $y = \frac{250xz}{w^2}$

24. $(-\infty, -12] \cup [5, \infty)$

Chapter 3, Test Form B

1. a) Quartic; b) $-3x^4$; c) –3; d) 4

2. 0 has multiplicity 2; $-\frac{1}{2}$ has multiplicity 1; 1 has multiplicity 2

3. 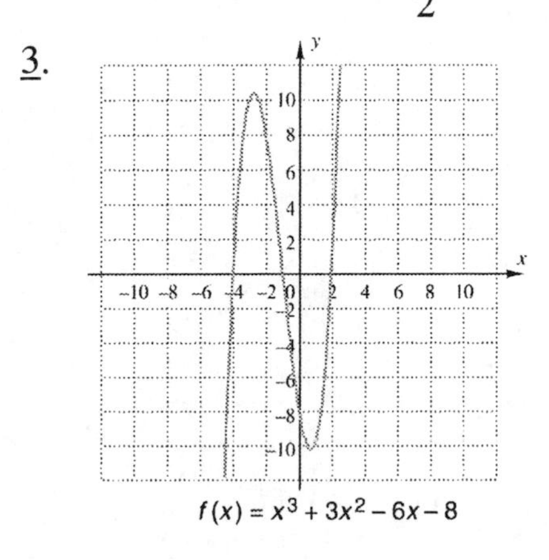

4. Yes 5. $P(x) = (x-4)(x^3 + 4x^2 + 14x + 59) + 231$
6. $4x^2 + 6x + 20$, R 35 7. –23 8. Yes
9. $f(x) = x^4 - 8x^3 - 3x^2 + 126x - 216$ 10. $-\sqrt{2}, 7-4i$
11. $f(x) = x^3 - 3x^2 - 6x + 18$ 12. $\pm\frac{1}{2}, \pm\frac{3}{2}, \pm 1, \pm 3$
13. a) $-2, \pm\sqrt{5}$; b) $P(x) = (x+2)(x+\sqrt{5})(x-\sqrt{5})$
14. a) 3 or 1; b) 1

Chapter 3, Test Form B (continued)

15.

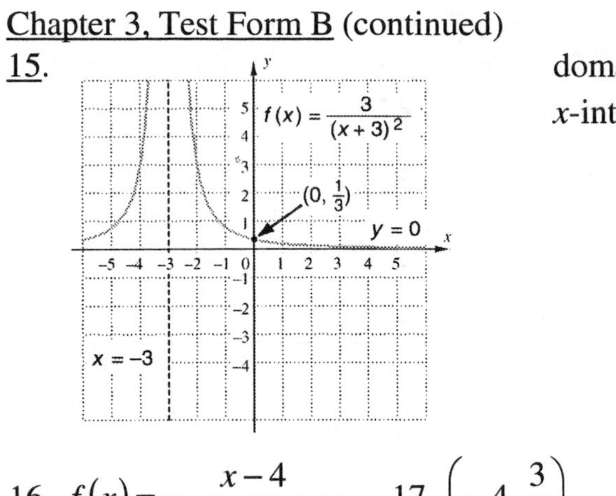

domain: $(-\infty, -3) \cup (-3, \infty)$

x-intercept: none

16. $f(x) = \dfrac{x-4}{(x+3)(x-5)}$ 17. $\left(-4, \dfrac{3}{2}\right)$ 18. $\left(5, \dfrac{31}{5}\right]$ 19. 5 sec

20. $[0, 0.54) \cup (4.46, \infty)$ years 21. $y = \dfrac{7}{3}x$ 22. 0.16 ampere 23. $y = \dfrac{125x^2z^2}{9w}$

24. $(-2, 2)$

Chapter 3, Test Form C

1. a) Quadratic; b) $-x^2$; c) -1; d) 2

2. 0 has multiplicity 2; 3 has multiplicity 2; $-\dfrac{5}{4}$ has multiplicity 1

3.

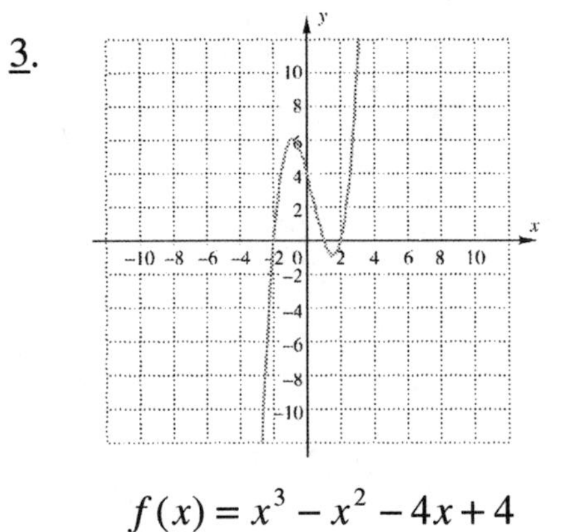

$f(x) = x^3 - x^2 - 4x + 4$

4. Not possible 5. $P(x) = (x+2)(x^3 - 2x^2 + x - 1) + (-4)$

6. $5x^3 - 5x^2 + 4x - 3$, R 1 7. -10 8. Yes

9. $f(x) = x^4 - 2x^3 - 15x^2$ 10. $\sqrt{5}, 3 - i$

11. $f(x) = x^3 + 4x^2 + 4x + 16$ 12. $\pm\dfrac{1}{6}, \pm\dfrac{1}{3}, \pm\dfrac{1}{2}, \pm 1$

13. a) $-1, 3, \pm\sqrt{2}$; b) $P(x) = (x+1)(x-3)(x+\sqrt{2})(x-\sqrt{2})$

14. a) 2 or 0; b) 1

15.

domain: $(-\infty, -1) \cup (-1, 4) \cup (4, \infty)$

x-intercept: -3

Chapter 3, Test Form C (continued)

16. $f(x)=\dfrac{x}{(x+3)(x-1)}$ 17. $\left[-2, \dfrac{5}{3}\right]$ 18. $\left[-\dfrac{17}{2}, -5\right)$ 19. 4 sec 20. $(0.65, 7.68)$ days

21. $y = 5x$ 22. 3.75 W/m^2 23. $y=\dfrac{10xz}{\sqrt{w}}$ 24. $(-\infty, -3]\cup[5, \infty)$

Chapter 3, Test Form D

1. a) Linear; b) $-2x$; c) -2; d) 1 2. 0 has multiplicity 1; $\dfrac{3}{4}$ has multiplicity 2; -2 has multiplicity 1

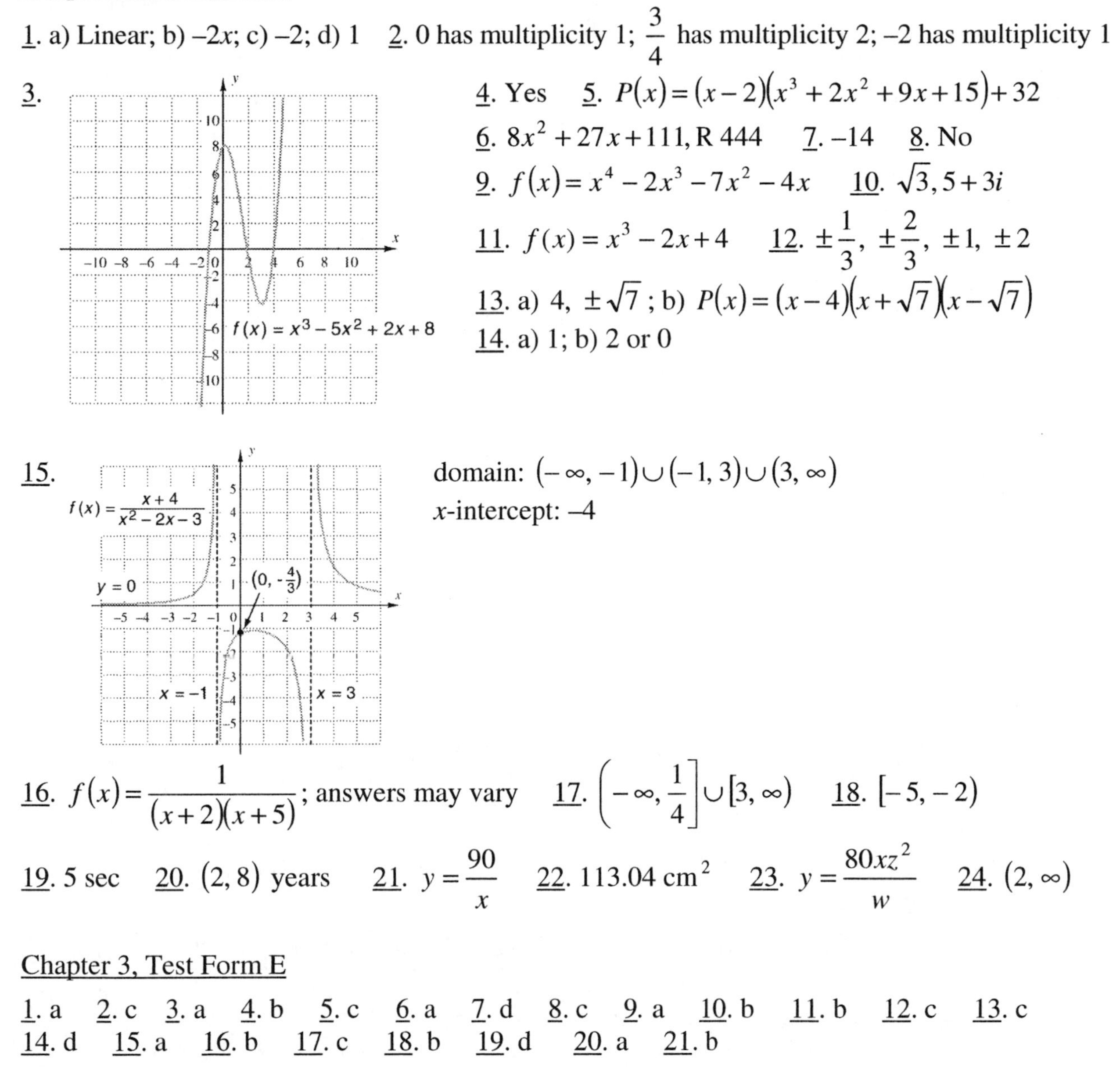

3.
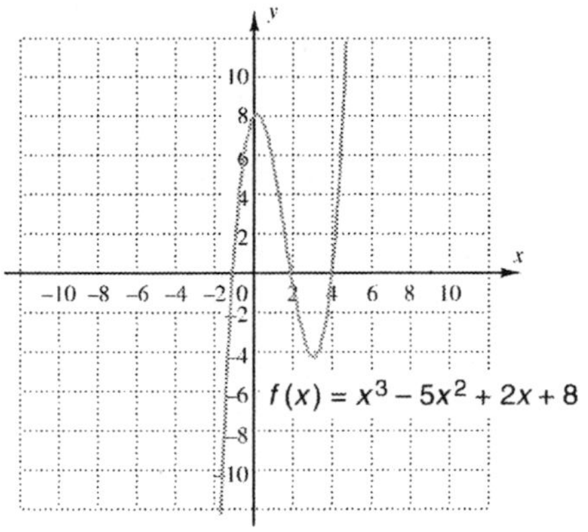

4. Yes 5. $P(x)=(x-2)(x^3+2x^2+9x+15)+32$

6. $8x^2+27x+111$, R 444 7. -14 8. No

9. $f(x)=x^4-2x^3-7x^2-4x$ 10. $\sqrt{3}, 5+3i$

11. $f(x)=x^3-2x+4$ 12. $\pm\dfrac{1}{3}, \pm\dfrac{2}{3}, \pm1, \pm2$

13. a) 4, $\pm\sqrt{7}$; b) $P(x)=(x-4)(x+\sqrt{7})(x-\sqrt{7})$

14. a) 1; b) 2 or 0

15.
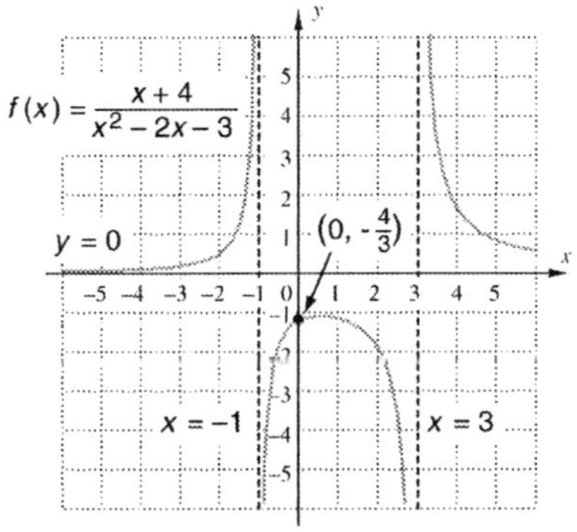

domain: $(-\infty, -1)\cup(-1, 3)\cup(3, \infty)$

x-intercept: -4

16. $f(x)=\dfrac{1}{(x+2)(x+5)}$; answers may vary 17. $\left(-\infty, \dfrac{1}{4}\right]\cup[3, \infty)$ 18. $[-5, -2)$

19. 5 sec 20. $(2, 8)$ years 21. $y=\dfrac{90}{x}$ 22. 113.04 cm^2 23. $y=\dfrac{80xz^2}{w}$ 24. $(2, \infty)$

Chapter 3, Test Form E

1. a 2. c 3. a 4. b 5. c 6. a 7. d 8. c 9. a 10. b 11. b 12. c 13. c
14. d 15. a 16. b 17. c 18. b 19. d 20. a 21. b

Chapter 3, Test Form F

1. d 2. c 3. d 4. d 5. b 6. a 7. d 8. d 9. a 10. b 11. d 12. a 13. a
14. d 15. c 16. d 17. a 18. b 19. c 20. a 21. c

Chapter 4, Test Form A

1. $\{(0,5),(2,-4),(-1,3),(6,2)\}$ 2. No 3. $f^{-1}(x)=\sqrt[3]{x-6}$ 4. $f^{-1}(x)=\dfrac{x+4}{2}$

5. $f^{-1}(x)=\dfrac{8x}{1+x}$ 6. Not one-to-one 7. $f^{-1}(f(x))=f^{-1}\left(\dfrac{1}{2}x-3\right)=2\left(\dfrac{1}{2}x-3+3\right)=x;$

$f\left(f^{-1}(x)\right)=f(2(x+3))=\dfrac{1}{2}[2(x+3)]-3=x+3-3=x$

8. a) $f^{-1}(x)=\sqrt[3]{x+2}$; b) $(-\infty,\infty)$; $(-\infty,\infty)$; c) $(-\infty,\infty)$; $(-\infty,\infty)$;

d) 9. 10.

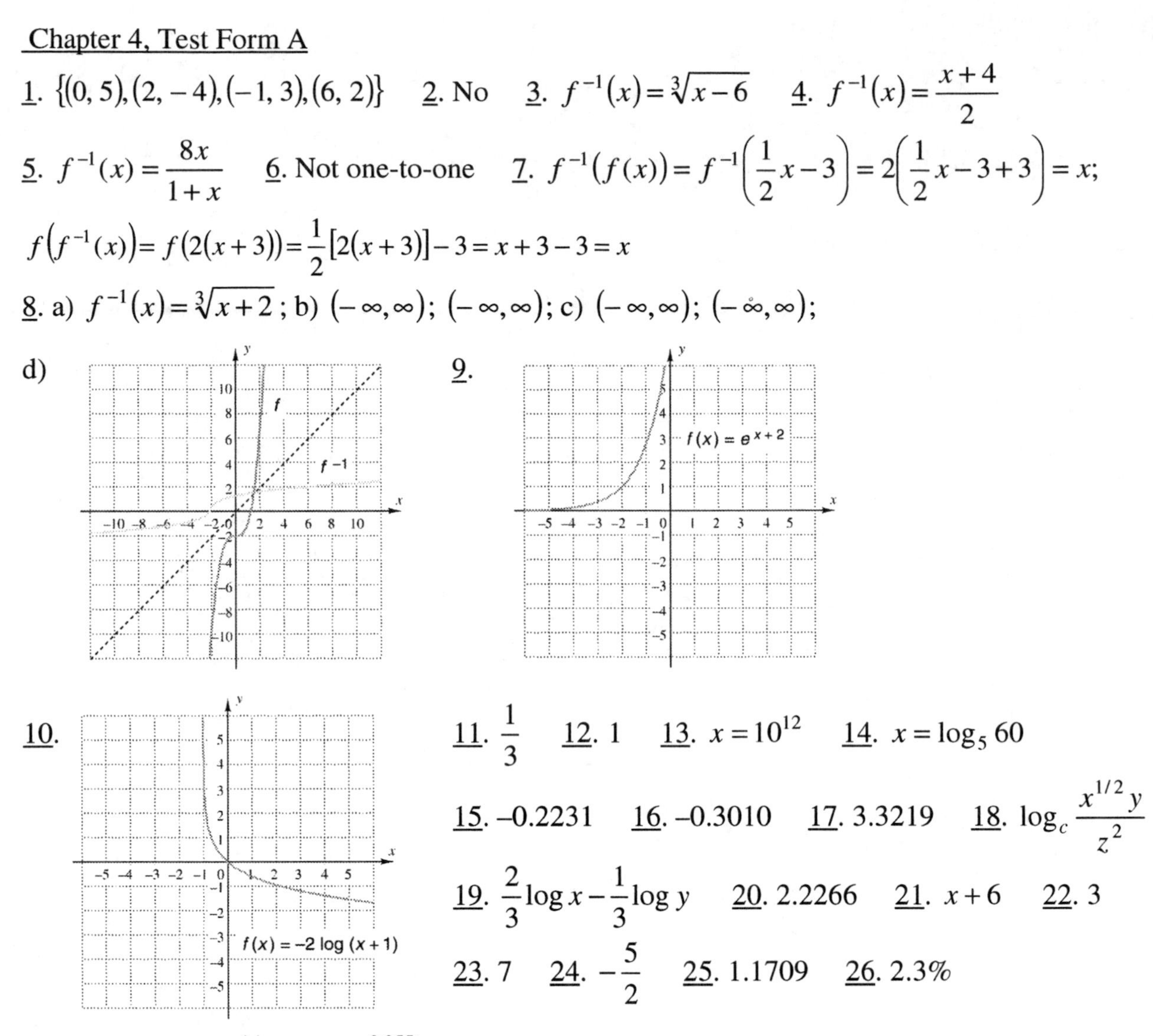

11. $\dfrac{1}{3}$ 12. 1 13. $x=10^{12}$ 14. $x=\log_5 60$

15. –0.2231 16. –0.3010 17. 3.3219 18. $\log_c \dfrac{x^{1/2}y}{z^2}$

19. $\dfrac{2}{3}\log x-\dfrac{1}{3}\log y$ 20. 2.2266 21. $x+6$ 22. 3

23. 7 24. $-\dfrac{5}{2}$ 25. 1.1709 26. 2.3%

27. a) 5.5%; b) $P(t)=5000e^{0.055t}$; c) \$8666.27; d) 12.6 yr 28. 81

Chapter 4, Test Form B

1. $\{(6,-3),(7,4),(8,0),(-2,-5)\}$ 2. Yes 3. $f^{-1}(x)=\sqrt[3]{x+8}$ 4. $f^{-1}(x)=\dfrac{x-2}{3}$

5. $f^{-1}(x)=\dfrac{5x}{1-x}$ 6. Not one-to-one 7. $f^{-1}(f(x))=f^{-1}\left(\dfrac{1}{4}x+6\right)=4\left(\dfrac{1}{4}x+6-6\right)=x;$

$f\left(f^{-1}(x)\right)=f(4(x-6))=\dfrac{1}{4}[4(x-6)]+6=x-6+6=x$

8. a) $f^{-1}(x)=\dfrac{2x+1}{x-1}$; b) $(-\infty,2)\cup(2,\infty)$; $(-\infty,1)\cup(1,\infty)$; c) $(-\infty,1)\cup(1,\infty)$; $(-\infty,2)\cup(2,\infty)$;

Chapter 4, Test Form B (continued)

d) 9. 10.

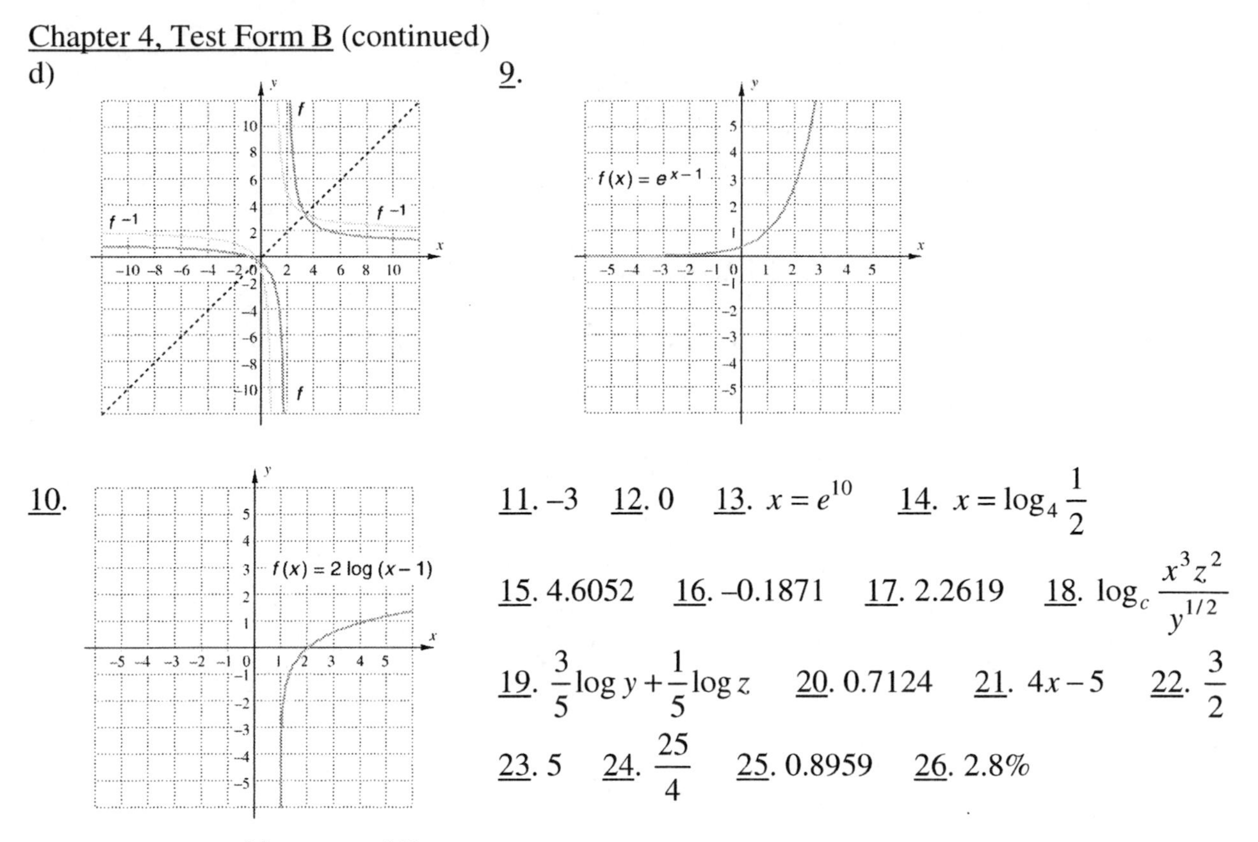

11. −3 12. 0 13. $x = e^{10}$ 14. $x = \log_4 \frac{1}{2}$

15. 4.6052 16. −0.1871 17. 2.2619 18. $\log_c \frac{x^3 z^2}{y^{1/2}}$

19. $\frac{3}{5}\log y + \frac{1}{5}\log z$ 20. 0.7124 21. $4x - 5$ 22. $\frac{3}{2}$

23. 5 24. $\frac{25}{4}$ 25. 0.8959 26. 2.8%

27. a) 6 %; b) $P(t) = 8000e^{0.06t}$; c) \$14,576.95; d) 11.6 yr 28. 9

Chapter 4, Test Form C

1. $\{(2, -6), (4, 5), (8, 0), (-2, 3)\}$ 2. Yes 3. $f^{-1}(x) = \sqrt[3]{x-1}$ 4. $f^{-1}(x) = \frac{x-1}{-2}$, or $\frac{1-x}{2}$

5. $f^{-1}(x) = \frac{3x}{1-x}$ 6. Not one-to-one 7. $f^{-1}(f(x)) = f^{-1}\left(-\frac{2}{3}x\right) = -\frac{3}{2} \cdot -\frac{2}{3}x = x;$

$f(f^{-1}(x)) = f\left(-\frac{3}{2}x\right) = -\frac{2}{3} \cdot -\frac{3}{2}x = x$

8. a) $f^{-1}(x) = \frac{3x-2}{x}$; b) $(-\infty, 3) \cup (3, \infty)$; $(-\infty, 0) \cup (0, \infty)$; c) $(-\infty, 0) \cup (0, \infty)$; $(-\infty, 3) \cup (3, \infty)$

d) 9.

y
x
10
8
6
4
2
−2
−4
−6
−8
−10
−10 −8 −6 −4 −2 0 2 4 6 8 10
f
f −1
f −1
f

y
x
5
4
3
2
1
−1
−2
−3
−4
−5
−5 −4 −3 −2 −1 0 1 2 3 4 5
f(x) = e^(x + 1)

Chapter 4, Test Form C (continued)

10.

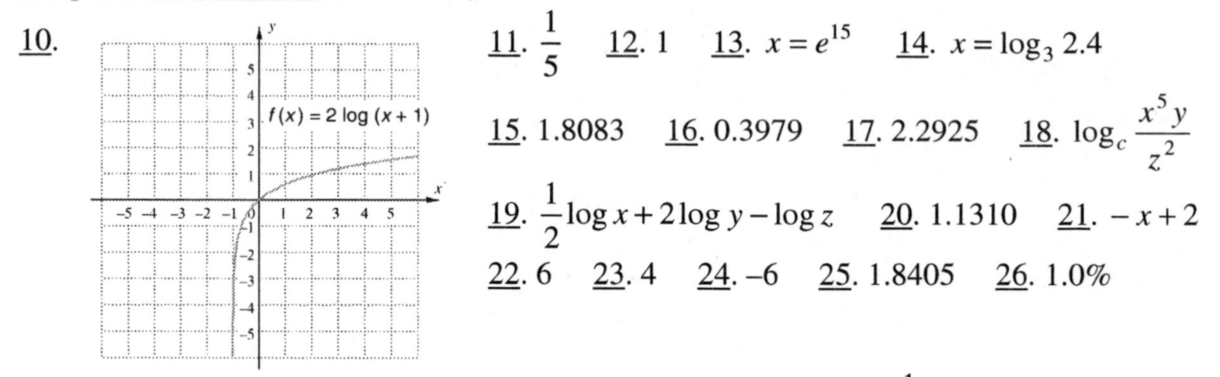

11. $\frac{1}{5}$ 12. 1 13. $x = e^{15}$ 14. $x = \log_3 2.4$

15. 1.8083 16. 0.3979 17. 2.2925 18. $\log_c \frac{x^5 y}{z^2}$

19. $\frac{1}{2}\log x + 2\log y - \log z$ 20. 1.1310 21. $-x + 2$

22. 6 23. 4 24. –6 25. 1.8405 26. 1.0%

27. a) 3.5%; b) $P(t) = 4000e^{0.035t}$; c) \$5676.27; d) 19.8 yr 28. $\pm\frac{1}{8}$

Chapter 4, Test Form D

1. $\{(-8,-6),(5,-3),(-2,6),(4,0)\}$ 2. Yes 3. $f^{-1}(x) = \sqrt[3]{x+2}$ 4. $f^{-1}(x) = \frac{x-4}{-3}$, or $\frac{4-x}{3}$

5. $f^{-1}(x) = \frac{x}{x-1}$ 6. Not one-to-one 7. $f^{-1}(f(x)) = f^{-1}(4x-5) = \frac{4x-5+5}{4} = \frac{4x}{4} = x$;

$f(f^{-1}(x)) = f\left(\frac{x+5}{4}\right) = 4\left(\frac{x+5}{4}\right) - 5 = x + 5 - 5 = x$

8. a) $f^{-1}(x) = 2(x-6)$; b) $(-\infty,\infty)$; $(-\infty,\infty)$; c) $(-\infty,\infty)$; $(-\infty,\infty)$;

d) 9.

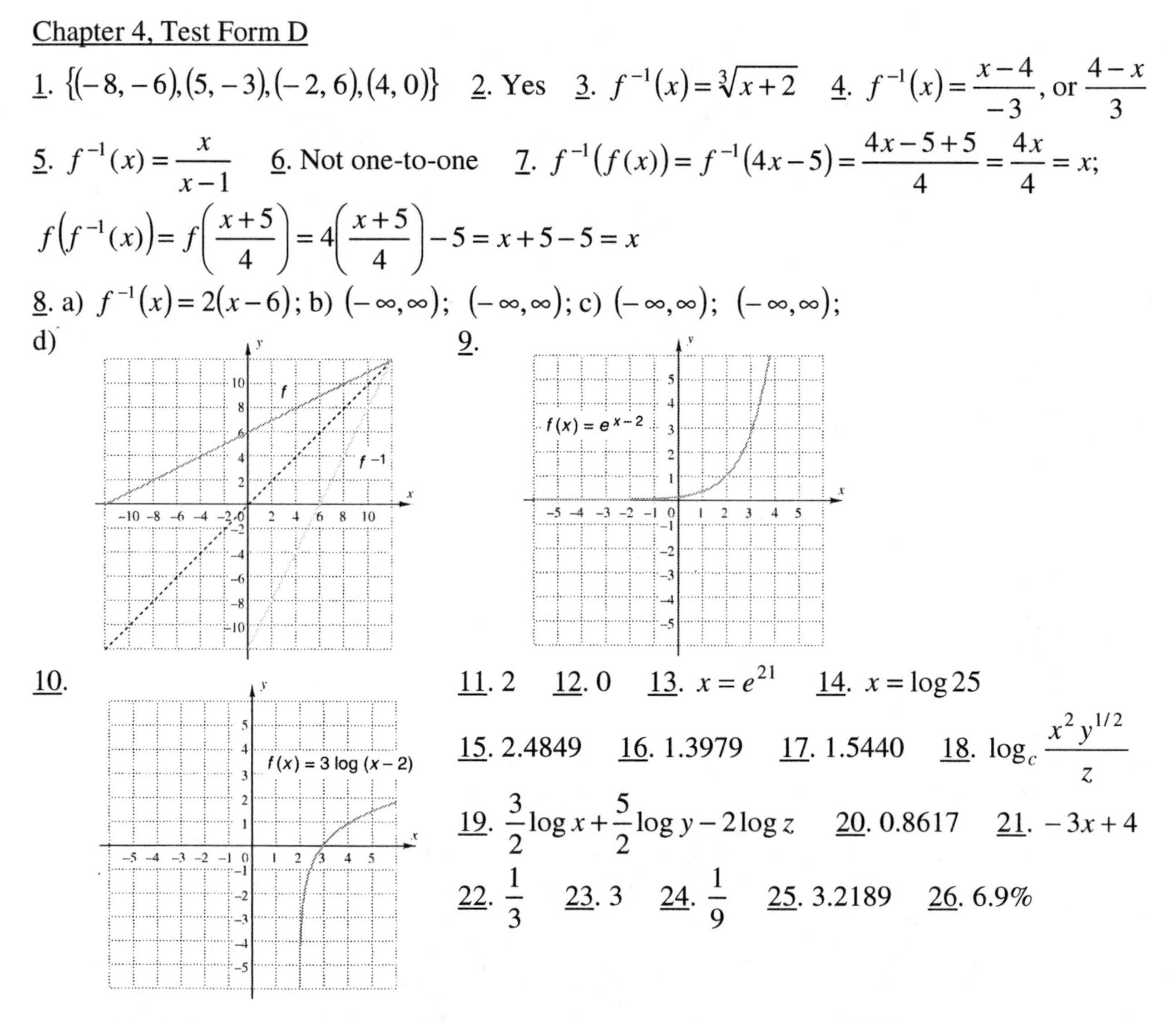

10.

11. 2 12. 0 13. $x = e^{21}$ 14. $x = \log 25$

15. 2.4849 16. 1.3979 17. 1.5440 18. $\log_c \frac{x^2 y^{1/2}}{z}$

19. $\frac{3}{2}\log x + \frac{5}{2}\log y - 2\log z$ 20. 0.8617 21. $-3x + 4$

22. $\frac{1}{3}$ 23. 3 24. $\frac{1}{9}$ 25. 3.2189 26. 6.9%

27. a) 6.5%; b) $P(t) = 10{,}000e^{0.065t}$; c) \$19,155.41; d) 10.7 yr 28. $\frac{8000}{27}$

Chapter 4, Test Form E

1. d 2. a 3. c 4. b 5. a 6. a 7. d 8. d 9. b 10. a 11. c 12. c 13. a
14. b 15. c 16. d 17. c 18. a 19. b 20. c 21. b 22. d 23 a 24. b

Chapter 4, Test Form F

1. c 2. d 3. a 4. b 5. a 6. b 7. d 8. a 9. d 10. a 11. b 12. c 13. d
14. a 15. b 16. b 17. a 18. c 19. d 20. b 21. c 22.a 23. d 24. b

Chapter 5, Test Form A

1. $(x, 5x-4)$ or $\left(\frac{y+4}{5}, y\right)$ 2. $(3, -2)$ 3. No solution 4. $(-1, 5, 3)$

5. Consistent; dependent 6. Consistent; independent 7. Peanuts: $15\frac{5}{9}$ lb; almonds: $4\frac{4}{9}$ lb

8. $\begin{bmatrix} 4 & 2 \\ 2 & 13 \end{bmatrix}$ 9. Not possible 10. $\begin{bmatrix} 10 & 40 \\ 11 & 8 \\ -1 & 2 \end{bmatrix}$ 11. Not possible 12. $\begin{bmatrix} 12 & 8 \\ -6 & 4 \\ 2 & 0 \end{bmatrix}$

13. $\begin{bmatrix} \frac{1}{5} & 0 \\ \frac{1}{15} & \frac{1}{6} \end{bmatrix}$ 14. a) $\begin{bmatrix} 100 & 70 & 50 \\ 120 & 80 & 60 \\ 80 & 80 & 40 \\ 60 & 100 & 30 \end{bmatrix}$; b) $\begin{bmatrix} 120 & 84 & 60 \\ 144 & 96 & 72 \\ 96 & 96 & 48 \\ 72 & 120 & 36 \end{bmatrix}$; c) $\begin{bmatrix} 220 & 154 & 110 \\ 264 & 176 & 132 \\ 176 & 176 & 88 \\ 132 & 220 & 66 \end{bmatrix}$;

d) total order of each item in each store for the first two weeks in August

15. $\begin{bmatrix} 5 & 1 & 6 \\ 2 & -1 & 1 \\ 4 & -2 & 3 \end{bmatrix}\begin{bmatrix} x \\ y \\ z \end{bmatrix} = \begin{bmatrix} 8 \\ -1 \\ -4 \end{bmatrix}$ 16. 12 17. 60 18. $\left(\frac{7}{2}, \frac{9}{2}\right)$

19.

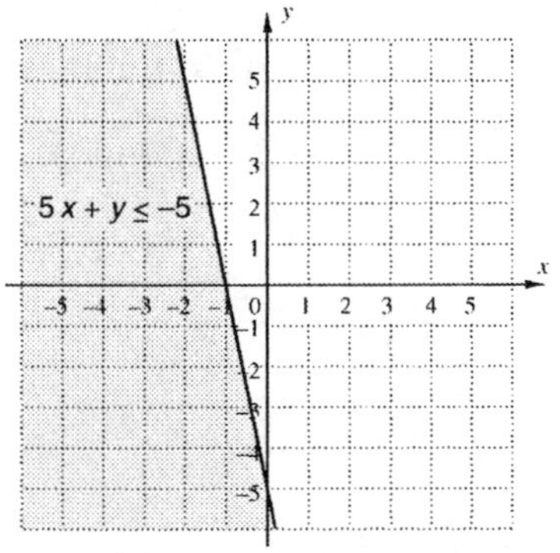

20. Maximum: 17 at $(6, -5)$; minimum: 5 at $(0, -5)$

21. $54; hotdogs: 36; popcorns: 24 22. $\frac{-2}{x+1} + \frac{6}{x-4}$

23. $A = 2, B = 4, C = -2$

Chapter 5, Test Form B

1. No solution 2. $(-4, 6)$ 3. $(x, x-5)$ or $(y+5, y)$ 4. $(5, -4, -3)$ 5. Inconsistent; independent 6. Consistent; dependent 7. Watermelon: $6\frac{2}{3}$ lb; honeydew melon: $3\frac{1}{3}$ lb

8. Not possible 9. $\begin{bmatrix} 2 & -9 \\ 0 & 2 \end{bmatrix}$ 10. Not possible 11. $\begin{bmatrix} 11 & 21 \\ 9 & -7 \end{bmatrix}$ 12. $\begin{bmatrix} 2 & -8 \\ -6 & -4 \end{bmatrix}$

13. $\begin{bmatrix} -\frac{1}{7} & \frac{2}{7} \\ \frac{3}{14} & \frac{1}{14} \end{bmatrix}$ 14. a) $\begin{bmatrix} 6.25 & 1.20 & 1.00 \\ 3.00 & 1.20 & 2.25 \\ 5.50 & 1.20 & 1.50 \end{bmatrix}$; b) $[19 \quad 12 \quad 30]$; c) $[319.75 \quad 73.20 \quad 91]$;

d) the total cost, in dollars, for each type of food item served on the given day

15. $\begin{bmatrix} 2 & 1 & -5 \\ -3 & -4 & 1 \\ -1 & 2 & -4 \end{bmatrix}\begin{bmatrix} x \\ y \\ z \end{bmatrix} = \begin{bmatrix} 10 \\ 1 \\ 6 \end{bmatrix}$ 16. -44 17. 60 18. $(30, 23)$

19.

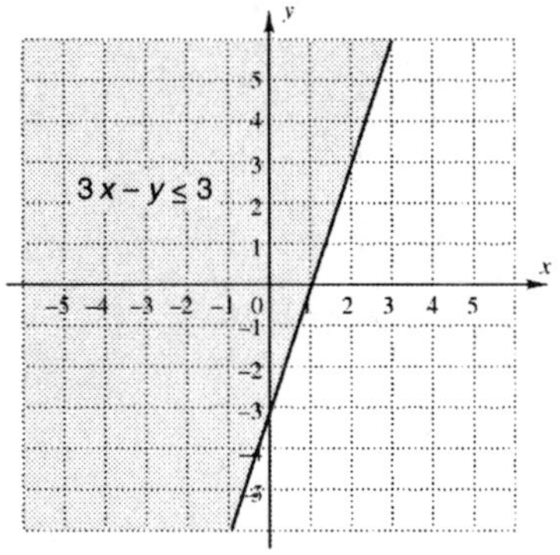

20. Maximum: 16 at $\left(\frac{16}{3}, 0\right)$; minimum: -2 at $(2, -4)$

21. \$25,000 each; \$2500 22. $\frac{3}{x-5} + \frac{-2}{x+1}$

23. $A = -2$, $B = -3$, $C = 2$

Chapter 5, Test Form C

1. $(3, -1)$ 2. No solution 3. $\left(x, \frac{2}{5}x + \frac{13}{5}\right)$ or $\left(\frac{5}{2}y - \frac{13}{2}, y\right)$ 4. $(-2, -3, 5)$

5. Consistent; independent 6. Consistent; dependent 7. Adult's ticket: \$22; child's ticket: \$16

8. $\begin{bmatrix} -6 & -1 \\ 4 & -2 \end{bmatrix}$ 9. Not possible 10. Not possible 11. $\begin{bmatrix} -3 & -12 \\ 32 & -2 \end{bmatrix}$ 12. $\begin{bmatrix} 3 & 0 & -9 \\ 6 & 12 & 18 \end{bmatrix}$

13. $\begin{bmatrix} \frac{2}{13} & \frac{1}{13} \\ -\frac{1}{26} & \frac{3}{13} \end{bmatrix}$ 14. a) $\begin{bmatrix} 30 & 45 & 25 \\ 50 & 20 & 55 \end{bmatrix}$; b) $\begin{bmatrix} 2.00 \\ 1.80 \\ 2.25 \end{bmatrix}$; c) $\begin{bmatrix} 197.25 \\ 259.75 \end{bmatrix}$;

d) the total cost, in dollars, for hot lunches at each seating the second week of February

15. $\begin{bmatrix} 6 & 4 & 1 \\ -5 & 2 & 4 \\ 3 & 1 & 2 \end{bmatrix}\begin{bmatrix} x \\ y \\ z \end{bmatrix} = \begin{bmatrix} 4 \\ 6 \\ 0 \end{bmatrix}$ 16. -13 17. 52 18. $\left(\frac{29}{27}, \frac{17}{9}\right)$

Chapter 5, Test Form C (continued)

19.

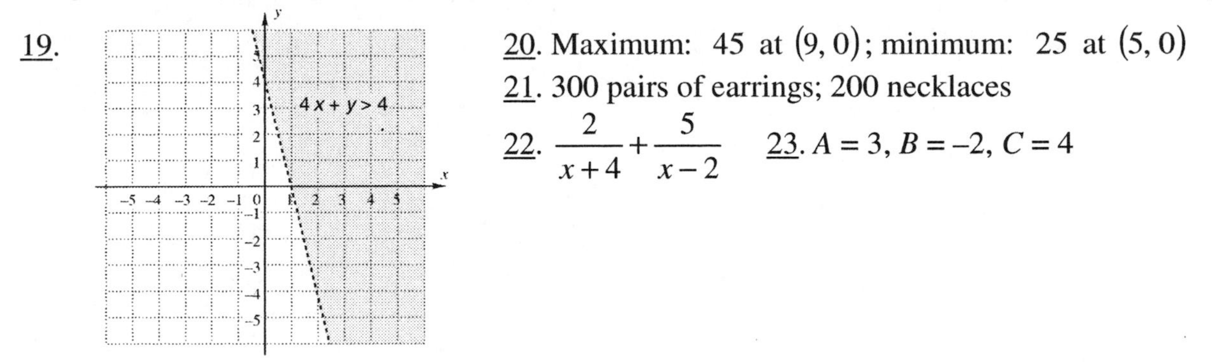

20. Maximum: 45 at $(9, 0)$; minimum: 25 at $(5, 0)$
21. 300 pairs of earrings; 200 necklaces
22. $\dfrac{2}{x+4} + \dfrac{5}{x-2}$ 23. $A = 3, B = -2, C = 4$

Chapter 5, Test Form D

1. $(-6, -3)$ 2. $(x, 3x+2)$ or $\left(\dfrac{y-2}{3}, y\right)$ 3. No solution 4. $(5, -4, 1)$ 5. Consistent; independent 6. Inconsistent; independent 7. 5.5%: \$4200; 4%: \$3800 8. Not possible

9. $\begin{bmatrix} -4 & 3 \\ 3 & -8 \end{bmatrix}$ 10. $\begin{bmatrix} 24 & -8 \\ 8 & -6 \\ 3 & 4 \end{bmatrix}$ 11. Not possible 12. $\begin{bmatrix} 0 & -16 \\ 4 & -8 \\ -6 & 2 \end{bmatrix}$ 13. $\begin{bmatrix} \frac{1}{5} & \frac{1}{5} \\ \frac{3}{5} & -\frac{2}{5} \end{bmatrix}$

14. a) $\begin{bmatrix} 30 & 40 & 50 \\ 40 & 50 & 70 \\ 60 & 80 & 120 \end{bmatrix}$; b) $[0.80 \quad 0.60 \quad 1.00]$; c) $[108 \quad 142 \quad 202]$; d) total profit, in dollars, for concessions at each location 15. $\begin{bmatrix} 1 & 3 & 1 \\ 3 & -4 & 3 \\ -1 & 6 & -2 \end{bmatrix} \begin{bmatrix} x \\ y \\ z \end{bmatrix} = \begin{bmatrix} 8 \\ 2 \\ 12 \end{bmatrix}$ 16. 22 17. –124 18. $\left(\dfrac{33}{8}, \dfrac{15}{8}\right)$

19. $3x + 2y \le -6$

20. Maximum: 18 at $(4, 1)$; minimum: $\dfrac{34}{3}$ at $\left(2, \dfrac{5}{3}\right)$

21. Pies: 60; cakes: 60; maximum profit: \$660

22. $\dfrac{5}{x+4} + \dfrac{4}{x-2}$ 21. $A = 3, B = -4, C = -1$

Chapter 5, Test Form E

1. c 2. a 3. d 4. a 5. d 6. b 7. b 8. d 9. a 10. b 11. c 12. a 13. d
14. b 15. b 16. a 17. d 18. c

Chapter 5, Test Form F

1. a 2. b 3. c 4. d 5. a 6. d 7. b 8. d 9. a 10. b 11. c 12. c 13. a
14. c 15. d 16. a 17. c 18. d

Chapter 6, Test Form A

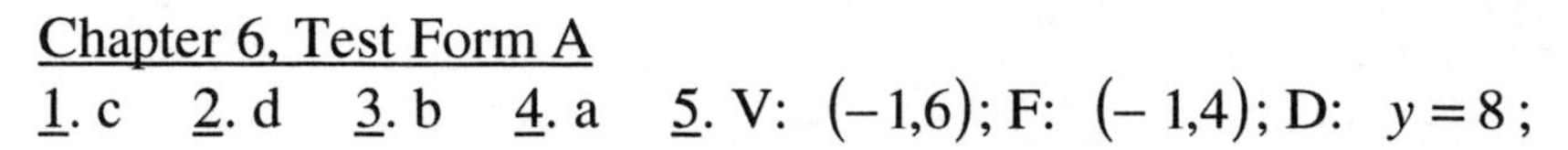

1. c 2. d 3. b 4. a 5. V: $(-1,6)$; F: $(-1,4)$; D: $y=8$;

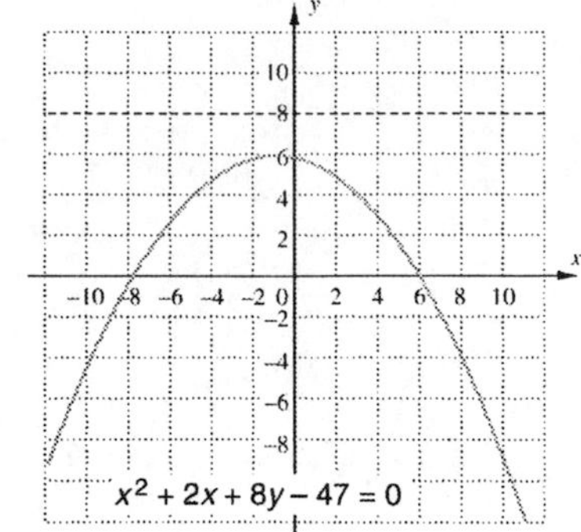

6. $x^2 = -8y$ 7. Center: $(-2,5)$; radius: 6;

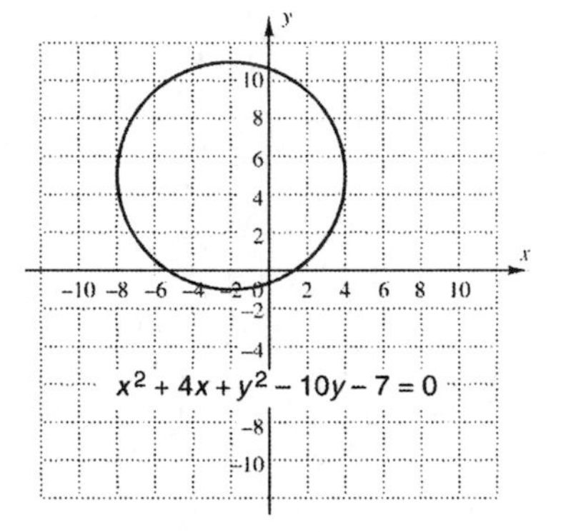

8. C: $(0,0)$; V: $(-4,0), (4,0)$; F: $(-\sqrt{7},0), (\sqrt{7},0)$;

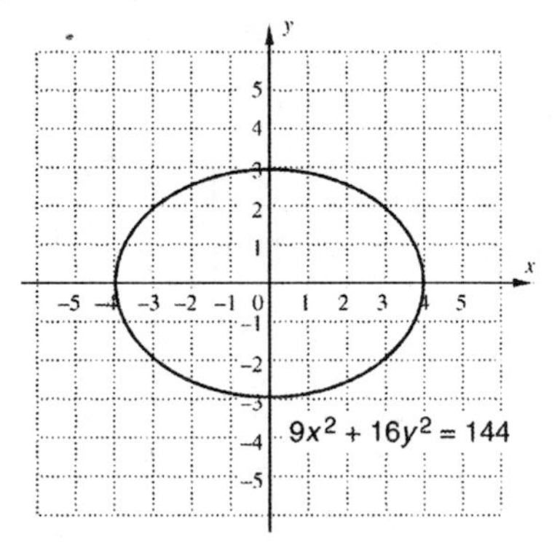

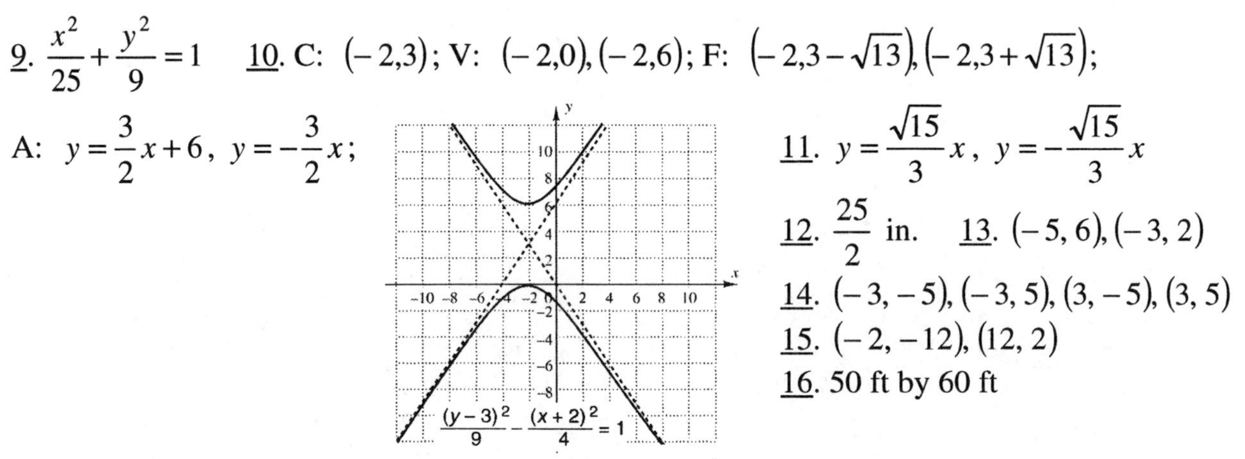

9. $\dfrac{x^2}{25}+\dfrac{y^2}{9}=1$ 10. C: $(-2,3)$; V: $(-2,0), (-2,6)$; F: $(-2,3-\sqrt{13}), (-2,3+\sqrt{13})$;

A: $y=\dfrac{3}{2}x+6$, $y=-\dfrac{3}{2}x$;

11. $y=\dfrac{\sqrt{15}}{3}x$, $y=-\dfrac{\sqrt{15}}{3}x$

12. $\dfrac{25}{2}$ in. 13. $(-5, 6), (-3, 2)$

14. $(-3, -5), (-3, 5), (3, -5), (3, 5)$

15. $(-2, -12), (12, 2)$

16. 50 ft by 60 ft

Chapter 6, Test Form A (continued)

17. 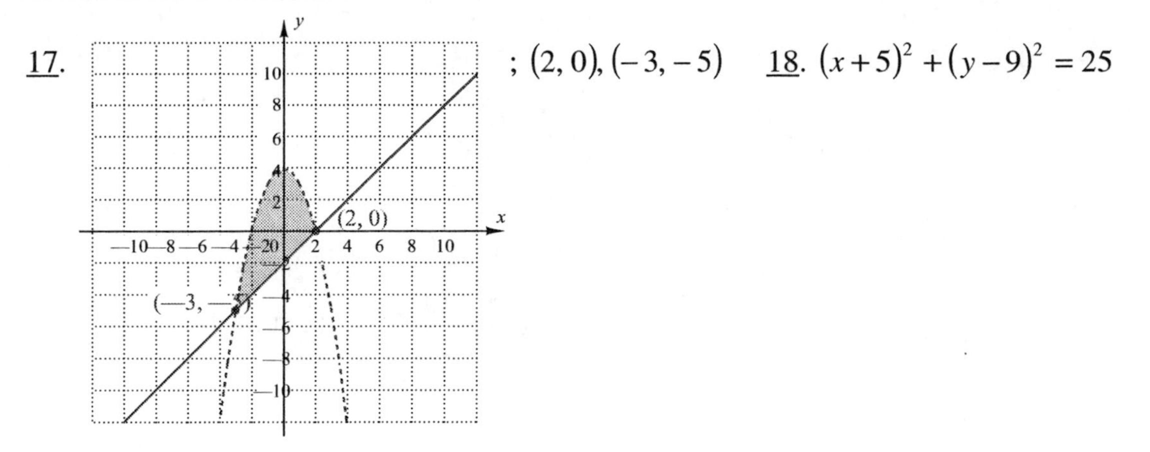

; $(2, 0), (-3, -5)$ 18. $(x+5)^2 + (y-9)^2 = 25$

Chapter 6, Test Form B

1. b 2. a 3. d 4. c 5. V: $(3, -4)$; F: $(3, -2)$; D: $y = -6$;

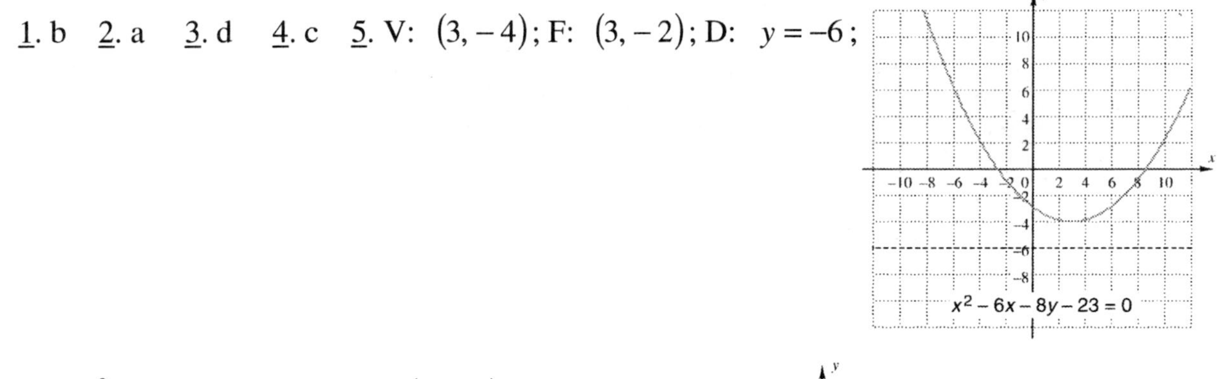

6. $x^2 = -12y$ 7. Center: $(-3, 2)$; radius: 4;

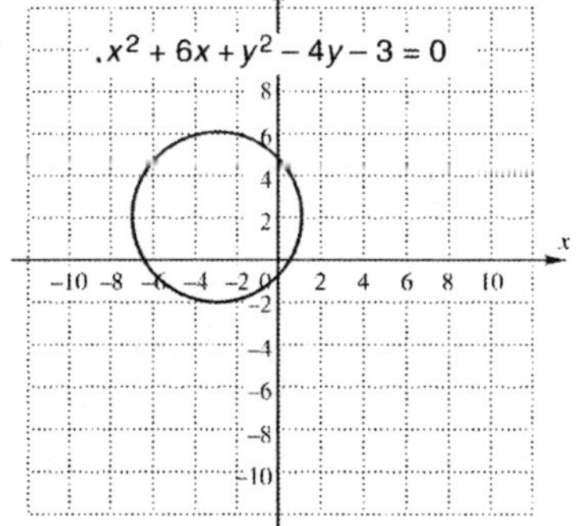

8. C: $(0, 0)$; V: $(-2, 0), (2, 0)$; F: $(-\sqrt{3}, 0), (\sqrt{3}, 0)$;

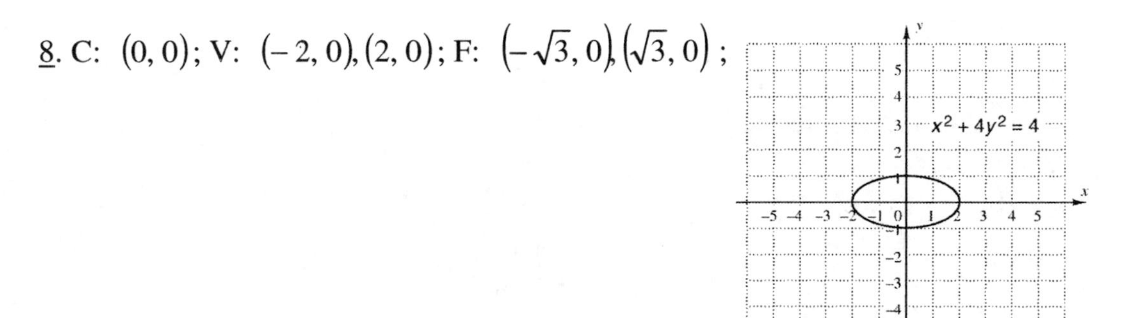

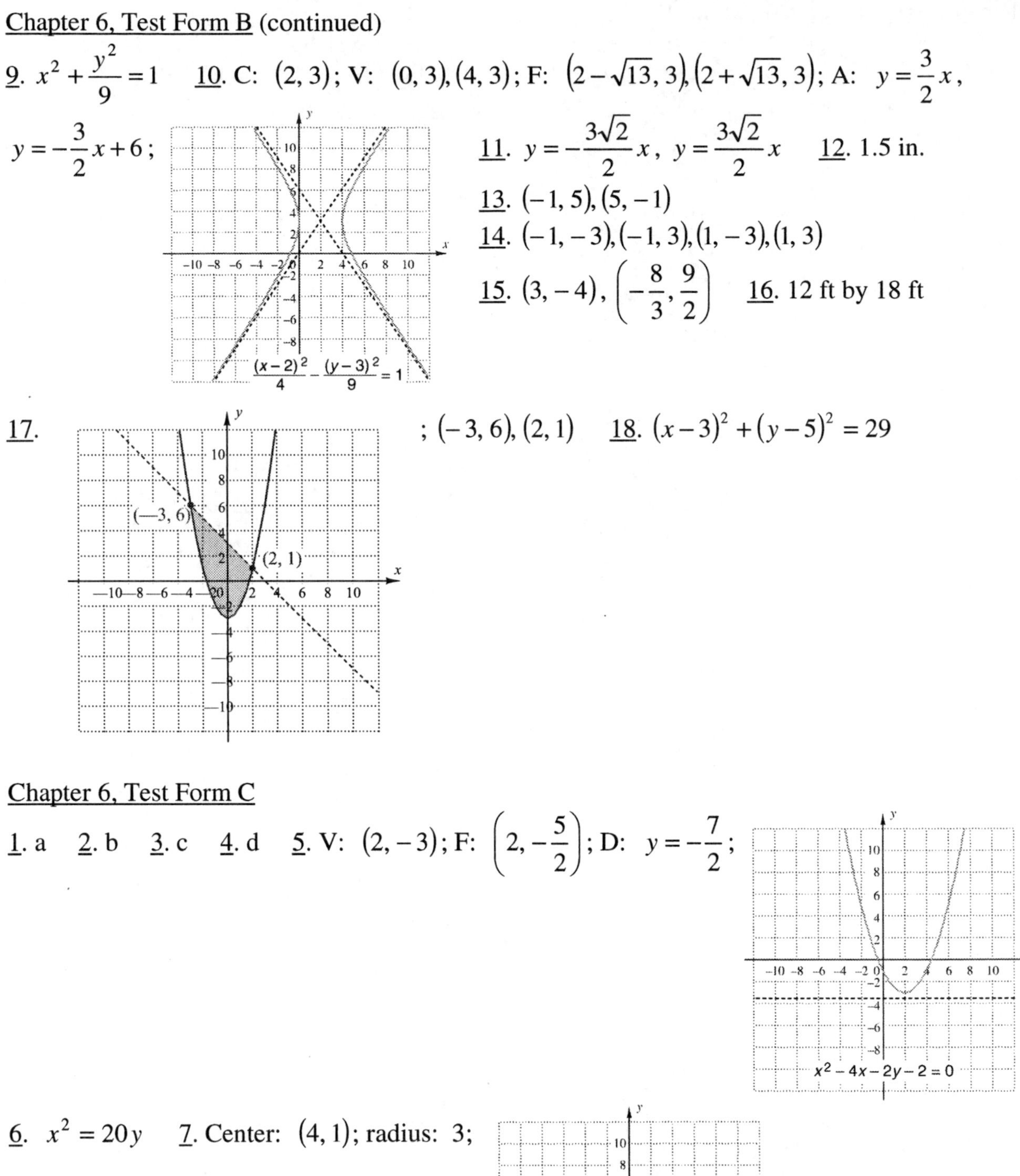

Chapter 6, Test Form B (continued)

9. $x^2 + \frac{y^2}{9} = 1$ 10. C: $(2, 3)$; V: $(0, 3), (4, 3)$; F: $(2-\sqrt{13}, 3), (2+\sqrt{13}, 3)$; A: $y = \frac{3}{2}x$, $y = -\frac{3}{2}x + 6$;

11. $y = -\frac{3\sqrt{2}}{2}x$, $y = \frac{3\sqrt{2}}{2}x$ 12. 1.5 in.

13. $(-1, 5), (5, -1)$

14. $(-1, -3), (-1, 3), (1, -3), (1, 3)$

15. $(3, -4)$, $\left(-\frac{8}{3}, \frac{9}{2}\right)$ 16. 12 ft by 18 ft

17.

; $(-3, 6), (2, 1)$ 18. $(x-3)^2 + (y-5)^2 = 29$

Chapter 6, Test Form C

1. a 2. b 3. c 4. d 5. V: $(2, -3)$; F: $\left(2, -\frac{5}{2}\right)$; D: $y = -\frac{7}{2}$;

6. $x^2 = 20y$ 7. Center: $(4, 1)$; radius: 3;

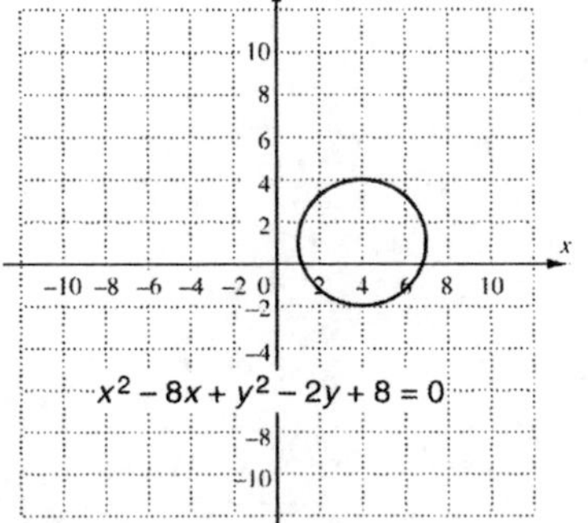

Chapter 6, Test Form C (continued)

8. C: $(0,0)$; V: $(0,-3),(0,3)$; F: $\left(0,-\sqrt{5}\right),\left(0,\sqrt{5}\right)$;

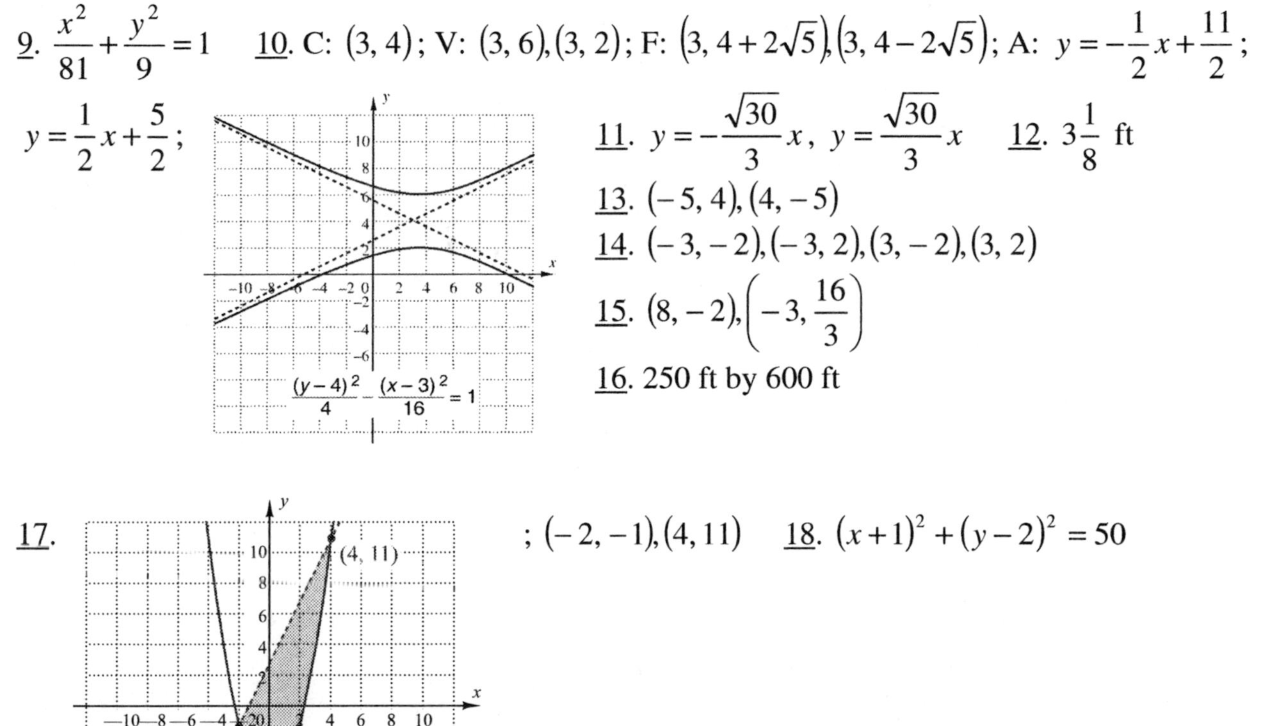

9. $\dfrac{x^2}{81}+\dfrac{y^2}{9}=1$ 10. C: $(3, 4)$; V: $(3, 6),(3, 2)$; F: $\left(3, 4+2\sqrt{5}\right),\left(3, 4-2\sqrt{5}\right)$; A: $y=-\dfrac{1}{2}x+\dfrac{11}{2}$; $y=\dfrac{1}{2}x+\dfrac{5}{2}$;

11. $y=-\dfrac{\sqrt{30}}{3}x,\ y=\dfrac{\sqrt{30}}{3}x$ 12. $3\dfrac{1}{8}$ ft

13. $(-5, 4),(4, -5)$

14. $(-3, -2),(-3, 2),(3, -2),(3, 2)$

15. $(8, -2),\left(-3, \dfrac{16}{3}\right)$

16. 250 ft by 600 ft

17. ; $(-2, -1),(4, 11)$ 18. $(x+1)^2+(y-2)^2=50$

Chapter 6, Test Form D

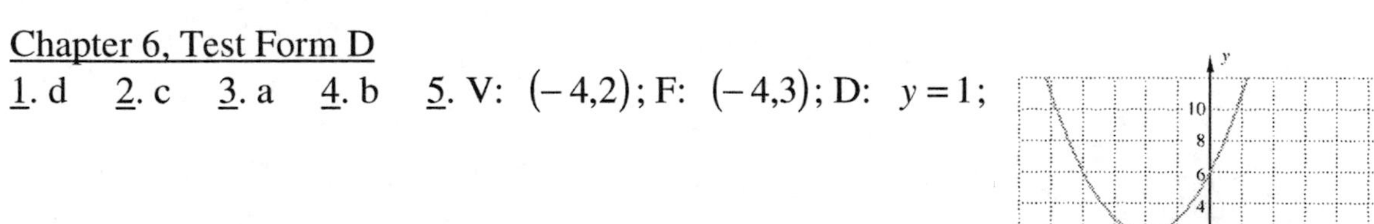

1. d 2. c 3. a 4. b 5. V: $(-4,2)$; F: $(-4,3)$; D: $y=1$;

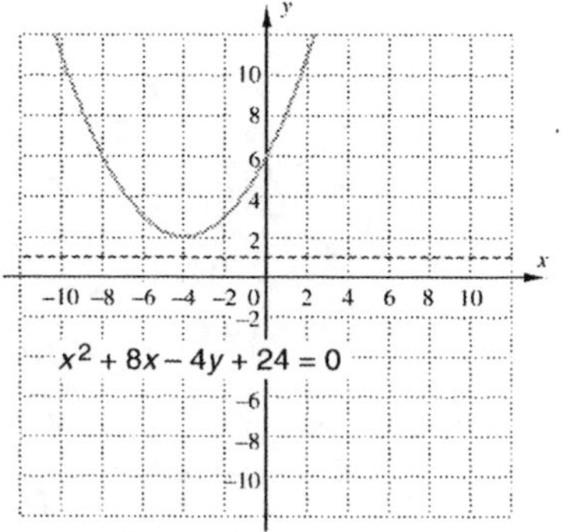

Chapter 6, Test Form D (continued)

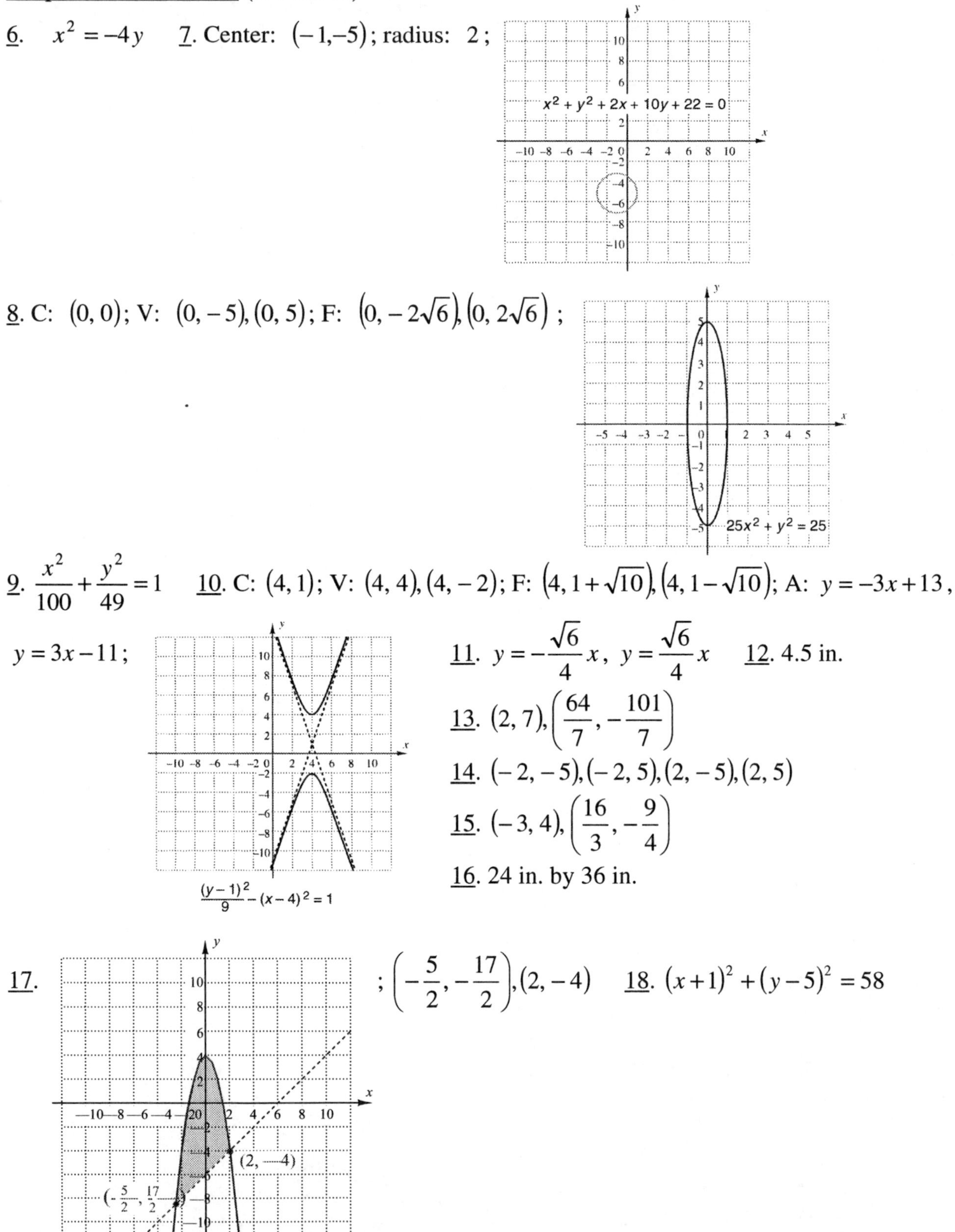

6. $x^2 = -4y$ 7. Center: $(-1, -5)$; radius: 2;

8. C: $(0, 0)$; V: $(0, -5), (0, 5)$; F: $(0, -2\sqrt{6}), (0, 2\sqrt{6})$;

9. $\frac{x^2}{100} + \frac{y^2}{49} = 1$ 10. C: $(4, 1)$; V: $(4, 4), (4, -2)$; F: $(4, 1+\sqrt{10}), (4, 1-\sqrt{10})$; A: $y = -3x + 13$, $y = 3x - 11$;

11. $y = -\frac{\sqrt{6}}{4}x$, $y = \frac{\sqrt{6}}{4}x$ 12. 4.5 in.

13. $(2, 7), \left(\frac{64}{7}, -\frac{101}{7}\right)$

14. $(-2, -5), (-2, 5), (2, -5), (2, 5)$

15. $(-3, 4), \left(\frac{16}{3}, -\frac{9}{4}\right)$

16. 24 in. by 36 in.

17. ; $\left(-\frac{5}{2}, -\frac{17}{2}\right), (2, -4)$ 18. $(x+1)^2 + (y-5)^2 = 58$

Chapter 6, Test Form E

1. c 2. a 3. b 4. d 5. d 6. a 7. c 8. a 9. b 10. d 11. d 12. c 13. b 14. d
15. c 16. a 17. d 18. b

Chapter 6, Test Form F

1. d 2. b 3. a 4. c 5. c 6. d 7. a 8. b 9. d 10. c 11. c 12. a 13. b 14. d
15. c 16. a 17. b 18. c

Chapter 7, Test Form A

1. $\frac{225}{64}$ 2. −1, −2, 5, −8, 11 3. 2 + 6 + 12 + 20 = 40 4. $\sum_{k=1}^{5} 800(0.1)^{k-1}$; answers may vary

5. 2, 11, 38, 119 6. −44 7. $-\frac{1}{2}$ 8. 1940 9. −624 10. 46,875 11. 5 12. 6138

13. 500,000 14. $\frac{496}{99}$ 15. $23,154.82 16. $13.55

17. $S_n : 5+10+15+\cdots+5n = \frac{5n(n+1)}{2}$

$S_1 : 5 = \frac{5\cdot 1(1+1)}{2}$

$S_k : 5+10+15+\cdots+5k = \frac{5k(k+1)}{2}$

$S_{k+1} : 5+10+15+\cdots+5k+(5k+5) = \frac{5(k+1)(k+2)}{2}$

1. Basis step: $5 = \frac{5\cdot 1(1+1)}{2} = \frac{10}{2} = 5$ is true.

2. Induction step: Let k be any natural number. Assume S_k is true. Deduce S_{k+1}.

$$\begin{aligned} 5+10+15+\cdots+5k &= \frac{5k(k+1)}{2} \\ 5+10+15+\cdots+5k+(5k+5) &= \frac{5k(k+1)}{2}+(5k+5) \\ &= \frac{5k(k+1)}{2}+\frac{2(5k+5)}{2} \\ &= \frac{5k^2+5k+10k+10}{2} \\ &= \frac{5k^2+15k+10}{2} \\ &= \frac{5(k+1)(k+2)}{2} \end{aligned}$$

Chapter 7, Test Form A (continued)

18. 1320 19. 1716 20. $\frac{n(n-1)(n-2)(n-3)}{24}$ 21. ${}_7P_4 = 840$ 22. $1 \cdot 5^3 = 125$

23. ${}_9C_3 \cdot {}_6C_2 = 1260$ 24. $x^6 - 6x^5a + 15x^4a^2 - 20x^3a^3 + 15x^2a^4 - 6xa^5 + a^6$ 25. $80x^3y^2$

26. 256 27. $\frac{7}{12}$ 28. $\frac{224}{4845}$ 29. 12

Chapter 7, Test Form B

1. 448 2. $0, \frac{4}{3}, \frac{10}{3}, 6, \frac{28}{3}$ 3. $1 + \frac{4}{3} + 2 + \frac{16}{5} = \frac{113}{15}$ 4. $\sum_{k=1}^{\infty} -13 + 5k$; answers may vary

5. 4, 7, 13, 25 6. 71 7. 10 8. –2750 9. 804 10. $\frac{2}{125}$ 11. 4 12. –4

13. Does not exist 14. $\frac{104}{33}$ 15. \$46,153.85 16. \$13.90

17. $S_n : 5 + 9 + 13 + \cdots + (4n+1) = n(2n+3)$

$S_1 : 5 = 1(2 \cdot 1 + 3)$

$S_k : 5 + 9 + 13 + \cdots + (4k+1) = k(2k+3)$

$S_{k+1} : 5 + 9 + 13 + \cdots + (4k+1) + (4(k+1)+1) = (k+1)(2(k+1)+3)$

1. Basis step: $5 = 1(2 \cdot 1 + 3) = 1 \cdot 5 = 5$ is true.
2. Induction step: Let k be any natural number. Assume S_k. Deduce S_{k+1}.

$$\begin{aligned} 5 + 9 + 13 + \cdots + (4k+1) &= k(2k+3) \\ 5 + 9 + 13 + \cdots + (4k+1) + (4(k+1)+1) &= k(2k+3) + (4(k+1)+1) \\ &= 2k^2 + 3k + 4k + 4 + 1 \\ &= 2k^2 + 7k + 5 \\ &= (k+1)(2k+5) \\ &= (k+1)(2(k+1)+3) \end{aligned}$$

18. 154,440 19. 120 20. $\frac{n(n-1)(n-2)}{6}$ 21. ${}_6P_5 = 720$ 22. $5^3 \cdot 1 = 125$

23. ${}_{75}C_3 = 67{,}525$ 24. $x^5 - 5x^4d + 10x^3d^2 - 10x^2d^3 + 5xd^4 - d^5$ 25. $120p^7q^3$ 26. 32

27. $\frac{1}{13}$ 28. $\frac{75}{1012}$ 29. 12

Chapter 7, Test Form C

1. 20 2. $1, \frac{3}{2}, \frac{5}{3}, \frac{7}{4}, \frac{9}{5}$ 3. $\frac{1}{2} + 1 + \frac{3}{2} + 2 = 5$ 4. $\sum_{k=1}^{\infty} (-1)^k 3 \cdot 2^{k-1}$; answers may vary

5. 10, 6, 4, 3 6. $\frac{25}{4}$ 7. 23.5 8. 1800 9. 1152 10. –486 11. 3 12. $\frac{1365}{16}$

Chapter 7, Test Form C (continued)

13. 180 14. $\frac{74}{99}$ 15. \$7,321,366,588 16. \$16.55

17. $S_n: 1+2+2^2+\cdots+2^{n-1}=2^n-1$

$S_1: 1=2^1-1$

$S_k: 1+2+2^2+\cdots+2^{k-1}=2^k-1$

$S_{k+1}: 1+2+2^2+\cdots+2^{k-1}+2^k=2^{k+1}-1$

1. Basis step: $1=2^1-1=2-1=1$ is true.
2. Induction step: Let k be any natural number. Assume S_k is true. Deduce S_{k+1}.

$$\begin{aligned} 1+2+2^2+\cdots+2^{k-1} &= 2^k-1 \\ 1+2+2^2+\cdots+2^{k-1}+2^k &= 2^k-1+2^k \\ &= 2\cdot 2^k-1 \\ &= 2^{k+1}-1 \end{aligned}$$

18. 259,459,200 19. 167,960 20. $\frac{n(n-1)(n-2)(n-3)(n-4)}{120}$ 21. ${}_6P_4=360$

22. $1\cdot 5^2=25$ 23. ${}_9C_2\cdot{}_{100}C_5=2{,}710{,}350{,}720$ 24. $x^5-10x^4+40x^3-80x^2+80x-32$

25. $21s^5t^2$ 26. 64 27. $\frac{3}{13}$ 28. $\frac{1}{969}$ 29. 15

Chapter 7, Test Form D

1. 68 2. $-7, \frac{11}{2}, -5, \frac{19}{4}, -\frac{23}{5}$ 3. $1+\frac{3}{4}+\frac{5}{9}+\frac{7}{16}=\frac{395}{144}$ 4. $\sum_{k=1}^{6}(-1)^k k$ 5. 0.5, 5, 14, 32

6. –68 7. –6 8. –520 9. –876 10. 68.34375 11. –0.25 12. $\frac{5115}{256}$ 13. –32

14. $\frac{23}{11}$ 15. $50\frac{14}{27}$ ft 16. \$23.90

Chapter 7, Test Form D (continued)

17. $S_n : 1^2 + 2^2 + 3^2 + \cdots + n^2 = \dfrac{n(n+1)(2n+1)}{6}$

$S_1 : 1^2 = \dfrac{1(1+1)(2\cdot 1+1)}{6}$

$S_k : 1^2 + 2^2 + 3^2 + \cdots + k^2 = \dfrac{k(k+1)(2k+1)}{6}$

$S_{k+1} : 1^2 + 2^2 + \cdots + k^2 + (k+1)^2 = \dfrac{(k+1)(k+1+1)(2(k+1)+1)}{6}$

1. Basis step: $1^2 = \dfrac{1(1+1)(2\cdot 1+1)}{6} = \dfrac{1\cdot 2\cdot 3}{6} = 1$ is true.

2. Induction step: Let k be any natural number. Assume S_k. Deduce S_{k+1}.

$$
\begin{aligned}
1^2 + 2^2 + \cdots + k^2 &= \frac{k(k+1)(2k+1)}{6} \\
1^2 + 2^2 + \cdots + k^2 + (k+1)^2 &= \frac{k(k+1)(2k+1)}{6} + (k+1)^2 \\
&= \frac{k(k+1)(2k+1) + 6(k+1)^2}{6} \\
&= \frac{(k+1)(2k^2 + 7k + 6)}{6} \\
&= \frac{(k+1)(k+2)(2k+3)}{6} \\
&= \frac{(k+1)(k+1+1)(2(k+1)+1)}{6}
\end{aligned}
$$

18. 5040 19. 66 20. $\dfrac{n(n-1)(n-2)}{6}$ 21. ${}_6P_4 = 360$ 22. $1\cdot 5^4 = 625$ 23. $4\cdot 3\cdot 2 = 24$

24. $a^5 - 10a^4 + 40a^3 - 80a^2 + 80a - 32$ 25. $12xy^3$ 26. 128 27. $\dfrac{2}{15}$ 28. $\dfrac{14}{255}$ 29. 6

Chapter 7, Test Form E

1. a 2. d 3. b 4. c 5. b 6. d 7. a 8. c 9. b 10. a 11. b 12. c 13. d
14. c 15. a 16. d 17. b 18. c 19. d 20. a 21. a 22. c 23. b 24. d 25. a
26. c

Chapter 7, Test Form F

1. a 2. d 3. c 4. d 5. b 6. c 7. b 8. a 9. d 10. b 11. d 12. c 13. a
14. b 15. c 16. d 17. b 18. c 19. a 20. a 21. d 22. b 23. a 24. c 25. b
26. a

FINAL EXAMINATION NAME____________________

TEST FORM A CLASS_____ SCORE_____ GRADE_____

ANSWERS

1. Compute: $5+3\left(2^2-1\right)^2$.

2. Simplify: $\left(3.5\times10^{-8}\right)\left(8.2\times10^{3}\right)$.

Make a graph of each equation.

3. $y=-x+4$

4. $y=-|x+1|+2$

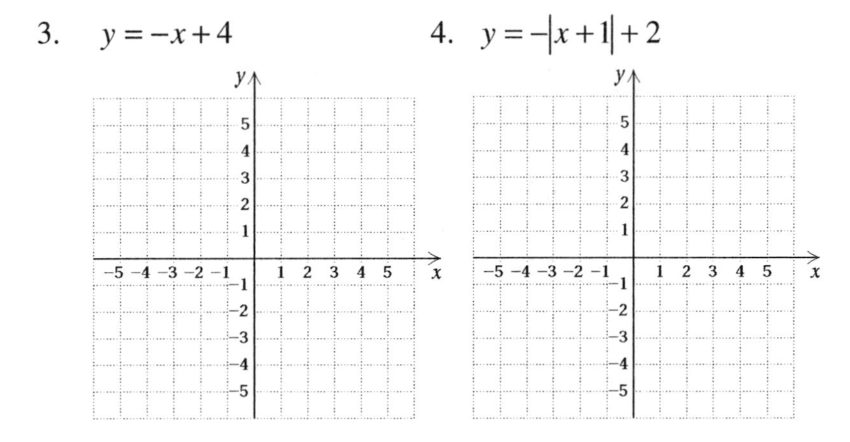

5. Visually estimate the range of the graph in Exercise 4.

6. a) Determine whether the relation $\{(3,-2),(4,-3),(5,-2),(6,-1)\}$ is a function. Answer "yes" or "no."

   b) Find the domain of the relation.

7. For the function $f(x)=2(x-1)^2+3$, find $f(a+2)$.

1. ____________

2. ____________

3. See graph.

4. See graph.

5. ____________

6. a)____________
   b)____________

7. ____________

FINAL EXAMINATION NAME______________________________

TEST FORM A

ANSWERS

8. ______________

9. ______________

10. See graph.

11. a)______________

b)______________

8. Find an equation of the line parallel to $4x+2y=3$ which passes through $(-2,5)$.

9. The table below shows the number of candles sold at a charity's fundraiser for 4 successive years.

Year	Number candles sold
0	80
1	60
2	50
3	64

Use years 0 and 3 to model the data with a linear function, and then estimate the number of candles that will be placed in year 5 using this function. Round to the nearest whole number.

10. The graph of the function $y=f(x)$ is shown below. No formula for *f* is given. Make hand-drawn graph of $y=f(x)-3$.

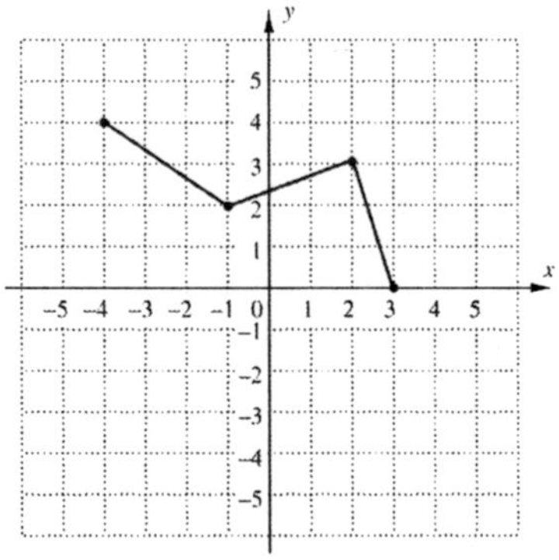

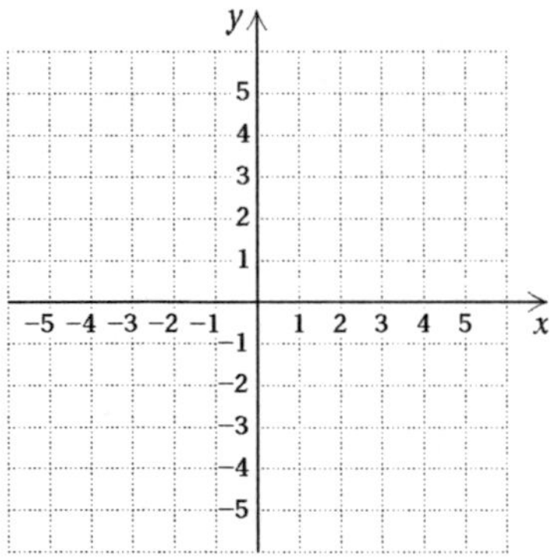

11. For $f(x)=\sqrt{x}$ and $g(x)=3x+1$,

a) find $(g \circ f)(x)$;

b) the domain of $(g \circ f)(x)$.

FINAL EXAMINATION **NAME**________________________

TEST FORM A

---

12. Simplify: $\sqrt{-6} \cdot \sqrt{-6}$.

Solve.

13. $|4x-2| = 6$

14. $x^2 - 5x + 3 = 0$.

15. $\sqrt{x+2} = 2x+1$

16. $x^2 > 8x - 15$

17. For the graph of the function $f(x) = 2x^2 + 4x + 5$,
    a) find the vertex;
    b) find the line of symmetry;
    c) state whether there is a maximum or minimum value and find that value;
    d) find the range;
    e) graph the function.

18. Find an equation of variation in which y varies directly as x, and $y = 0.8$ when $x = 6$.

19. Divide: $(2x^4 - x^3 + 3x - 2) \div (x + 2)$.

ANSWERS

12. ____________

13. ____________

14. ____________

15. ____________

16. ____________

17. a)____________
    b)____________
    c)____________
    d)____________
    e) See graph.

18. ____________

19. ____________

FINAL EXAMINATION **NAME**________________________

TEST FORM A

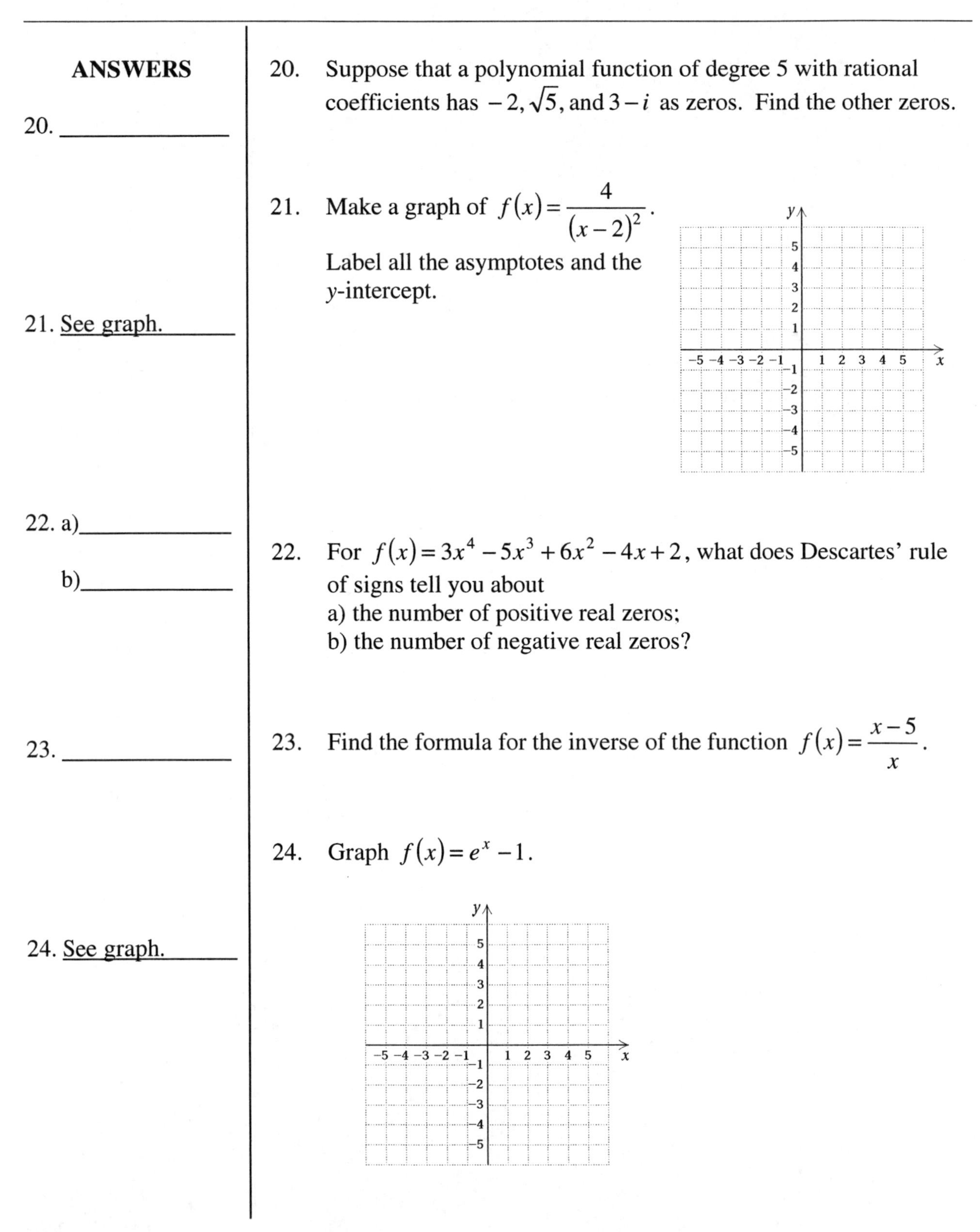

ANSWERS

20. ____________

21. See graph.

22. a)____________

b)____________

23. ____________

24. See graph.

20. Suppose that a polynomial function of degree 5 with rational coefficients has $-2, \sqrt{5}$, and $3-i$ as zeros. Find the other zeros.

21. Make a graph of $f(x)=\dfrac{4}{(x-2)^2}$.

Label all the asymptotes and the y-intercept.

22. For $f(x)=3x^4-5x^3+6x^2-4x+2$, what does Descartes' rule of signs tell you about
a) the number of positive real zeros;
b) the number of negative real zeros?

23. Find the formula for the inverse of the function $f(x)=\dfrac{x-5}{x}$.

24. Graph $f(x)=e^x-1$.

FINAL EXAMINATION **NAME**________________________

TEST FORM A

25. Solve: $\dfrac{3^x}{3^4} = 27^{x^2-4x}$.

26. Convert to an exponential equation: $\log x = 8$.

27. Given that $\log_b 12 = 1.7925$ and $\log_b 2 = 0.5000$, find $\log_b 6$.

28. The population of a bacteria culture doubled in 6 hr. What was the exponential growth rate?

Solve, if possible. If there is no solution, state this. Use any method.

29. $2x + 6y = 2,$
 $x - y = -7$

30. $3x - 2y + z = 6,$
 $-2x + 5y + 3z = -26,$
 $-x + 3y - 2z = 8$

Use $A = \begin{bmatrix} 3 & 1 & 2 \\ -1 & 0 & 7 \end{bmatrix}$ and $B = \begin{bmatrix} 2 & 3 \\ -4 & 5 \end{bmatrix}$ for Exercises 31 and 32.

31. Find BA, if possible.

32. Find B^{-1}, if possible.

ANSWERS

25. ____________

26. ____________

27. ____________

28. ____________

29. ____________

30. ____________

31. ____________

32. ____________

FINAL EXAMINATION **NAME**________________________

TEST FORM A

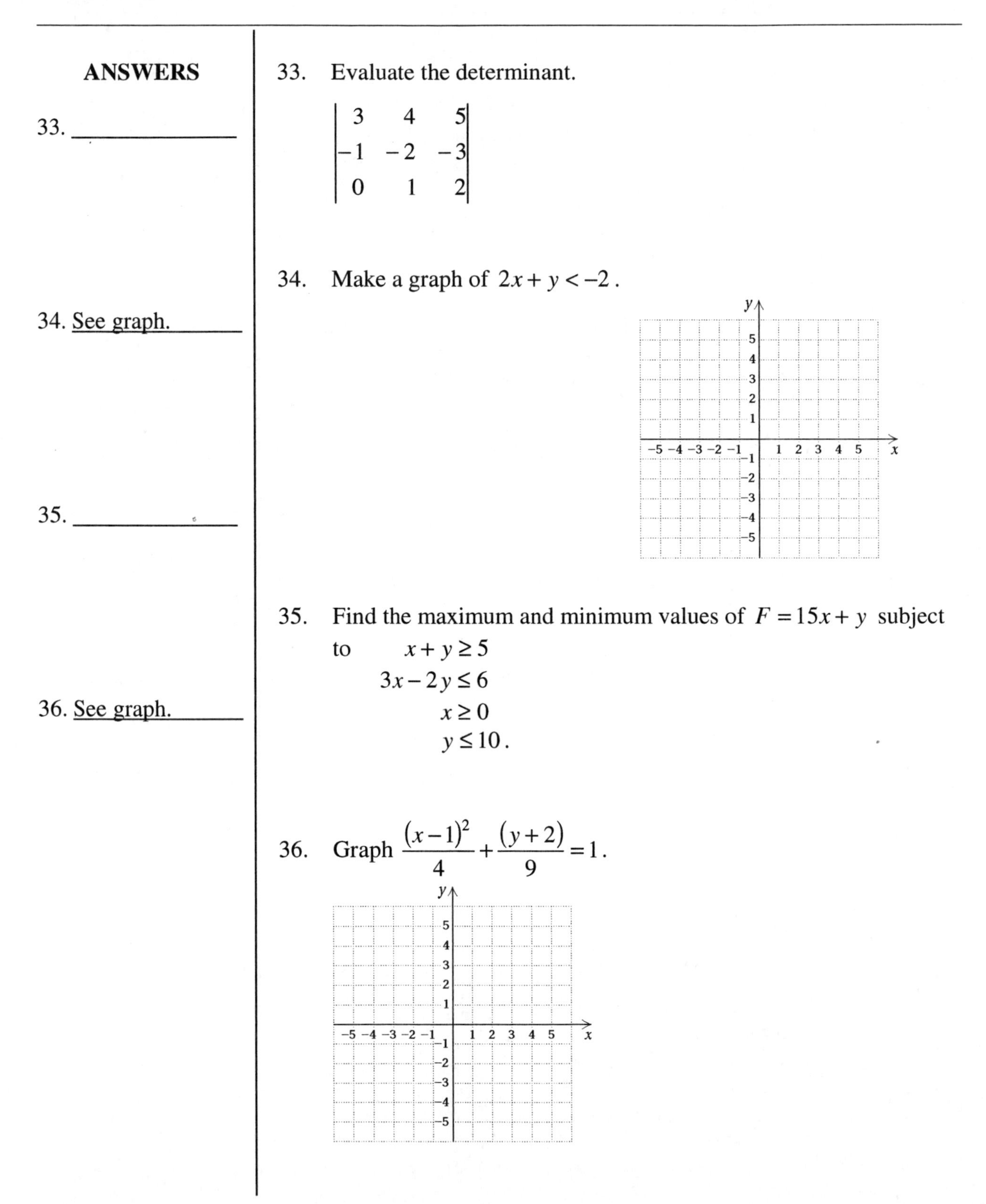

ANSWERS

33. ____________

34. See graph.

35. ____________

36. See graph.

33. Evaluate the determinant.

$$\begin{vmatrix} 3 & 4 & 5 \\ -1 & -2 & -3 \\ 0 & 1 & 2 \end{vmatrix}$$

34. Make a graph of $2x + y < -2$.

35. Find the maximum and minimum values of $F = 15x + y$ subject to

$$\begin{aligned} x + y &\geq 5 \\ 3x - 2y &\leq 6 \\ x &\geq 0 \\ y &\leq 10. \end{aligned}$$

36. Graph $\dfrac{(x-1)^2}{4} + \dfrac{(y+2)}{9} = 1$.

FINAL EXAMINATION **NAME**________________________

TEST FORM A

ANSWERS

37. Find the asymptotes of the hyperbola given by $4x^2 - 5y^2 = 100$.

37. ____________

38. Find the center and the radius of a circle given by $x^2 + 8x + y^2 - 10y - 23 = 0$.

38. ____________

39. Solve: $2x^2 + 5y^2 = 38$,
$6x - y = -16$.

39. ____________

40. The 1st term of an arithmetic sequence is –3 and the 13th term is 6. Find the 8th term.

40. ____________

41. Evaluate: $\sum_{k=1}^{5}(-1)^k(3k-2)$.

41. ____________

42. If $a_1 = -2$ and $a_{n+1} = 2a_n - 1$, find a_4.

42. ____________

43. *Amount of an Annuity*. To create a college fund, a parent makes a sequence of 15 yearly deposits of $3000 each in a savings account on which interest is compounded annually at 4.5 %. Find the amount of the annuity.

43. ____________

FINAL EXAMINATION **NAME**____________________________

TEST FORM A

ANSWERS

44. ______________

45. ______________

46. ______________

47. ______________

48. ______________

49. ______________

50. ______________

44. Use mathematical induction to prove that for every natural number n, $4+8+12+\cdots+4n=2n(n+1)$.

45. Find: ${}_{10}C_3$.

46. Expand: $(x-n)^4$.

47. How many license plates can be formed using three letters followed by 3 digits?

48. *Card Drawing*. Suppose we draw a card from a well-shuffled deck of 52 cards. What is the probability of drawing a king or a two?

---

49. Find the domain of $\dfrac{x}{\sqrt{x-2}}$.

50. If $(4,-6)$ is on the graph of $y=f(x)$, what point do you know is on the graph of $f(x-2)$?

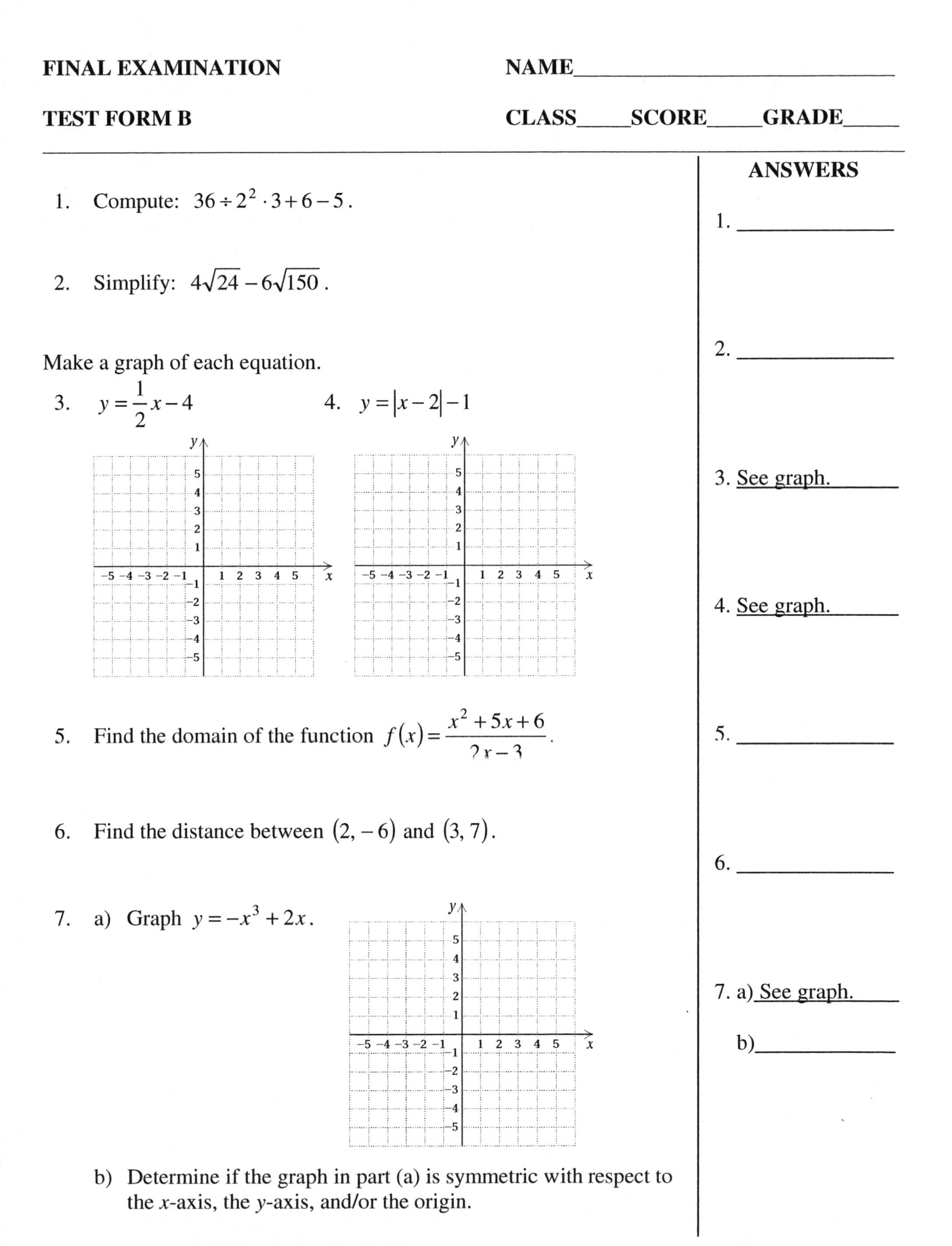

FINAL EXAMINATION **NAME**____________________

TEST FORM B **CLASS**_____**SCORE**_____**GRADE**_____

1. Compute: $36 \div 2^2 \cdot 3 + 6 - 5$.

2. Simplify: $4\sqrt{24} - 6\sqrt{150}$.

Make a graph of each equation.

3. $y = \frac{1}{2}x - 4$

4. $y = |x - 2| - 1$

5. Find the domain of the function $f(x) = \frac{x^2 + 5x + 6}{2x - 3}$.

6. Find the distance between $(2, -6)$ and $(3, 7)$.

7. a) Graph $y = -x^3 + 2x$.

   b) Determine if the graph in part (a) is symmetric with respect to the x-axis, the y-axis, and/or the origin.

ANSWERS

1. ____________

2. ____________

3. See graph.

4. See graph.

5. ____________

6. ____________

7. a) See graph.

   b) ____________

FINAL EXAMINATION **NAME**______________________________

TEST FORM B

ANSWERS

8. ______________

9. ______________

10. ______________

11. a)______________

b)______________

8. Write an equation for a line with slope $-\frac{5}{6}$ that passes through the point $(8, 2)$.

9. The table below shows the number of trips over 50 mi made for 4 successive years.

Year	Number of trips over 50 mi
0	20
1	22
2	30
3	32

Use years 1 and 3 to model the data with a linear function, and then estimate the number of trips over 50 mi in year 6 using this function.

10. Write an equation for a function that has the shape of $y = \sqrt{x}$, but shifted left 2 units and up 4 units.

11. For $f(x) = x - 3$ and $g(x) = x^2 + 1$, find
a) $(f - g)(x)$;
b) the domain of $(f - g)(x)$.

FINAL EXAMINATION **NAME**______________________

TEST FORM B

12. Simplify: $(-3+i)(8-2i)$.

Solve.

13. $\frac{5}{x+3}-\frac{2x+1}{11-x}=2$

14. $n-2\sqrt{n}-8=0$

15. $x^2+6x+4=0$

16. $-5\leq 4x+3<12$

17. For the graph of the function $f(x)=-x^2+4x$,
    a) find the vertex;
    b) find the line of symmetry;
    c) state whether there is a maximum or minimum value and find that value;
    d) find the range;
    e) graph the function.

18. The distance traveled varies directly as the time. If the distance traveled is 3 laps when the time is 4 min, find the number of laps when the time is 7 min.

19. Use the intermediate value theorem to determine whether $f(x)=x^3-4x+2$ has a real zero between -1 and 0, if possible. Show your work. If it is not possible to make a determination using this method, state this.

ANSWERS

12. ____________

13. ____________

14. ____________

15. ____________

16. ____________

17. a)____________
    b)____________
    c)____________
    d)____________
    e) See graph.

18. ____________

19. ____________

FINAL EXAMINATION **NAME**______________________

TEST FORM B

ANSWERS

20. ______________

21. ______________

22. a)____________

b)____________

23. ______________

24. See graph.______

20. Divide: $(12x^3 - 4x^2 - 3x + 5) \div (2x - 1)$.

21. Find a rational function that has vertical asymptotes of $x = 3$ and $x = -6$, and a y-intercept of $(0, 2)$.

22. For $f(x) = 2x^5 - 3x^3 + 6x^2 - 4$, what does Descartes' rule of signs tell you about
a) the number of positive real zeros;
b) the number of negative real zeros?

23. Determine whether the function shown below is one-to-one. Answer "yes" or "no."

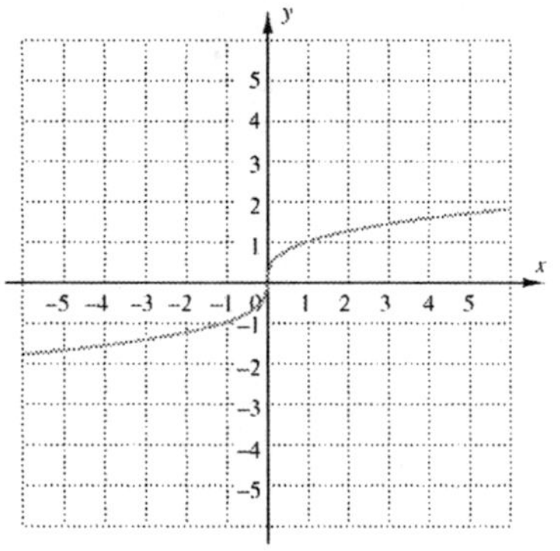

24. Graph $f(x) = e^{x+2}$.

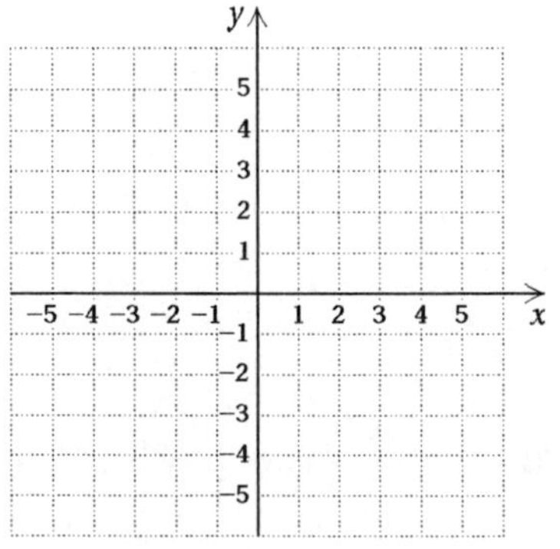

FINAL EXAMINATION **NAME**____________________________

TEST FORM B

Solve:

25. $2^{x-6} = 16^{3x}$.

26. $\ln x = 0.1$

27. Given that $\log_a 12 = 1.5440$ and $\log_a 16 = 1.7227$, find $\log_a 4$.

28. Suppose $\$5000$ is invested at interest rate *k*, compounded continuously, and grows to $\$5950.28$ in 3 yr.

    a) Find the exponential growth rate.
    b) Find the doubling time to the nearest tenth of a year.

Solve, if possible. If there is no solution, state this. Use any method.

29. $5x - 7y = 12,$
    $-10x + 14y = -6$

30. $3x - y + 2z = -8,$
    $-4x - 3y + 8z = -10,$
    $x + 2y + 4z = 13$

Use $A = \begin{bmatrix} -1 & 5 & -2 \\ 4 & 2 & 8 \end{bmatrix}$ and $B = \begin{bmatrix} 2 & -3 \\ 4 & -5 \end{bmatrix}$ for Exercises 31 and 32.

31. Find AB, if possible.

32. Find B^{-1}, if possible.

ANSWERS

25. ____________

26. ____________

27. ____________

28. a)____________
    b)____________

29. ____________

30. ____________

31. ____________

32. ____________

FINAL EXAMINATION **NAME**______________________________

TEST FORM B

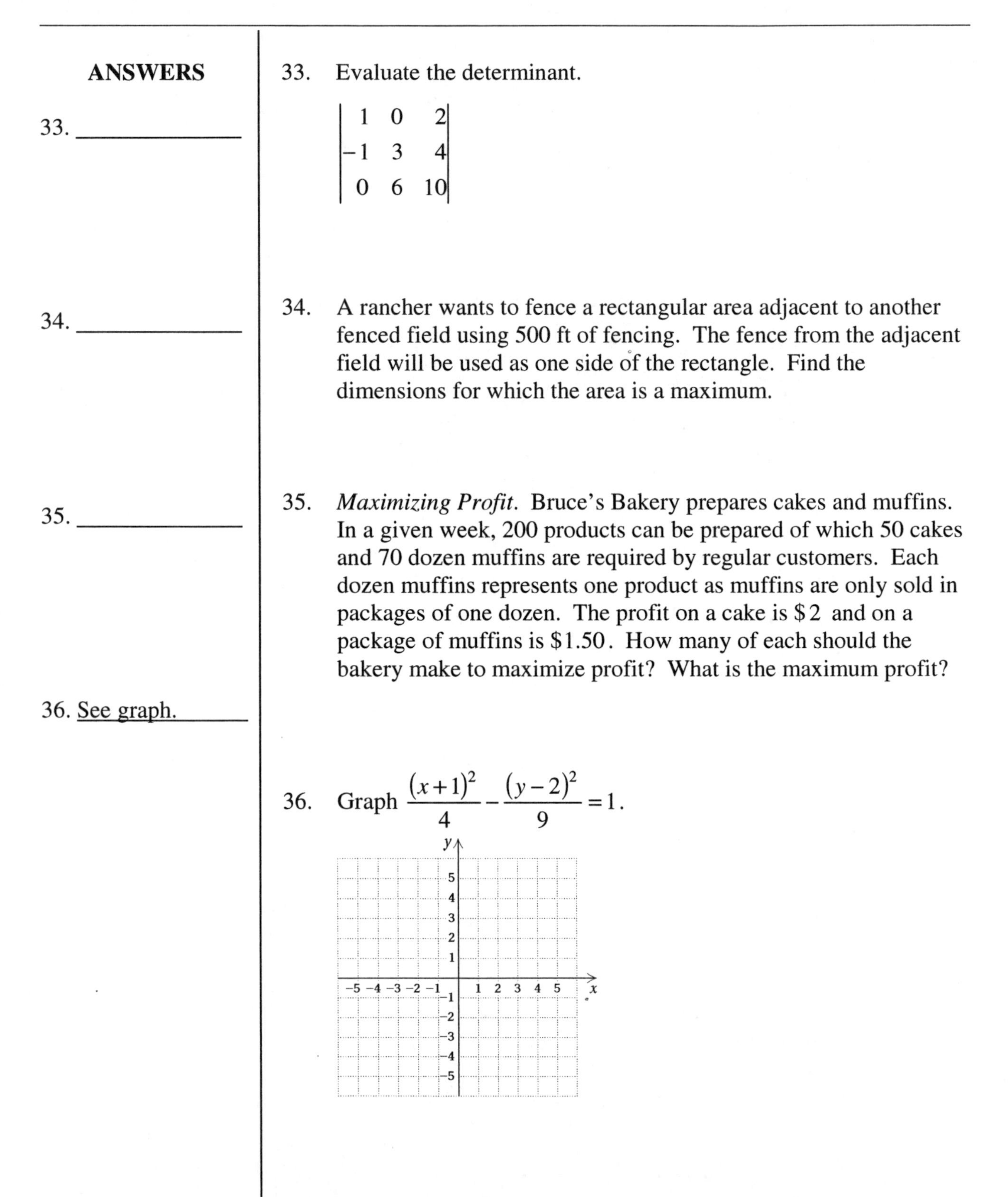

ANSWERS

33. ____________

34. ____________

35. ____________

36. See graph.

33. Evaluate the determinant.

$$\begin{vmatrix} 1 & 0 & 2 \\ -1 & 3 & 4 \\ 0 & 6 & 10 \end{vmatrix}$$

34. A rancher wants to fence a rectangular area adjacent to another fenced field using 500 ft of fencing. The fence from the adjacent field will be used as one side of the rectangle. Find the dimensions for which the area is a maximum.

35. *Maximizing Profit.* Bruce's Bakery prepares cakes and muffins. In a given week, 200 products can be prepared of which 50 cakes and 70 dozen muffins are required by regular customers. Each dozen muffins represents one product as muffins are only sold in packages of one dozen. The profit on a cake is $\$2$ and on a package of muffins is $\$1.50$. How many of each should the bakery make to maximize profit? What is the maximum profit?

36. Graph $\frac{(x+1)^2}{4}-\frac{(y-2)^2}{9}=1$.

FINAL EXAMINATION **NAME**________________________

TEST FORM B

ANSWERS

37. Find the center and the radius of the circle given by $x^2 - 8x + y^2 + 12y - 29 = 0$.

38. A satellite dish has a parabolic cross-section that is 18 in. wide at the opening and 3 in. deep at the vertex. How far from the vertex is the focus?

39. Solve: $2x + y = 31$,
    $xy = -16$.

40. For sequence whose nth term is $a_n = (-1)^n (3n-1)$, find a_6.

41. Find the sum of the first 500 even natural numbers.

42. If $a_1 = 3$ and $a_{n+1} = 3a_n + 1$, find a_4.

43. Find the sum, if it exists: $120 + (-72) + 43.2 + (-25.92) + \cdots$.

37. ____________

38. ____________

39. ____________

40. ____________

41. ____________

42. ____________

43. ____________

FINAL EXAMINATION **NAME**______________________________

TEST FORM B

ANSWERS

44. ______________

45. ______________

46. ______________

47. ______________

48. ______________

49. ______________

50. ______________

44. Use mathematical induction to prove that for every natural number, $n > 1, n^2 > n$.

45. Find: ${}_8P_2$.

46. Expand: $(2x-1)^4$.

47. *Test Options.* On a test with 10 questions, a student must answer 4 out of the first 5 questions and 2 out of the last 5. In how many ways can this be done?

48. *Card Drawing.* Suppose we draw a card from a well-shuffled deck of 52 cards. What is the probability of drawing a red face card (jack, queen, or king)?

---

49. Solve for n: $8\binom{n-1}{6} = \binom{n}{5}$.

50. Solve: $\log|x+6| = 2$.

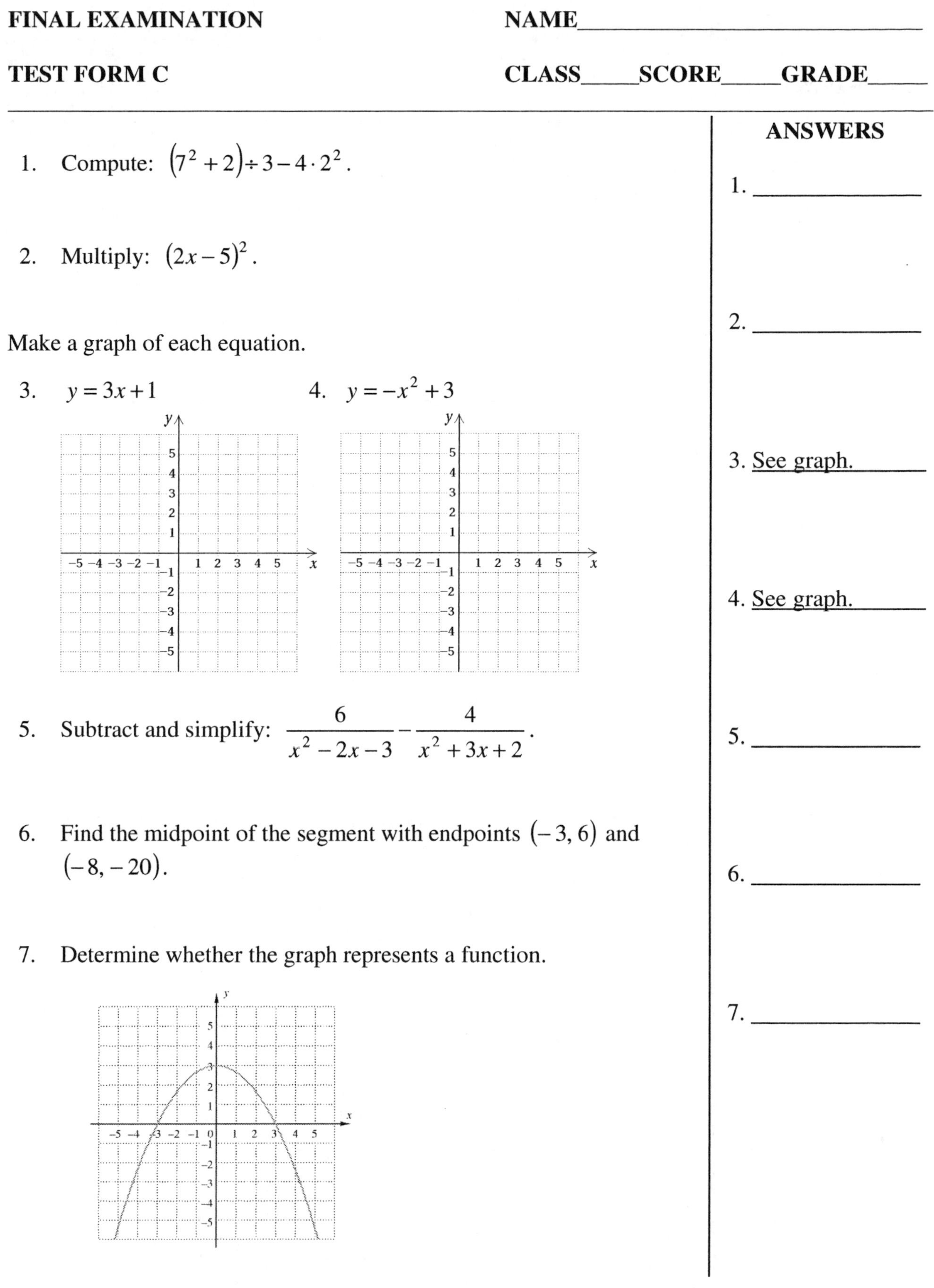

FINAL EXAMINATION NAME______________________

TEST FORM C CLASS____ SCORE____ GRADE____

ANSWERS

1. Compute: $\left(7^2+2\right)\div 3-4\cdot 2^2$.

1. ______________

2. Multiply: $(2x-5)^2$.

2. ______________

Make a graph of each equation.

3. $y=3x+1$

4. $y=-x^2+3$

3. See graph.

4. See graph.

5. Subtract and simplify: $\dfrac{6}{x^2-2x-3}-\dfrac{4}{x^2+3x+2}$.

5. ______________

6. Find the midpoint of the segment with endpoints $(-3, 6)$ and $(-8, -20)$.

6. ______________

7. Determine whether the graph represents a function.

7. ______________

FINAL EXAMINATION **NAME**________________________

TEST FORM C

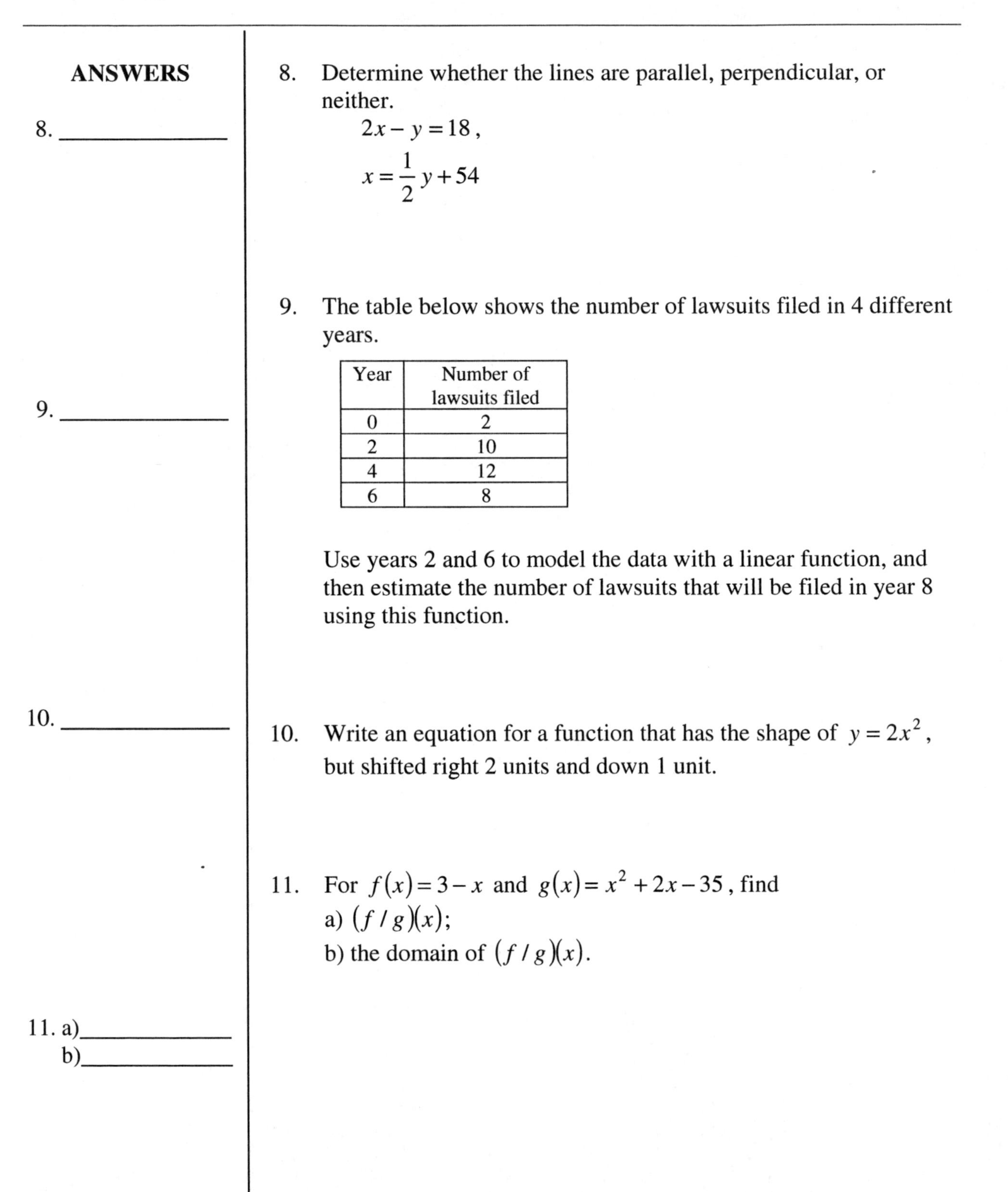

ANSWERS

8. ____________

9. ____________

10. ____________

11. a)____________
    b)____________

8. Determine whether the lines are parallel, perpendicular, or neither.

$$2x - y = 18,$$

$$x = \frac{1}{2}y + 54$$

9. The table below shows the number of lawsuits filed in 4 different years.

Year	Number of lawsuits filed
0	2
2	10
4	12
6	8

Use years 2 and 6 to model the data with a linear function, and then estimate the number of lawsuits that will be filed in year 8 using this function.

10. Write an equation for a function that has the shape of $y = 2x^2$, but shifted right 2 units and down 1 unit.

11. For $f(x) = 3 - x$ and $g(x) = x^2 + 2x - 35$, find
    a) $(f/g)(x)$;
    b) the domain of $(f/g)(x)$.

FINAL EXAMINATION NAME______________________

TEST FORM C

---

12. Simplify: $\frac{4+3i}{5-2i}$.

Solve.

13. $m+6\sqrt{m}-16=0$

14. $x^2+x+1=0$

15. $\frac{x-2}{x+3}\le 2$

16. $|-x+3|<10$

17. For the graph of the function $f(x)=-x^2+4x-1$,
a) find the vertex;
b) find the line of symmetry;
c) state whether there is a maximum or minimum value and find that value;
d) find the range;
e) graph the function.

18. y varies jointly as x and the square of z. If $y=\frac{5}{8}$ when $x=3$ and $z=\frac{1}{8}$, find y when $x=4$ and $z=\frac{1}{2}$.

19. For $f(x)=5-3x+4x^2$,
a) classify $f(x)$ as linear, quadratic, cubic, or quartic;
b) find the leading term;
c) find the leading coefficient;
d) find the degree of the polynomial.

ANSWERS

12. ______________

13. ______________

14. ______________

15. ______________

16. ______________

17 a)______________
b)______________
c)______________
d)______________
e) See graph.

18. ______________

19. a)______________
b)______________
c)______________
d)______________

FINAL EXAMINATION **NAME**______________________

TEST FORM C

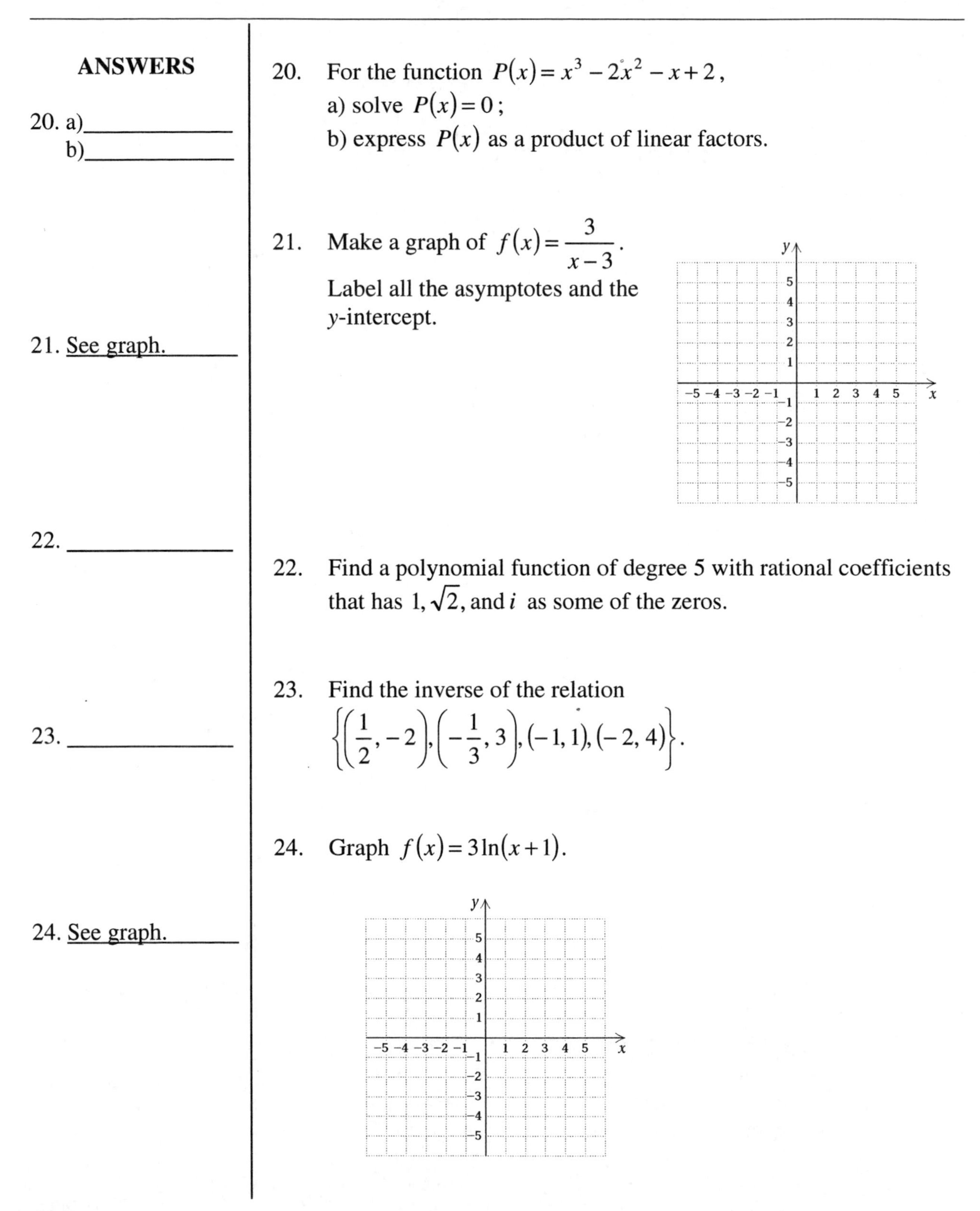

ANSWERS

20. a)____________
    b)____________

21. See graph.

22. ____________

23. ____________

24. See graph.

20. For the function $P(x) = x^3 - 2x^2 - x + 2$,
    a) solve $P(x) = 0$;
    b) express $P(x)$ as a product of linear factors.

21. Make a graph of $f(x) = \frac{3}{x-3}$.
    Label all the asymptotes and the y-intercept.

22. Find a polynomial function of degree 5 with rational coefficients that has $1, \sqrt{2}$, and i as some of the zeros.

23. Find the inverse of the relation
    $\left\{\left(\frac{1}{2}, -2\right), \left(-\frac{1}{3}, 3\right), (-1, 1), (-2, 4)\right\}$.

24. Graph $f(x) = 3\ln(x+1)$.

FINAL EXAMINATION **NAME**______________________________

TEST FORM C

Solve.

25. $\ln x = 8$

26. $2^8 = 4^{\sqrt{x}}$

27. Express in terms of sums and differences of logarithms: $\dfrac{x^2 y^{1/2}}{z^3}$.

28. Suppose $\$4000$ is invested at interest rate k, compounded continuously, and grows to $\$4555.31$ in 5 yr.

    a) Find the exponential growth function.
    b) Find the balance after 10 yr.

Solve, if possible. If there is no solution, state this. Use any method.

29. $4x - y = -9$,
    $-6x + y = 11$

30. $3x - y + z = -4$,
    $-6x + 2y - 4z = 10$,
    $y + 15z = -10$

Use $A = \begin{bmatrix} -1 & -2 \\ 5 & 6 \end{bmatrix}$ and $B = \begin{bmatrix} -5 & 2 & -4 \\ 3 & -1 & 0 \end{bmatrix}$ for Exercises 31 and 32.

31. Find $B - A$, if possible.

32. Find A^{-1}, if possible.

ANSWERS

25. ____________

26. ____________

27. ____________

28. a)____________
    b)____________

29. ____________

30. ____________

31. ____________

32. ____________

FINAL EXAMINATION **NAME**____________________________

TEST FORM C

ANSWERS

33. ______________

34. See graph.

35. ______________

33. Evaluate the determinant.

$$\begin{vmatrix} 5 & 0 & 6 \\ -2 & 1 & 4 \\ -1 & 3 & 2 \end{vmatrix}$$

34. Make a graph of $2x - 3y \geq 6$.

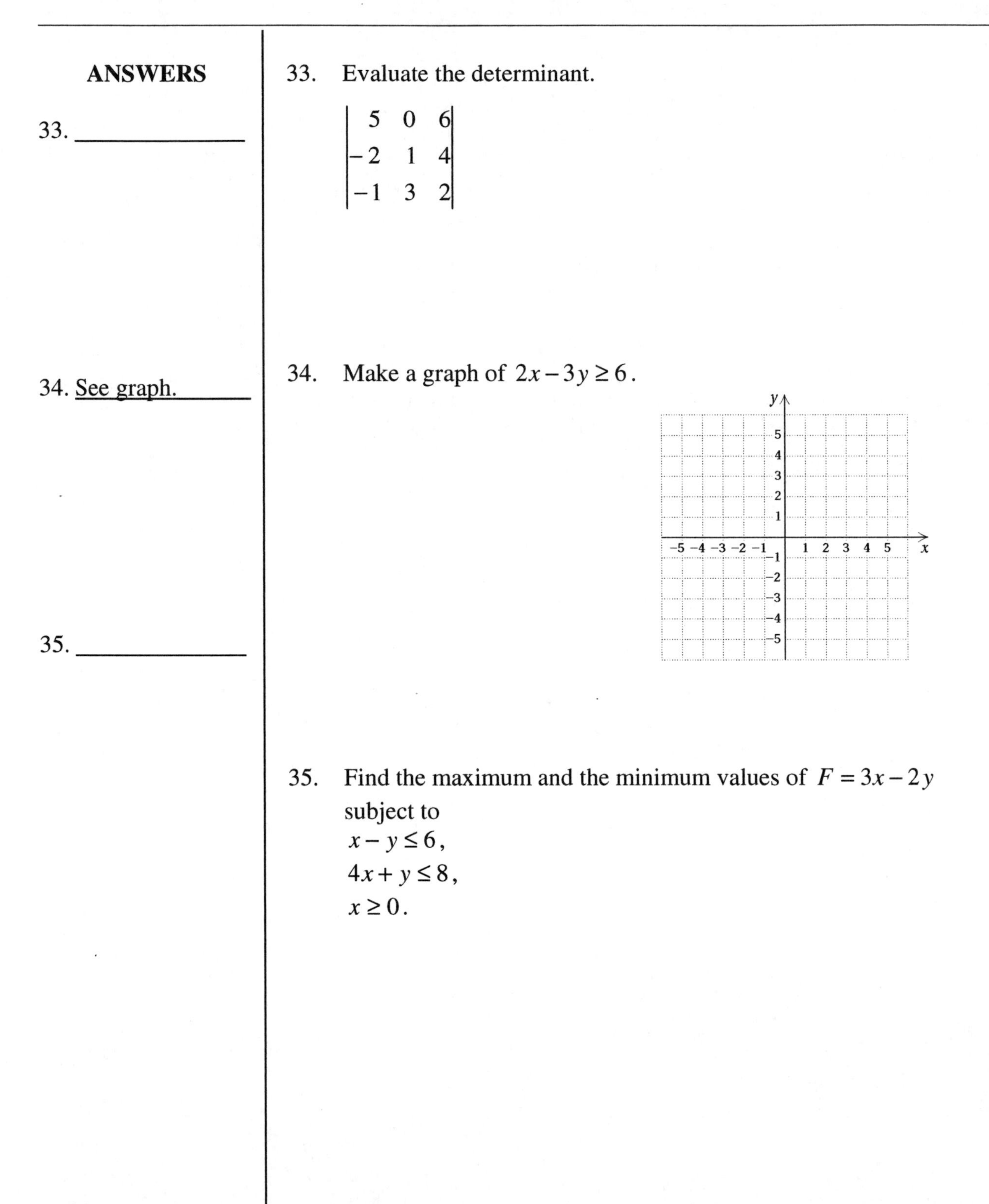

35. Find the maximum and the minimum values of $F = 3x - 2y$ subject to
$x - y \leq 6$,
$4x + y \leq 8$,
$x \geq 0$.

FINAL EXAMINATION **NAME**____________________

TEST FORM C

Match each of the following with its graph.

36. $9x^2 - 16y^2 - 144 = 0$

37. $9x^2 + 16y^2 = 144$

38. $x^2 - 6x + y^2 - 8y - 11 = 0$

39. $16y^2 - 9x^2 = 144$

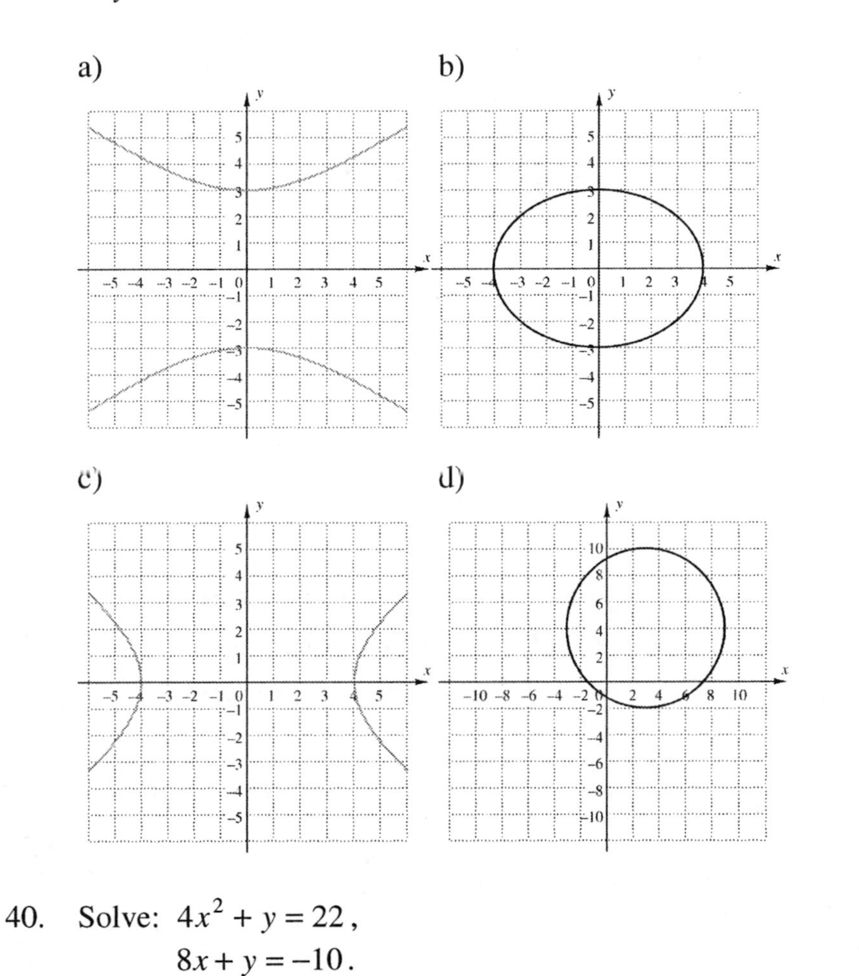

40. Solve: $4x^2 + y = 22$,
$8x + y = -10$.

41. For a geometric sequence, $r = 0.5$ and $S_5 = 11.625$, find a_1.

ANSWERS

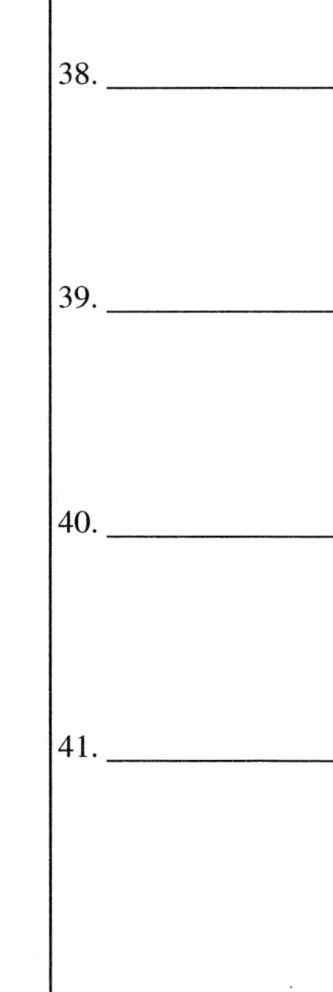

36. ____________

37. ____________

38. ____________

39. ____________

40. ____________

41. ____________

FINAL EXAMINATION **NAME**________________________

TEST FORM C

ANSWERS

42. ____________

43. ____________

44. ____________

45. See work.

46. ____________

47. ____________

48. ____________

49. ____________

50. ____________

42. If $a_1 = 0$ and $a_{n+1} = 2a_n - 3$, find a_4.

43. *A Daily Doubling Salary.* Suppose someone offered you a 12-week summer job under the following conditions. You will be paid $40 for the first week, $60 for the second, $90 for the third, and so on, earning one and a half times your previous week's salary each week. How much would you earn altogether?

44. Find fraction notation for $0.\overline{7}$.

45. Use mathematical induction to prove that for every natural number n, $2+4+6+\cdots+2n = n(n+1)$.

46. Expand: $(x-a)^4$.

47. *License Plates.* How many license plates can be made if they are formed by 3 letters, followed by 3 digits, followed by a letter? Digits and letters may be repeated.

48. *Marbles.* Suppose we select, without looking, one marble from a bag containing 12 red marbles, 8 blue marbles, and 4 white marbles. What is the probability of selecting a red marble?

---

49. Solve: $3^{4\sqrt{x}} = 27^{2/3}$.

50. Find the domain of $f(x) = \dfrac{x^2 + 2x - 15}{\sqrt{x-9}}$.

FINAL EXAMINATION **NAME**______________________

TEST FORM D **CLASS**____ **SCORE**____ **GRADE**____

ANSWERS

1. Compute: $\left(32 \div 2^4\right) \cdot 5 - 3$.

1. ______________

2. Simplify: $\dfrac{8.5 \times 10^{-8}}{3.4 \times 10^3}$.

2. ______________

Make a graph of each equation.

3. $y = 2x - 3$

4. $y = \sqrt{x^2 - 9}$

3. See graph.

4. See graph.

5. Rationalize the denominator $\dfrac{4+\sqrt{2}}{3-\sqrt{2}}$.

5. ______________

6. Given that $f(x) = -3x^3 - 4x^2 + 5x - 10$, find $f(-2)$.

6. ______________

7. For $f(x) = 3x^2 + x$, find $f(x+h)$.

7. ______________

FINAL EXAMINATION **NAME**____________________________

TEST FORM D

ANSWERS

8. ______________

9. ______________

10. ______________

11. ______________

8. Find an equation for the line that passes through $(3, -4)$ and $(-5, 6)$.

9. The table below shows the average score on an entrance exam for 4 different years.

Year	Average score
0	110
2	115
4	113
6	119

Use years 0 and 4 to model the data with a linear function, and then estimate the average score in year 5.

10. The graph of the function $y = f(x)$ is shown below. No formula for f is given. Make hand-drawn graph of $y = f(x+2)$.

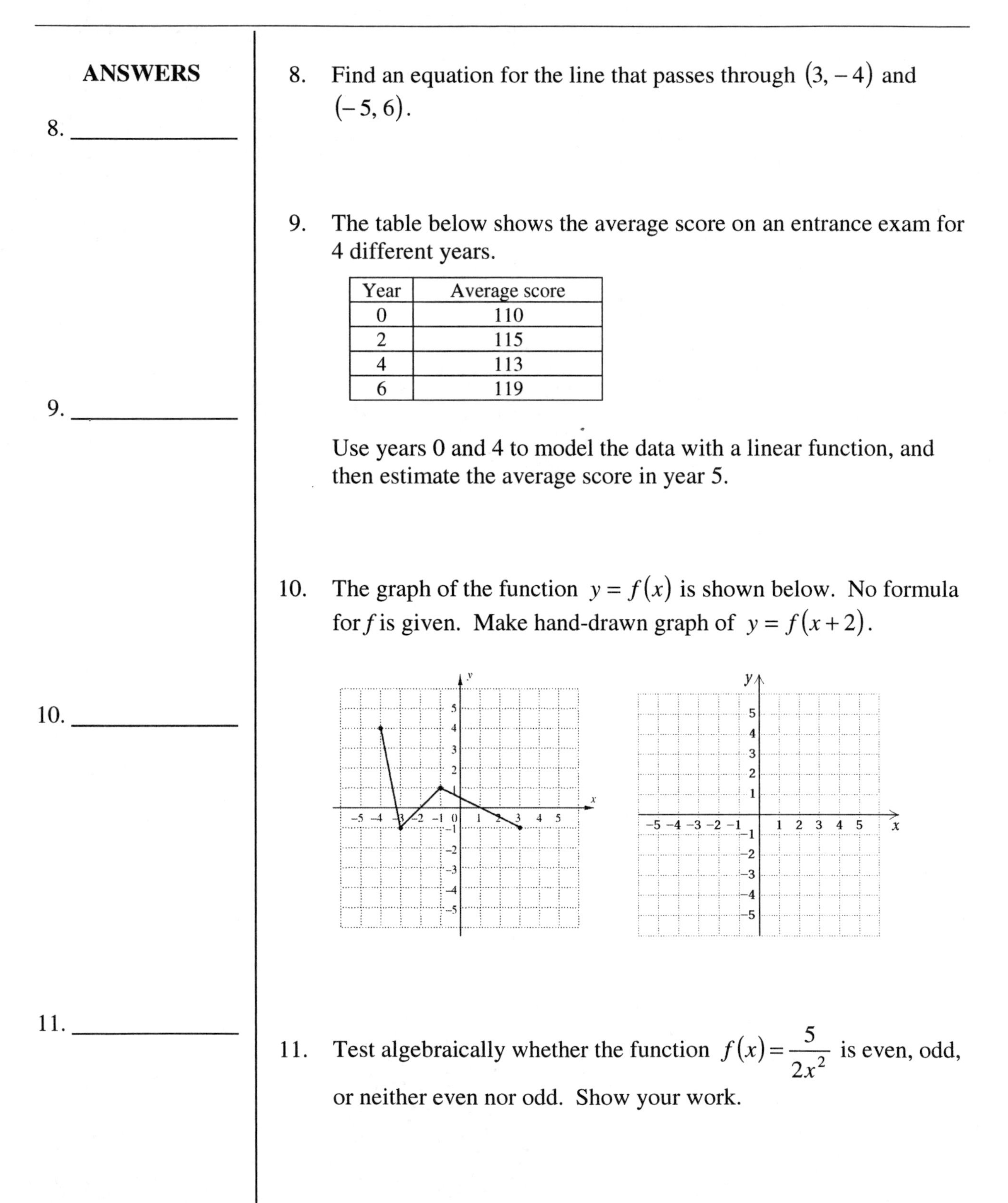

11. Test algebraically whether the function $f(x) = \dfrac{5}{2x^2}$ is even, odd, or neither even nor odd. Show your work.

FINAL EXAMINATION **NAME**________________________

TEST FORM D

---

12. Simplify: i^{15}.

Solve.

13. $x-1=\sqrt{3x+7}$

14. $-3<3x-6\leq 1$

15. $\dfrac{x+3}{x-4}\geq 2$

16. $3x^2+13x+30=0$

17. For the graph of the function $f(x)=x^2+2x-3$,
    a) find the vertex;
    b) find the line of symmetry;
    c) state whether there is a maximum or minimum value and find that value;
    d) find the range;
    e) graph the function.

y, x axes from −5 to 5

18. Find an equation of variation in which y varies inversely as x, and $y=8$ when $x=5$.

19. For $f(x)=x^3-6x$,
    a) classify $f(x)$ as linear, quadratic, cubic, or quartic;
    b) find the leading term;
    c) find the leading coefficient;
    d) find the degree of the polynomial.

ANSWERS

12. ______________

13. ______________

14. ______________

15. ______________

16. ______________

17. a)______________
    b)______________
    c)______________
    d)______________
    e) See graph.

18. ______________

19. a)______________
    b)______________
    c)______________
    d)______________

FINAL EXAMINATION **NAME**______________________

TEST FORM D

ANSWERS

20. ____________

21. ____________

22. ____________

23. ____________

24. See graph.

20. Use synthetic division to find $P(-10)$ for $P(x)=5x^4-6x^3+2x^2-3x+4$.

21. Find a rational function that has $x=3$ and $x=-2$ as vertical asymptotes, and a *y*-intercept of $(0,1)$.

22. Use long division to find the quotient $Q(x)$ and remainder $R(x)$, when $P(x)$ is divided by $d(x)$, and express $P(x)$ in the form $d(x)\cdot Q(x)+R(x)$. Show your work.
$P(x)=4x^3-3x^2+x-5$,
$d(x)=x+1$

23. Find the formula for the inverse of $f(x)=3-8x$.

24. Graph $f(x)=\ln(x+3)$.

y
5
4
3
2
1
−5 −4 −3 −2 −1
1 2 3 4 5
x
−1
−2
−3
−4
−5

FINAL EXAMINATION **NAME**__________________________

TEST FORM D

Solve.

25. $\log \frac{1}{1000} = x$

26. $e^{3x} = 15$

27. Express in terms of sums and differences of logarithms:
$\log \frac{y\sqrt{x}}{z^2}$.

28. The population of a town doubles in 15 yr. Find the exponential growth rate.

Solve, if possible. If there is no solution, state this. Use any method.

29. $4x - 5y = 8,$
$2x + y = 10$

30. $-2x + y + 3z = 0,$
$14x - 6y - 5z = -13,$
$7x + 3y - z = 4$

Use $A = \begin{bmatrix} 5 & 0 \\ 9 & -8 \end{bmatrix}$ and $B = \begin{bmatrix} -1 & 5 & -3 \\ 4 & 8 & 1 \end{bmatrix}$ for Exercises 31 and 32.

31. Find AB, if possible.

32. Find $4B$, if possible.

ANSWERS

25. ______________

26. ______________

27. ______________

28. ______________

29. ______________

30. ______________

31. ______________

32. ______________

FINAL EXAMINATION **NAME**__________________________

TEST FORM D

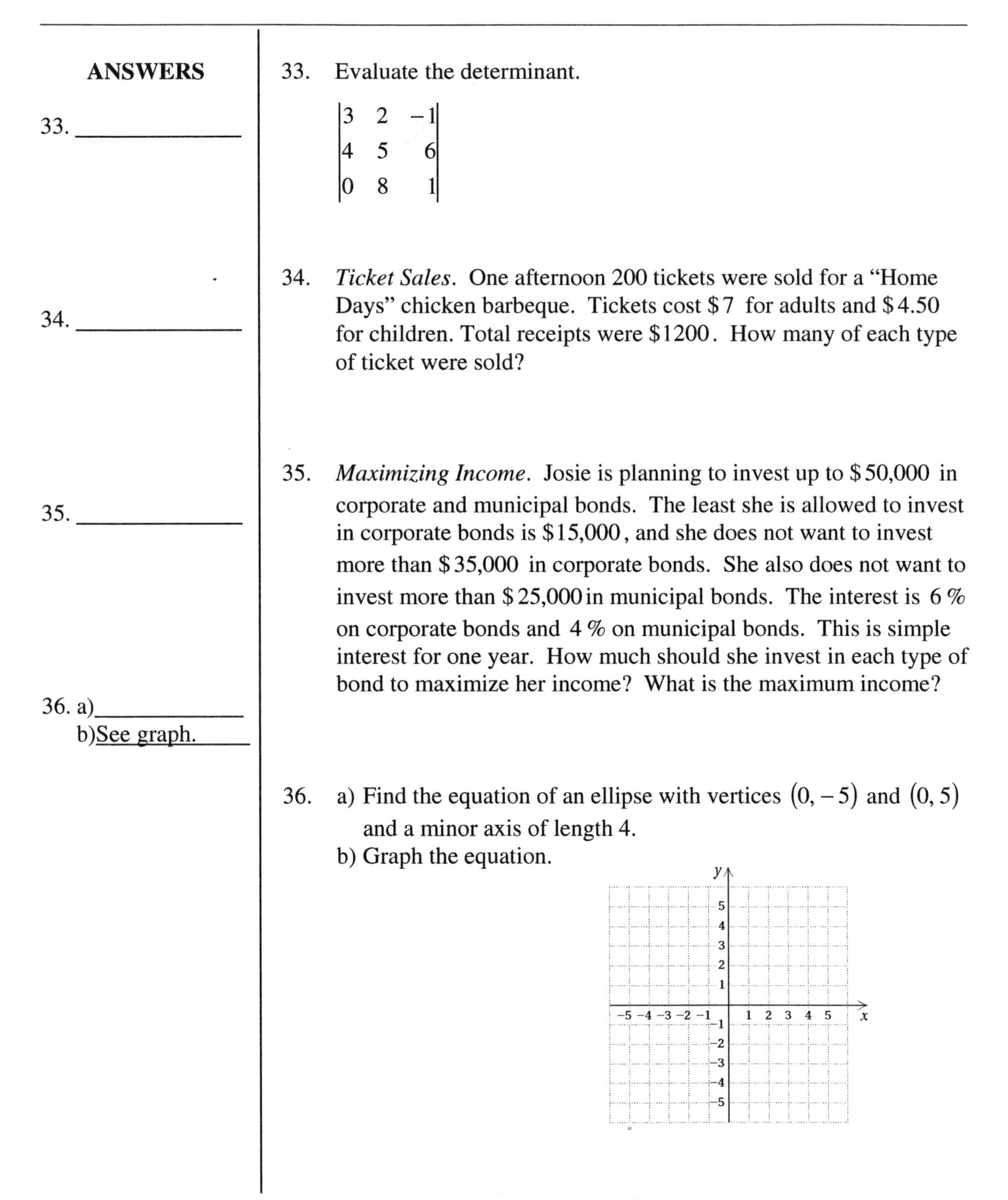

ANSWERS

33. ____________

34. ____________

35. ____________

36. a)____________
b)See graph.

33. Evaluate the determinant.

$$\begin{vmatrix} 3 & 2 & -1 \\ 4 & 5 & 6 \\ 0 & 8 & 1 \end{vmatrix}$$

34. *Ticket Sales.* One afternoon 200 tickets were sold for a "Home Days" chicken barbeque. Tickets cost \$7 for adults and \$4.50 for children. Total receipts were \$1200. How many of each type of ticket were sold?

35. *Maximizing Income.* Josie is planning to invest up to \$50,000 in corporate and municipal bonds. The least she is allowed to invest in corporate bonds is \$15,000, and she does not want to invest more than \$35,000 in corporate bonds. She also does not want to invest more than \$25,000 in municipal bonds. The interest is 6 % on corporate bonds and 4 % on municipal bonds. This is simple interest for one year. How much should she invest in each type of bond to maximize her income? What is the maximum income?

36. a) Find the equation of an ellipse with vertices $(0, -5)$ and $(0, 5)$ and a minor axis of length 4.
b) Graph the equation.

FINAL EXAMINATION **NAME**______________________________

TEST FORM D

ANSWERS

37. Find an equation of the parabola with focus $(0,3)$ and directrix $y=-3$.

38. Find the equation of a circle with center $(-2, 6)$ and radius 9.

39. Solve: $x^2+3y^2=37$,
$x^2-2y^2=17$.

40. Find the 20th term of the sequence $15, 12, 9, \ldots$.

41. Evaluate: $\sum_{k=1}^{4} \frac{(-1)^{k+1}}{k+2}$.

42. If $a_1=10$, and $a_{n+1}=\frac{1}{2}a_n+2$, find a_4.

43. *The Economic Multiplier*. The government is making a \$2,300,000 expenditure on a border crossing. If 60% of this is spent again, and so on, what is the total effect on the economy?

37. ______________

38. ______________

39. ______________

40. ______________

41. ______________

42. ______________

43. ______________

FINAL EXAMINATION **NAME**______________________

TEST FORM D

ANSWERS

44. ____________

45. ____________

46. ____________

47. ____________

48. ____________

49. ____________

50. ____________

44. Use mathematical induction to prove that for every natural number n, $1+4+7+\cdots+(3n-2)=\dfrac{n(3n-1)}{2}$.

45. Find: $\dbinom{6}{2}$.

46. Determine the number of subsets of a set containing 8 members.

47. *Set-up Crew.* There are 30 participants in a conference. In how many ways can a set-up crew of 4 people be chosen?

48. *Rolling Dice.* Suppose a 6-sided die is rolled. What is the probability that a number less than five is rolled?

---

49. Solve: $2^{2\sqrt{x}}=64^{4/3}$.

50. Find the domain of $f(x)=\dfrac{\sqrt{x+1}}{\sqrt{x-1}}$.

FINAL EXAMINATION NAME____________________________

TEST FORM E CLASS_____SCORE_____GRADE_____

1. Divide and simplify: $\dfrac{x^2-3x-10}{x^2-x-6} \div \dfrac{x^2-25}{x^2-10x+25}$.

   a) $\dfrac{(x-5)(x+5)}{(x-3)(x+2)}$ b) $\dfrac{(x-5)^2}{(x-3)(x+5)}$

   c) $\dfrac{(x+2)^2}{(x+1)(x+5)}$ d) $\dfrac{(x+2)}{(x-3)}$

2. Simplify: $\dfrac{\dfrac{x^2-y^2}{2x}}{\dfrac{x+y}{x^2}}$.

   a) $\dfrac{(x-y)(x+y)^2}{2x^3}$ b) $\dfrac{x(x-y)}{2}$

   c) $\dfrac{2}{x(x-y)}$ d) $\dfrac{x(x-y^2)}{2y}$

3. Simplify: $3\sqrt{18}+4\sqrt{50}$.

   a) $29\sqrt{2}$ b) $127\sqrt{2}$ c) $15\sqrt{2}$ d) 210

4. Which equation corresponds to the given graph?

   a) $y=3x-2$

   b) $y=-3x-2$

   c) $y=-2x-\dfrac{2}{3}$

   d) $y=-3x+2$

ANSWERS

1. ______________

2. ______________

3. ______________

4. ______________

FINAL EXAMINATION **NAME**____________________

TEST FORM E

ANSWERS

5. __________

6. __________

7. __________

8. __________

9. __________

10. __________

5. Calculate: $24 \div 2^3 + 1 + 4(5-3)$.

a) 12 b) 1737 c) 13 d) $\frac{48}{13}$

6. Given that $f(x) = 2x^2 + x - 5$, find $f(-3)$.

a) –26 b) –20 c) 16 d) 10

7. Write an equation for a line that passes through $(6, 5)$ and $(-4, 2)$.

a) $y = \frac{3}{2}x - 4$ b) $y = \frac{9}{4} - \frac{17}{2}$

c) $y = \frac{3}{10}x + \frac{16}{5}$ d) $y = \frac{10}{3}x - 15$

8. For the function $f(x) = -8 + 4x + 3x^2 - x^3$, find the leading coefficient.

a) 4 b) –8 c) 1 d) –1

9. Find the distance between $(3, -5)$ and $(-2, 1)$.

a) 11 b) $\sqrt{11}$ c) $\sqrt{61}$ d) $\sqrt{17}$

10. For $f(x) = x + 5$ and $g(x) = 3x + 1$, find the domain of $(f / g)x$.

a) $(-\infty, \infty)$ b) $\left(-\infty, -\frac{1}{3}\right) \cup \left(-\frac{1}{3}, \infty\right)$

c) $(-\infty, 5) \cup (5, \infty)$ d) $\left(-\infty, -\frac{1}{3}\right) \cup \left(-\frac{1}{3}, 5\right) \cup (5, \infty)$

FINAL EXAMINATION **NAME**____________________________

TEST FORM E

ANSWERS

11. ____________

12. ____________

13. ____________

14. ____________

15. ____________

11. Write an equation for a function that has the shape of $y = 4\sqrt{x}$, but shifted right 3 units and up 2 units.

a) $y = 4\sqrt{x-3} + 2$ b) $y = 4\sqrt{x+3} + 2$

c) $y = 4\sqrt{x+2} + 3$ d) $y = 4\sqrt{x+2} - 3$

12. Solve: $3m^2 + 2m + 1 = 0$

a) $\dfrac{-1 \pm \sqrt{2}}{3}$ b) $\dfrac{-2 \pm 2\sqrt{2}i}{3}$

c) $\dfrac{1}{3}, -1$ d) $\dfrac{-1 \pm \sqrt{2}i}{3}$

13. Solve: $-5 < 2x + 3 \le 4$.

a) $\left(-1, \dfrac{1}{2}\right]$ b) $(-\infty, -4) \cup \left[\dfrac{1}{2}, \infty\right)$

c) $\left(-4, \dfrac{1}{2}\right]$ d) $(-4, 2]$

14. Solve: $\dfrac{3-x}{x+2} \ge 1$.

a) $(-\infty, -2) \cup \left[\dfrac{1}{2}, \infty\right)$ b) $\left(-2, \dfrac{1}{2}\right]$

c) $\left[-2, \dfrac{1}{2}\right]$ d) $\left(-\infty, \dfrac{1}{2}\right]$

15. Simplify: $|2x - 5| < 4$.

a) $\left[\dfrac{1}{2}, \dfrac{9}{2}\right]$ b) $\left(-\infty, \dfrac{1}{2}\right) \cup \left(\dfrac{9}{2}, \infty\right)$

c) $\left(-\infty, \dfrac{9}{2}\right)$ d) $\left(\dfrac{1}{2}, \dfrac{9}{2}\right)$

FINAL EXAMINATION **NAME**________________________

TEST FORM E

ANSWERS

16. ____________

17. ____________

18. ____________

19. ____________

20. ____________

21. ____________

22. ____________

23. ____________

16. Simplify: $(4-3i)(5+i)$.
    a) $23-11i$ b) $9-2i$
    c) $17-11i$ d) $17-2i$

17. For the graph of the function $f(x)=3x^2+12x+17$, find the vertex.
    a) $(-2,-5)$ b) $(-4,17)$ c) $(2,53)$ d) $(-2,5)$

18. When P dollars is invested at interest rate i, compounded annually, for t years, the investment grows to A dollars, where $A=P(1+i)^t$. Find the interest rate i if \$1000 grows to \$1137.89 in 3 yr.
    a) 4.2% b) 4.4% c) 1.4% d) 4.7%

19. How many negative real zeros does Descartes' rule of signs indicate $f(x)=3x^5+x^4+2x^3+4x-4$ has?
    a) 2 or 0 b) 1 c) 5 d) 5 or 3 or 1

20. Find the quotient and remainder: $(6x^3-4x^2+3x-5)\div(x+2)$.
    a) $6x^2+8x+19$, R 33 b) $6x^2-16x-29$, R 53
    c) $6x^2-16x+35$, R -75 d) $6x^2-8x+19$, R -43

21. Use the rational zeros theorem to determine which number cannot be a zero of $P(x)=6x^4-3x^2-2x+2$.
    a) –3 b) $\frac{1}{3}$ c) 1 d) –1

22. Find the vertical asymptote: $f(x)=\frac{4-x}{2+x}$.
    a) $x=2$ b) $x=-2$ c) $x=-1$ d) $x=4$

23. Solve: $x^2+x-30\le 0$.
    a) $[-5,6]$ b) $(-\infty,-6]\cup[5,\infty)$
    c) $[-6,5]$ d) $(-\infty,-6)[5,\infty)$

FINAL EXAMINATION **NAME**____________________________

TEST FORM E

24. For $f(x)=2x^2$ and $g(x)=x+1$, find $(f \circ g)(x)$.
    a) $2x^2+2$ b) $2x^3+2x^2$
    c) $2x^2+1$ d) $2x^2+4x+2$

25. Find a formula for the inverse of $f(x)=4x+3$.
    a) $f^{-1}(x)=-4x-3$ b) $f^{-1}(x)=3x+4$
    c) $f^{-1}(x)=\frac{x}{4}-3$ d) $f^{-1}(x)=\frac{x-3}{4}$

26. Convert to an exponential equation: $\log x = 15$.
    a) $x=e^{15}$ b) $x=10^{15}$ c) $x=15^{10}$ d) $x^{15}=10$

27. Which of the following graphs illustrates the graph of $g(x)=\ln(x-4)$?
    a) b)

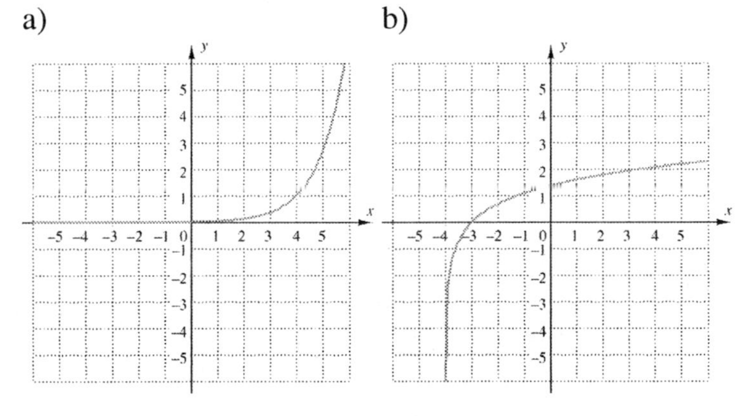

c) d)

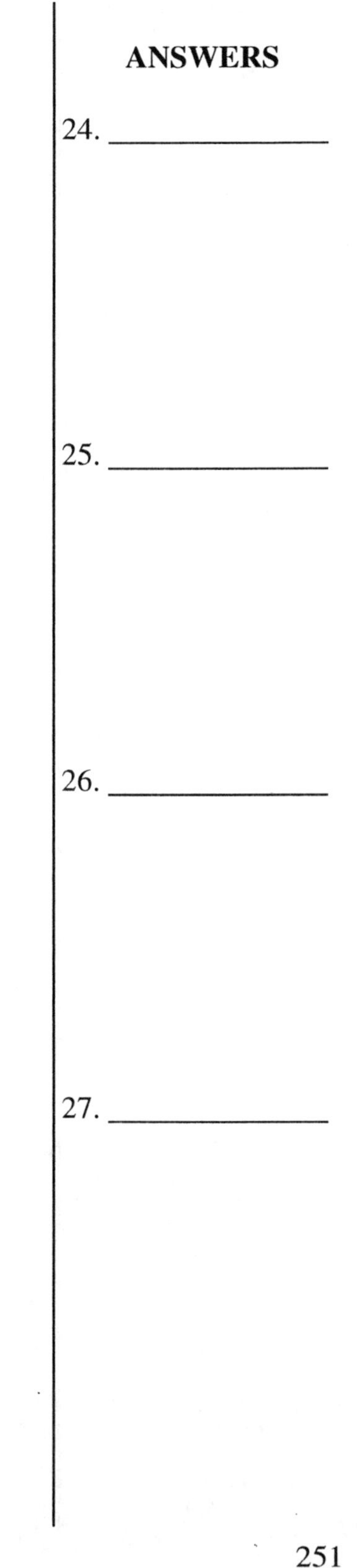

ANSWERS

24. ______________

25. ______________

26. ______________

27. ______________

FINAL EXAMINATION **NAME**____________________

TEST FORM E

ANSWERS

28. __________

29. __________

30. __________

31. __________

32. __________

33. __________

---

28. Solve: $4^x = 2^{3x-5}$.

a) $\frac{5}{2}$ b) 5 c) –5 d) $\frac{1}{5}$

29. Solve: $\log_2 x - \log_2(x+5) = -1$.

a) 5 b) $\frac{-5 \pm \sqrt{3}}{2}$

c) $-\frac{10}{3}$ d) –5

30. The population of a bacteria culture doubled in 8 hr. What was the exponential growth rate?

a) 5.5% b) 8.7% c) 3.8% d) 4.2%

31. Find the x-coordinate of the solution of $2x+4y=2$, $3x-2y=27$.

a) 7 b) –3 c) 3 d) 6

For Exercises 32 and 33, let $A = \begin{bmatrix} 3 & -2 \\ 5 & 4 \end{bmatrix}$ and $B = \begin{bmatrix} 4 & 8 & 6 \\ 0 & 1 & -3 \end{bmatrix}$.

32. Find AB.

a) $\begin{bmatrix} 12 & -16 & 6 \\ 0 & 4 & -3 \end{bmatrix}$ b) $\begin{bmatrix} 0 & -11 & -45 \\ 0 & 52 & 11 \end{bmatrix}$

c) $\begin{bmatrix} 12 & 22 & 24 \\ 20 & 44 & 18 \end{bmatrix}$ d) Not possible

33. Find $-3A$.

a) $\begin{bmatrix} \frac{6}{11} & \frac{3}{11} \\ -\frac{15}{22} & \frac{9}{22} \end{bmatrix}$ b) $\begin{bmatrix} 0 & -5 \\ 2 & 1 \end{bmatrix}$

c) $\begin{bmatrix} -9 & 6 \\ -15 & -12 \end{bmatrix}$ d) Not possible

FINAL EXAMINATION **NAME**____________________________

TEST FORM E

ANSWERS

34. Evaluate the determinant.

$$\begin{vmatrix} 4 & -1 & 0 \\ 1 & 3 & -5 \\ -2 & 4 & 2 \end{vmatrix}$$

a) 92 b) 112 c) –42 d) 96

34. ____________

35. *Tickets*. Admission to Jefferson County Field Days costs \$7 for adults and \$4 for children. One day \$730 was collected in admissions for 142 individuals. How many children attended?
a) 54 b) 71 c) 88 d) 41

35. ____________

36. Find one of the partial fractions when $\frac{-2x-22}{x^2-2x-8}$ is decomposed.

a) $\frac{5}{x-4}$ b) $\frac{3}{x-2}$ c) $\frac{3}{x+2}$ d) $\frac{5}{x+4}$

36. ____________

37. Which graph represents $4x^2+9y^2=36$?

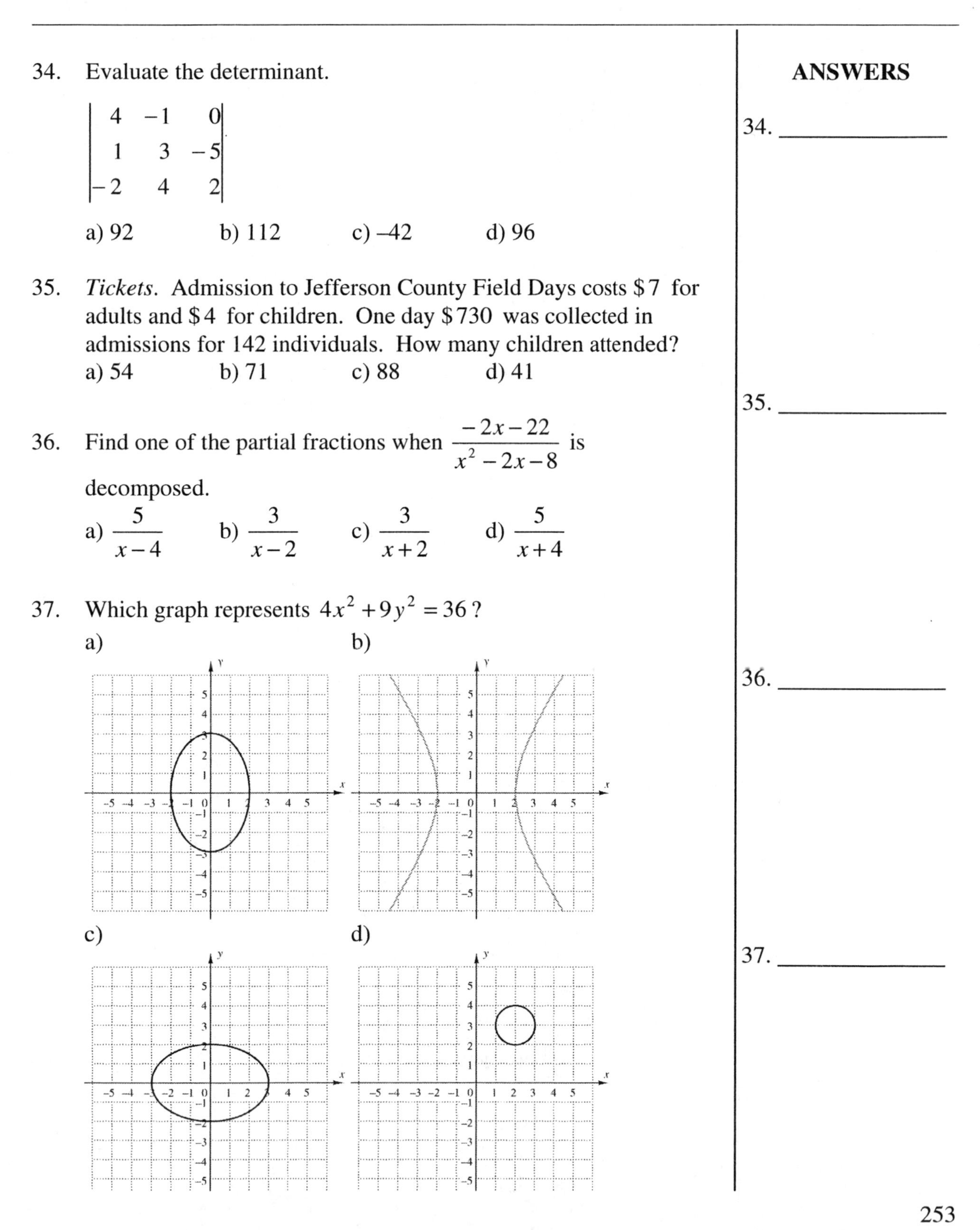

37. ____________

FINAL EXAMINATION **NAME**_______________

TEST FORM E

ANSWERS

38. ___________

39. ___________

40. ___________

41. ___________

38. Find the center and radius of the circle given by
$x^2 + y^2 - 4x + 16y + 52 = 0$.

a) $(2, -8); 2$ b) $(2, -8); 4$

c) $(-2, 8); 4$ d) $(2, -8); 16$

39. *Field Microphone*. A field microphone used at a baseball game has a parabolic cross-section and is 20 in. deep. The focus is 6 in. from the vertex. Find the width of the microphone at the opening.

a) About 42 in. b) About 4 in.

c) About 44 in. d) About 22 in.

40. Find an equation of the ellipse having vertices $(-7, 0)$ and $(7, 0)$ with minor axis of length 8.

a) $\frac{x^2}{49} + \frac{y^2}{16} = 1$ b) $\frac{x^2}{64} + \frac{y^2}{49} = 1$

c) $\frac{x^2}{16} + \frac{y^2}{49} = 1$ d) $\frac{x^2}{2} + \frac{y^2}{49} = 1$

41. Find the greater of the x-coordinates of the solutions of
$7x + y = 2$,
$xy = -24$.

a) 14 b) -12 c) 2 d) $-\frac{12}{7}$

FINAL EXAMINATION **NAME**________________

TEST FORM E

ANSWERS

42. For the sequence whose nth term is $a_n = (-1)^{n+1}(2n+5)$, find a_{17}.

a) 170 b) 44 c) 39 d) –39

42. ____________

43. Find the sum of the first 50 terms of the series $\frac{1}{3}+\frac{2}{3}+1+\cdots$.

a) 425 b) 850 c) $\frac{1300}{3}$ d) $\frac{1250}{3}$

43. ____________

44. Find the sum, if it exists: $\frac{1}{8}+\frac{1}{4}+\frac{1}{2}+\cdots$.

a) 2 b) 200 c) 1 d) Does not exist

44. ____________

45. Evaluate the statement: $n^2 > n$, for $n = 1, 2, 3, \ldots$.

a) It is sometimes true.
b) It is never true.
c) It is always true.
d) It is not possible to evaluate.

45. ____________

46. Find $\binom{9}{2}$.

a) $4\frac{1}{2}$ b) 72 c) 181,440 d) 36

46. ____________

47. A class has 12 boys and 8 girls. How many ways can a committee be chosen that has 2 boys and 2 girls?

a) 4 b) 384 c) 1848 d) 4845

47. ____________

FINAL EXAMINATION **NAME**______________________________

TEST FORM E

ANSWERS

48. ______________

49. ______________

50. ______________

48. A marble is randomly drawn from a bag containing 5 white marbles, 4 red marbles, and 3 blue marbles. What is the probability that a red or a blue marble is drawn?

    a) $\frac{1}{3}$ b) $\frac{7}{12}$ c) $\frac{1}{2}$ d) $\frac{7}{9}$

---

49. Find the domain of $f(x) = \log_5(x+3)$.

    a) $(-\infty, -3)$ b) $(-\infty, 3)$ c) $(-3, \infty)$ d) $(3, \infty)$

50. Suppose $\log_b x = 4$. Find $\log_b\left(\frac{1}{x}\right)$.

    a) –4 b) $\frac{1}{4}$ c) $-\frac{1}{4}$ d) 4

FINAL EXAMINATION NAME______________________________

TEST FORM F CLASS_____SCORE_____GRADE_____

ANSWERS

1. Rationalize the denominator: $\frac{6+\sqrt{3}}{\sqrt{6}}$.

a) $\sqrt{6}+3\sqrt{2}$ b) $\frac{11}{2\sqrt{6}-\sqrt{2}}$

c) $\frac{2\sqrt{6}+\sqrt{2}}{2}$ d) $\frac{1+\sqrt{2}}{6}$

1. ______________

2. Subtract and simplify: $\frac{x+1}{x-2}-\frac{x+3}{x}$.

a) 1 b) $\frac{x+2x-3}{x(x-2)}$

c) $\frac{-2}{x(x-2)}$ d) $\frac{6}{x(x-2)}$

2. ______________

3. Multiply: $(3x-4)^2$.

a) $9x^2-16$ b) $9x^2-12x+16$

c) $9x^2-24x-16$ d) $9x^2-24x+16$

3. ______________

4. Which equation corresponds to the given graph?

a) $y=x^2+4$

b) $y=-4x^2$

c) $y=-x^2-4$

d) $y=-x^2+4$

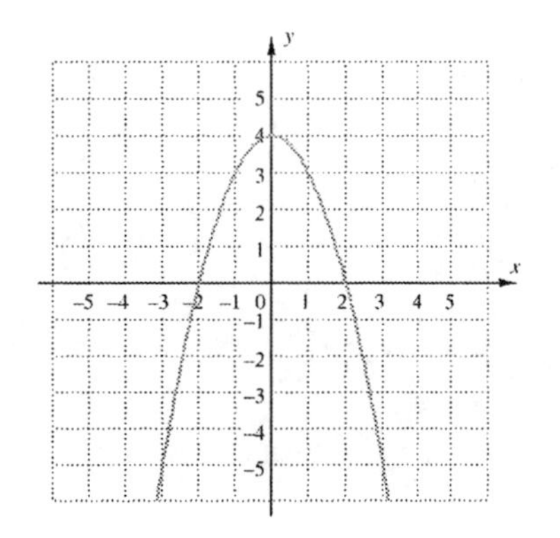

4. ______________

FINAL EXAMINATION **NAME**____________________________

TEST FORM F

ANSWERS

5. ____________

6. ____________

7. ____________

8. ____________

5. Find the domain of the function $f(x)=\dfrac{4x-12}{x^2-4x-5}$.

a) $(-\infty,0)\cup(0,\infty)$
b) $(-\infty,-1)\cup(-1,5)\cup(5,\infty)$
c) $(-\infty,-5)\cup(-5,1)\cup(1,\infty)$
d) $(-\infty,-1)\cup(-1,3)\cup(3,5)\cup(5,\infty)$

6. Given that $f(x)=(3x-1)^2$, find $f(a+2)$.

a) $9a^2+6a+1$ b) $9a+25$
c) $9a^2+30a+25$ d) $9a^2+15a+25$

7. Which of the following represents the graph of $f(x)=|x+2|-4$?

a) b) c) d)

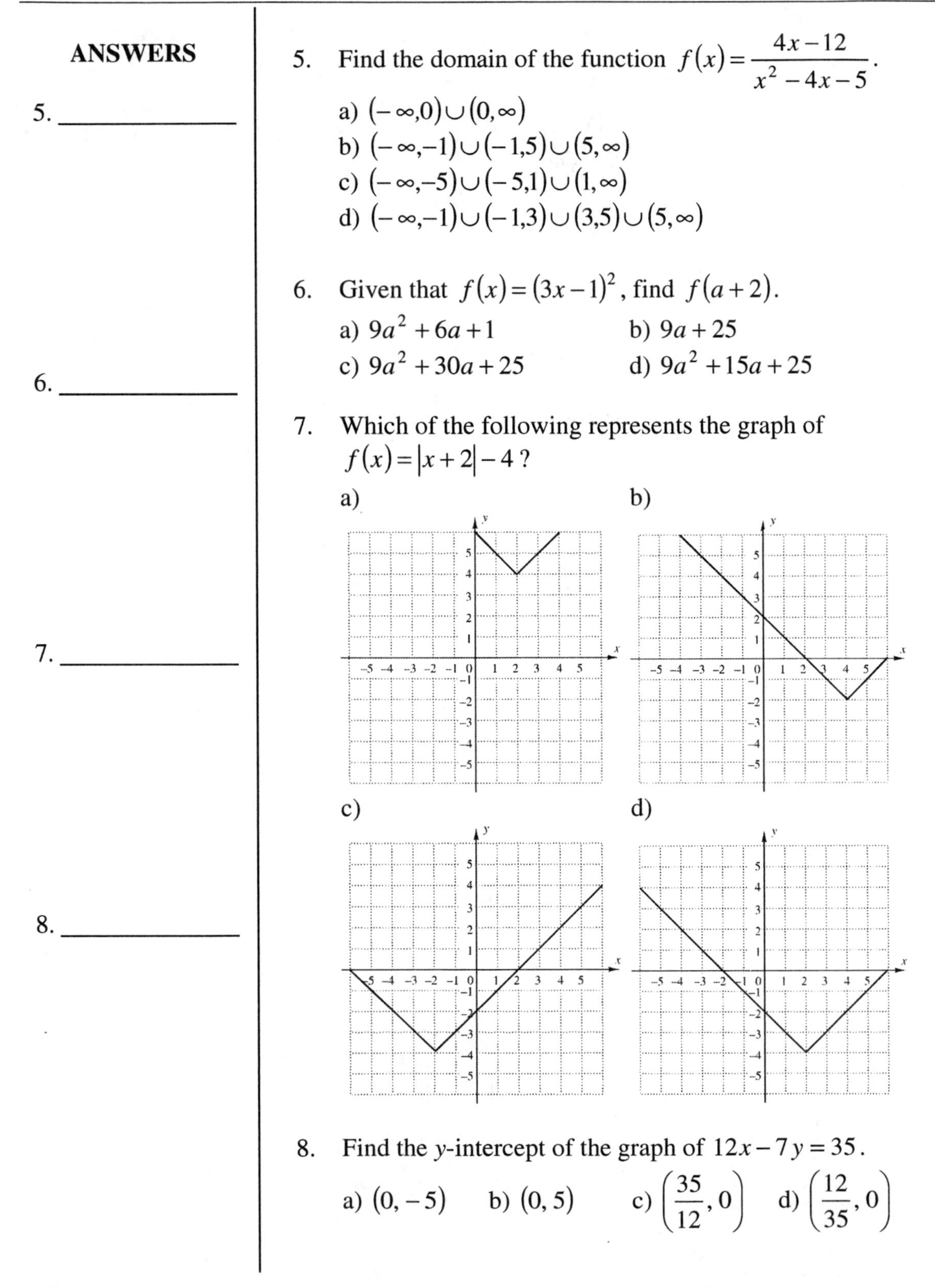

8. Find the y-intercept of the graph of $12x-7y=35$.

a) $(0,-5)$ b) $(0,5)$ c) $\left(\dfrac{35}{12},0\right)$ d) $\left(\dfrac{12}{35},0\right)$

FINAL EXAMINATION **NAME**________________________

TEST FORM F

---

9. Which of the following functions is even?
   a) $f(x)=2x^3-5x$ b) $f(x)=2x^4-4x^2-8x$
   c) $f(x)=|x|$ d) $f(x)=2x$

10. Which of the following functions is symmetric with respect to the origin?
   a) $f(x)=\sqrt{x}$ b) $f(x)=x^3+x$
   c) $f(x)=x^2-5$ d) $f(x)=|x+2|$

11. Solve: $3y^2-y-10=0$.
   a) $-\frac{3}{5}, 2$ b) $-2, \frac{3}{5}$ c) $-2, \frac{5}{3}$ d) $-\frac{5}{3}, 2$

12. Solve: $|n-3|\geq 5$.
   a) $[8, \infty)$ b) $(-\infty, -2]\cup[8, \infty)$
   c) $[-2, 8]$ d) $(-\infty, -2)\cup(8, \infty)$

13. Solve: $\frac{x}{3-x}\leq 6$.
   a) $\left(-\infty, \frac{18}{7}\right]$ b) $\left[\frac{18}{7}, 3\right)$
   c) $\left(-\infty, \frac{7}{18}\right]\cup(3, \infty)$ d) $\left(-\infty, \frac{18}{7}\right]\cup(3, \infty)$

14. Solve: $x^2-5x-2=0$.
   a) $\frac{5\pm\sqrt{33}}{2}$ b) $\frac{5\pm\sqrt{17}}{2}$
   c) $\frac{-5\pm 3\sqrt{3}}{2}$ d) $\frac{5\pm\sqrt{13}}{2}$

15. Simplify: i^{60}.
   a) –1 b) 1 c) i d) $-i$

ANSWERS

9. ____________

10. ____________

11. ____________

12. ____________

13. ____________

14. ____________

15. ____________

FINAL EXAMINATION **NAME**________________________

TEST FORM F

ANSWERS

16. ____________

17. ____________

18. ____________

19. ____________

20. ____________

21. ____________

22. ____________

16. Multiply: $(2+i)(3-i)$.
a) $7+i$ b) 7 c) $5+i$ d) $7-i$

17. For the graph of the function $f(x)=2x^2+12x+22$, find the vertex.
a) $(-4, 3)$ b) $(3, 4)$ c) $(-3, 4)$ d) $(3, -4)$

18. Find an equation of variation in which y varies inversely as x, and $y=8$ when $x=12$.
a) $y=\frac{96}{x}$ b) $y=\frac{2}{3}x$
c) $y=\frac{x}{96}$ d) $y=\frac{3}{2}x$

19. For $f(x)=-3x^3-2x^2+5x+5$, use the intermediate value theorem to determine which interval contains a zero of f.
a) between –2 and –1 b) between –1 and 0
c) between 0 and 1 d) between 1 and 2

20. Find the quotient and remainder: $(4x^3-5x^2+3x-2)\div(x-3)$.
a) $4x^2-17x+54$, R -164
b) $4x^2+17x+54$, R 160
c) $4x^2+7x+24$, R 70
d) $4x^2+7x+24$, R 25

21. Suppose that a polynomial function of degree 5 with rational coefficients has $-2, -\sqrt{3}$, and $5+i$ as zeros. Find one other zero.
a) 2 b) $-5+i$ c) $\sqrt{3}i$ d) $5-i$

22. Find a vertical asymptote of: $f(x)=\frac{49x^2-16}{3x^2-16x-12}$.
a) $x=\frac{4}{3}$ b) $x=\frac{2}{3}$ c) $x=0$ d) $x=6$

FINAL EXAMINATION **NAME**____________________________

TEST FORM F

23. Solve: $x^2 - 5x + 6 > 0$.

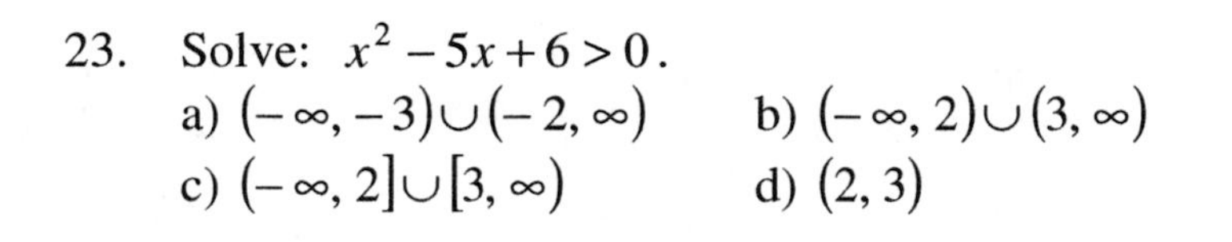

a) $(-\infty, -3) \cup (-2, \infty)$ b) $(-\infty, 2) \cup (3, \infty)$
c) $(-\infty, 2] \cup [3, \infty)$ d) $(2, 3)$

24. For $f(x) = x^2$ and $g(x) = x - 5$, find $(f \circ g)(x)$.

a) $x^2 - 5$ b) $x^3 - 5x^2$
c) $x^2 - 10x + 25$ d) $x^2 - 25$

25. Determine which of the following functions is one-to-one.

a) b)

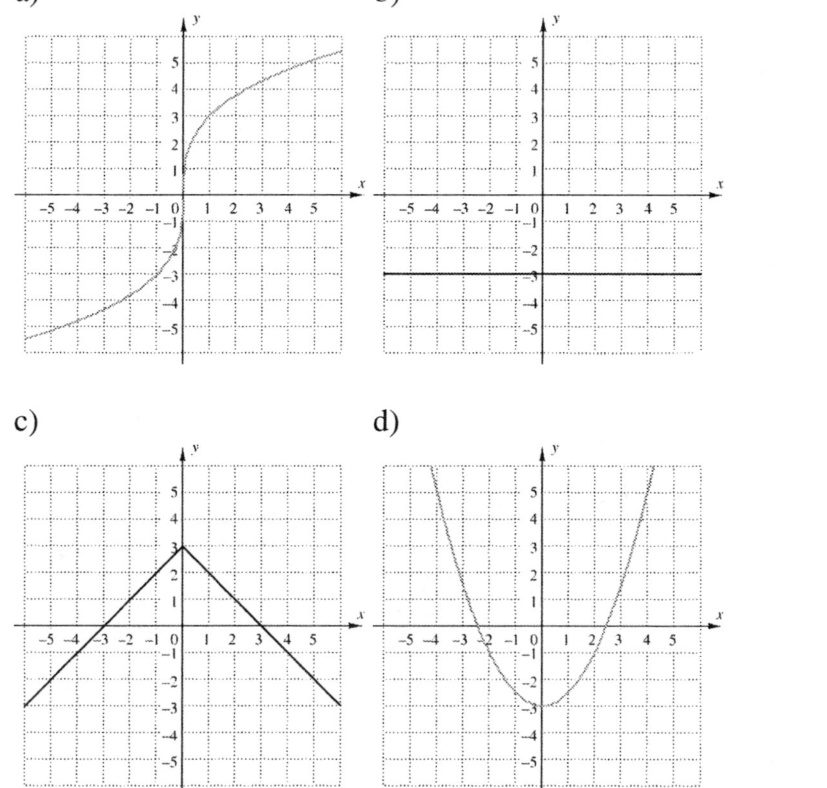

c) d)

ANSWERS

23. ______________

24. ______________

25. ______________

FINAL EXAMINATION NAME______________________________

TEST FORM F

ANSWERS

26. ______________

27. ______________

28. ______________

29. ______________

26. Convert to a logarithmic equation: $e^{3x} = 12$.

    a) $\log 12 = 3x$ b) $\ln 3x = 12$
    c) $x = 3\ln 12$ d) $\ln 12 = 3x$

27. Which of the following graphs illustrates the graph of $g(x) = -e^x + 1$?

    a) b)
    c) d)

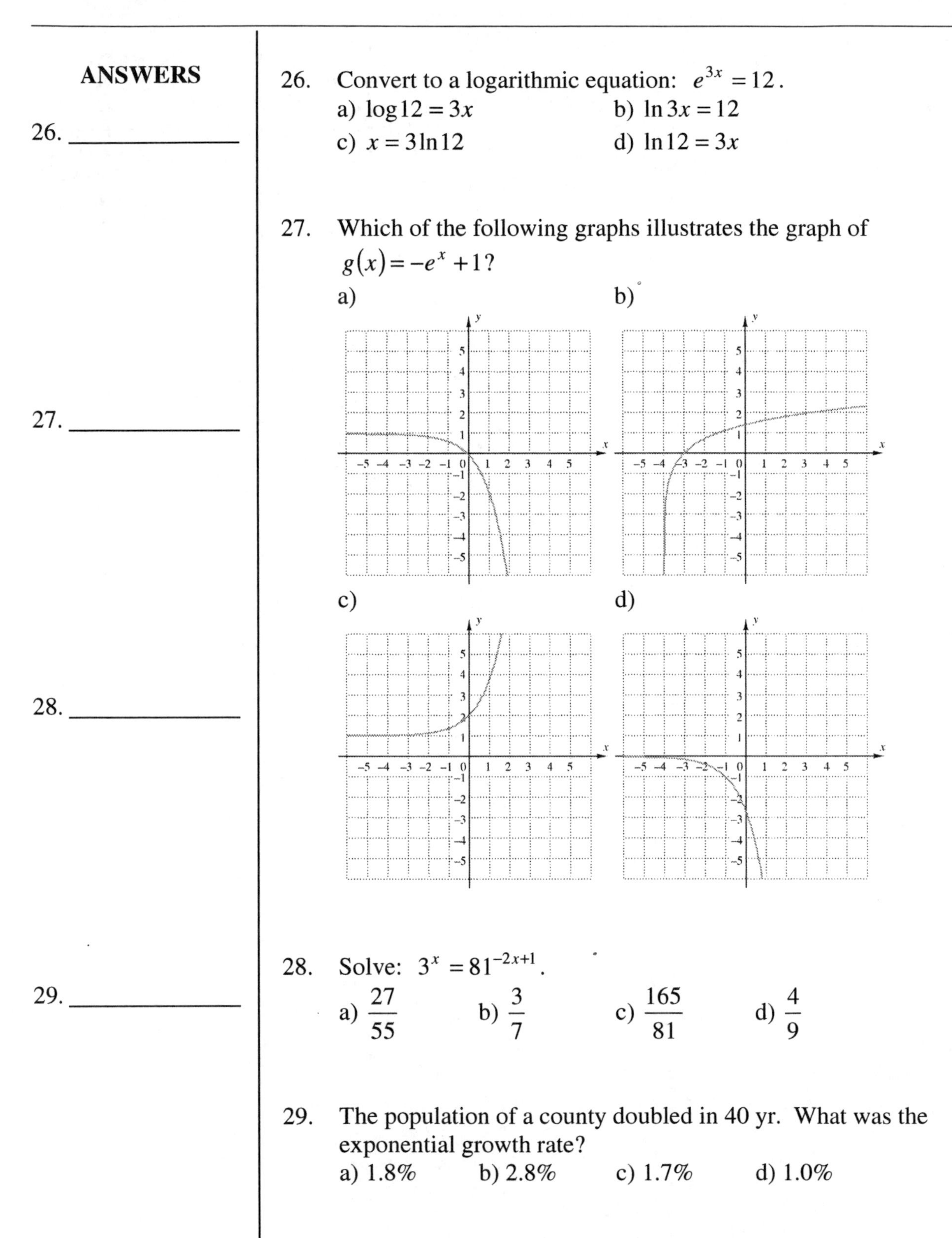

28. Solve: $3^x = 81^{-2x+1}$.

    a) $\frac{27}{55}$ b) $\frac{3}{7}$ c) $\frac{165}{81}$ d) $\frac{4}{9}$

29. The population of a county doubled in 40 yr. What was the exponential growth rate?

    a) 1.8% b) 2.8% c) 1.7% d) 1.0%

FINAL EXAMINATION **NAME**________________________

TEST FORM F

ANSWERS

30. Suppose \$1200 is invested at interest rate k, compounded continuously, and grows to \$1366.59 in 5 yr. Find the interest rate.
a) 1.1% b) 2.8% c) 2.6% d) 1.4%

31. Find the y-coordinate of the solution of $2x-3y=16$, $3x+4y=7$.
a) –2 b) 3 c) –3 d) 5

For Exercises 32 and 33, let $A=\begin{bmatrix}2 & 0\\ -4 & 3\end{bmatrix}$, $B=\begin{bmatrix}-6 & 4 & 7\\ -1 & -2 & 5\end{bmatrix}$, and $C=\begin{bmatrix}5 & -4 & 8\\ -1 & 6 & 0\end{bmatrix}$.

32. Find A^{-1}.

a) $\begin{bmatrix}-\frac{1}{2} & 1\\ 4 & -\frac{1}{3}\end{bmatrix}$ b) $\begin{bmatrix}\frac{1}{2} & 0\\ \frac{2}{3} & \frac{1}{3}\end{bmatrix}$

c) $\begin{bmatrix}3 & 0\\ -4 & 2\end{bmatrix}$ d) Not possible

33. Find $C-B$.

a) $\begin{bmatrix}11 & -8 & 1\\ 0 & 8 & -5\end{bmatrix}$ b) $\begin{bmatrix}-1 & 0 & 15\\ -2 & 4 & 5\end{bmatrix}$

c) $\begin{bmatrix}101 & 33\\ 33 & 30\end{bmatrix}$ d) Not possible

34. Evaluate the determinant.

$$\begin{vmatrix}3 & -1 & 0\\ 4 & 2 & -5\\ 1 & -2 & 6\end{vmatrix}$$

a) –13 b) 95 c) 47 d) 35

30. ____________

31. ____________

32. ____________

33. ____________

34. ____________

FINAL EXAMINATION **NAME**______________________

TEST FORM F

ANSWERS

35. ____________

36. ____________

37. ____________

38. ____________

35. *Investment.* Thomas inherited \$10,000 and invested it in two treasury bonds which pay 4% and 5% simple interest. The annual interest is \$435. Find the amount invested at 5%.
a) \$6500 b) \$5000 c) \$10,000 d) \$3500

36. Find the maximum value of $F = 7y - 4x$ subject to
$$x + y \le 8,$$
$$4x - 3y \le 12,$$
$$x \ge 0,$$
$$y \ge 0.$$
a) 56 b) 21 c) 68 d) 12

37. Find the equation of the figure shown in the graph.

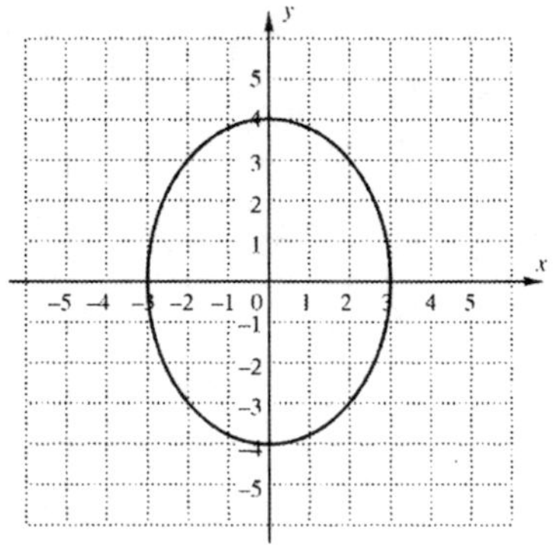

a) $16x^2 - 9y^2 = 144$ b) $4x^2 + 3y^2 = 12$
c) $16x^2 + 9y^2 = 144$ d) $9x^2 + 16y^2 = 144$

38. Find the center and radius of the circle given by $x^2 + y^2 - 8x + 4y + 15 = 0$.
a) $(-4, 2); \sqrt{5}$ b) $(4, -2); \sqrt{5}$
c) $(4, -2); 5$ d) $(4, -2); 3$

FINAL EXAMINATION **NAME**____________________________

TEST FORM F

ANSWERS

39. Find an equation of a parabola with focus $(0,5)$ and directrix $y=-5$.

a) $x^2=20y$ b) $x=20y$

c) $y^2=20x$ d) $y^2=-20x$

39. ____________

40. Find an asymptote of the hyperbola given by $\frac{(x-1)^2}{4}-\frac{(y+2)^2}{9}=1$.

a) $y=-\frac{3}{2}x$ b) $y=\frac{2}{3}x-\frac{8}{3}$

c) $y=\frac{2}{3}x+\frac{7}{2}$ d) $y=\frac{3}{2}x-\frac{7}{2}$

40. ____________

41. ____________

41. Find the least y-coordinate of the solution(s) of $x+y^2=10$, $x^2-2y^2=4$.

a) –4 b) –6 c) 4 d) –2

42. If $a_1=5$ and $a_{n+1}=-4a_n+3$, find a_5.

a) –17 b) –12,497 c) 1127 d) –4505

42. ____________

43. The first term of an arithmetic sequence is –2 and the 15th term is 82. Find the 9th term.

a) 6 b) $43\frac{5}{7}$ c) $48\frac{2}{5}$ d) 46

43. ____________

44. *A Daily Tripling Salary.* Suppose someone offered you a job for 10 days under the following conditions. You will be paid $5 for the first day, $15 for the second, and $45 for the third, and so on, tripling your previous day's salary each day. How much would you earn altogether?

a) $1500 b) $147,620 c) $49,205 d) $16,400

44. ____________

FINAL EXAMINATION **NAME**____________________

TEST FORM F

ANSWERS

45. __________

46. __________

47. __________

48. __________

49. __________

50. __________

45. Find S_{k+1}, the $(k+1)^{\text{st}}$ statement in the mathematical induction proof of $6+12+18+\cdots+6n=3n(n+1)$, for $n=1,2,3,\ldots$.

a) $6(k+1)=6k+6$

b) $6+12+18+\cdots+(6k+1)=3k^2+9k+6$

c) $6+12+18+\cdots+6(k+1)=3k^2+9k+1$

d) $6+12+18+\cdots+6(k+1)=3k^2+9k+6$

46. Find: ${}_{12}C_7$.

a) 3,991,680 b) 120
c) 792 d) 95,040

47. A class has 4 boys and 12 girls. How many ways can a team of 1 boy and 3 girls be chosen?

a) 224 b) 5280 c) 6912 d) 880

48. *Card Drawing*. A card is drawn from a well-shuffled standard deck of 52 cards. What is the probability that a black face card (jack, queen, or king) is chosen?

a) $\frac{3}{13}$ b) $\frac{3}{26}$ c) $\frac{1}{2}$ d) $\frac{1}{13}$

---

49. Solve: $\log_5|x+2|=3$.

a) –127, 123 b) –17, 13
c) 123 d) 13

50. Three solutions of the equation $Ax-By-Cz-5=0$ are $(2,4,-1)$, $(3,6,-2)$, and $(-2,-9,-4)$. Find C.

a) –1 b) –5 c) 7 d) 5

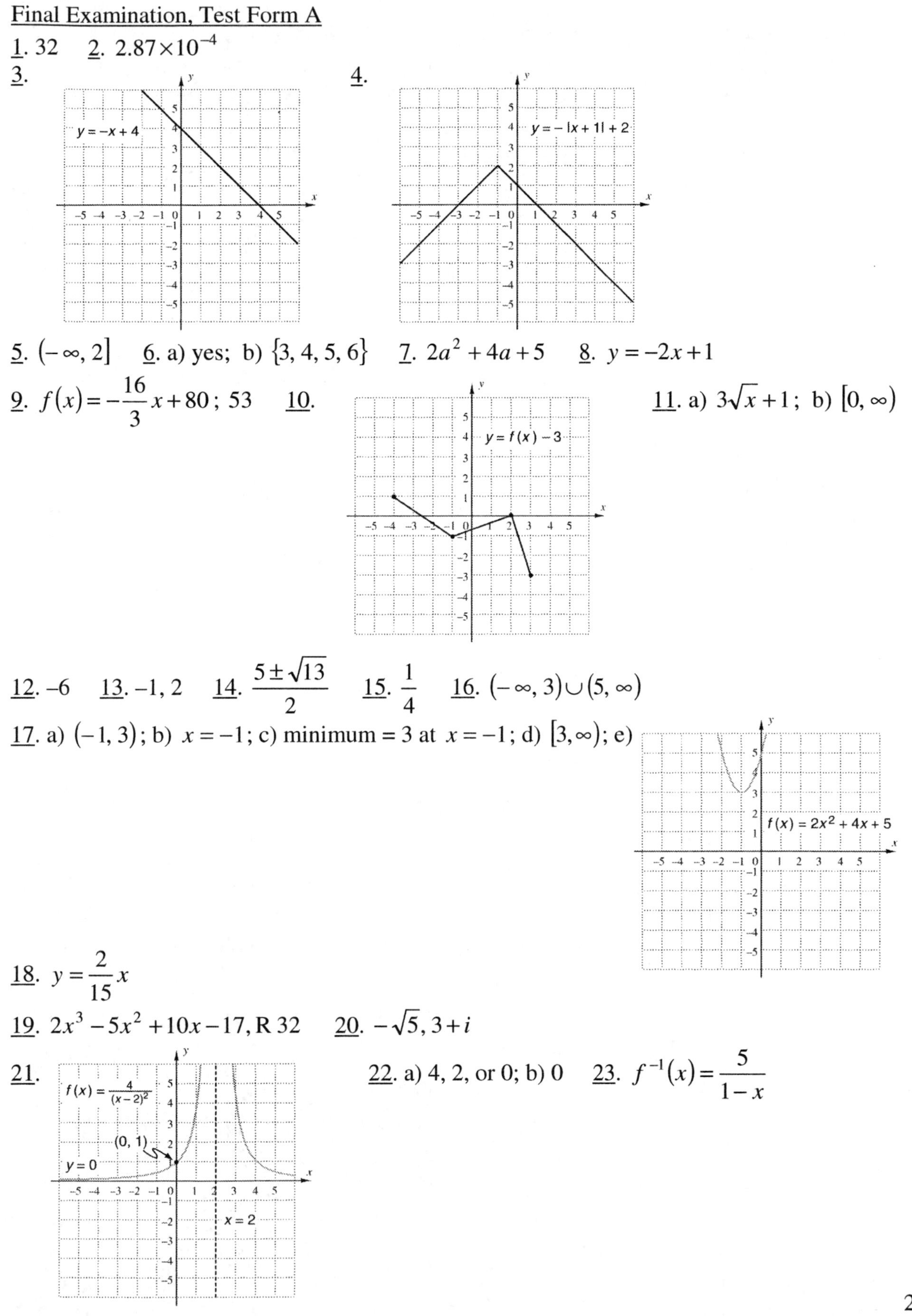

Final Examination, Test Form A

1. 32   2. 2.87×10^{-4}

3.

4.

5. $(-\infty, 2]$ 6. a) yes; b) $\{3, 4, 5, 6\}$ 7. $2a^2+4a+5$ 8. $y=-2x+1$

9. $f(x)=-\dfrac{16}{3}x+80$; 53   10.

11. a) $3\sqrt{x}+1$; b) $[0, \infty)$

12. –6   13. –1, 2   14. $\dfrac{5\pm\sqrt{13}}{2}$ 15. $\dfrac{1}{4}$ 16. $(-\infty, 3)\cup(5, \infty)$

17. a) $(-1, 3)$; b) $x=-1$; c) minimum = 3 at $x=-1$; d) $[3,\infty)$; e)

18. $y=\dfrac{2}{15}x$

19. $2x^3-5x^2+10x-17$, R 32   20. $-\sqrt{5}, 3+i$

21.

22. a) 4, 2, or 0; b) 0   23. $f^{-1}(x)=\dfrac{5}{1-x}$

24. 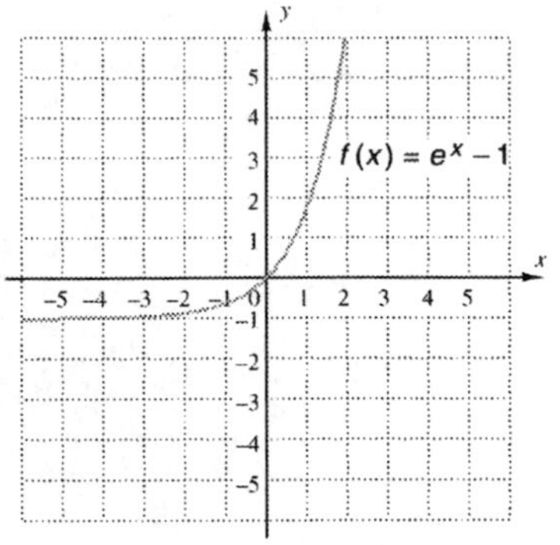

25. $\frac{1}{3}, 4$ 26. $x = 10^8$ 27. 1.2925 28. 11.6%

29. $(-5, 2)$ 30. $(4, 0, -6)$ 31. $\begin{bmatrix} 3 & 2 & 25 \\ -17 & -4 & 27 \end{bmatrix}$

32. $\begin{bmatrix} \frac{5}{22} & -\frac{3}{22} \\ \frac{2}{11} & \frac{1}{11} \end{bmatrix}$ 33. 0

34. 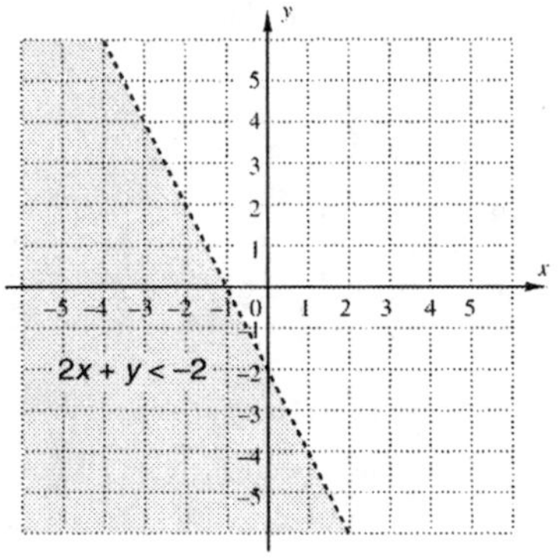

35. Maximum = 140 at $\left(\frac{26}{3}, 10\right)$; minimum = 5 at $(0, 5)$

36. 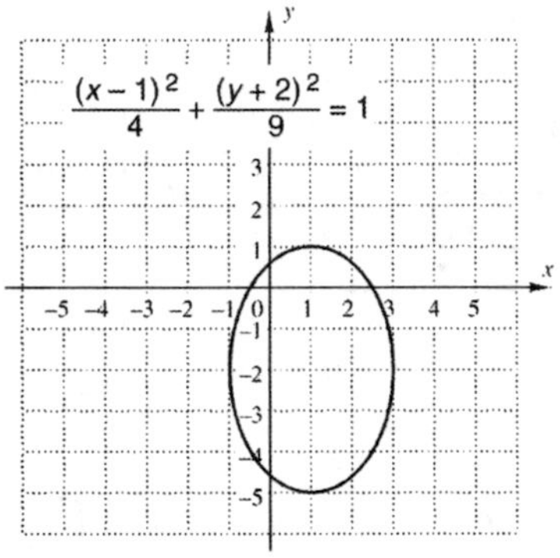

37. $y = \pm\frac{2\sqrt{5}}{5}x$ 38. $(-4, 5)$; 8 39. $(-3, -2)$, $\left(-\frac{207}{91}, \frac{214}{91}\right)$ 40. 2.25

41. $-1 + 4 + (-7) + 10 + (-13) = -7$ 42. -23 43. \$62,352.16

44. $S_n: 4 + 8 + 12 + \cdots + 4n = 2n(n+1)$

$S_1: 4 = 2 \cdot 1(1+1)$

$S_k: 4 + 8 + 12 + \cdots + 4k = 2k(k+1)$

$S_{k+1}: 4 + 8 + 12 + \cdots + 4k + 4(k+1) = 2(k+1)[(k+1)+1]$

1. Basis step: $4 = 2 \cdot 1(1+1) = 2 \cdot 2 = 4$ is true.
2. Induction step: Assume S_k is true. Deduce S_{k+1}.

$$\begin{aligned} 4 + 8 + 12 + \cdots + 4k &= 2k(k+1) \\ 4 + 8 + 12 + \cdots + 4k + 4(k+1) &= 2k(k+1) + 4(k+1) \\ &= 2k^2 + 2k + 4k + 4 \\ &= 2k^2 + 6k + 4 \\ &= 2(k+1)(k+2) \\ &= 2(k+1)[(k+1)+1] \end{aligned}$$

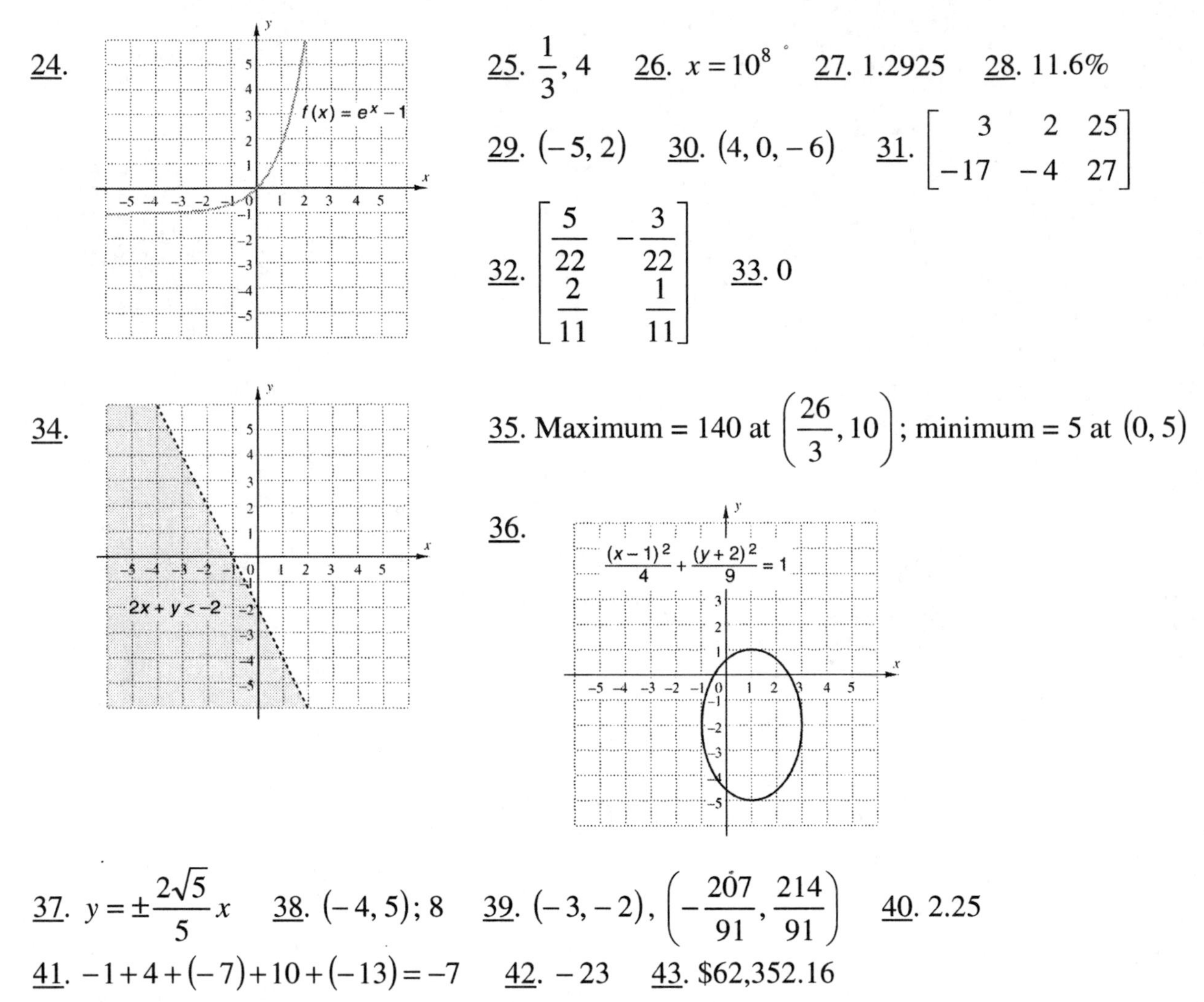

Final Examination, Test Form A (continued)

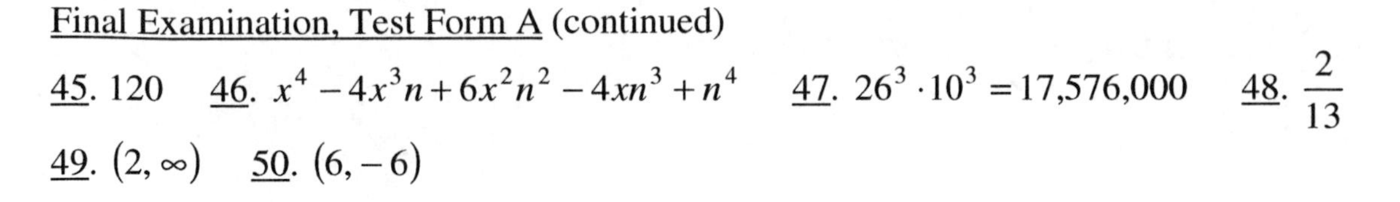

45. 120   46. $x^4 - 4x^3n + 6x^2n^2 - 4xn^3 + n^4$ 47. $26^3 \cdot 10^3 = 17{,}576{,}000$ 48. $\frac{2}{13}$

49. $(2, \infty)$ 50. $(6, -6)$

Final Examination, Test Form B

1. 28   2. $-22\sqrt{6}$

3.   4.

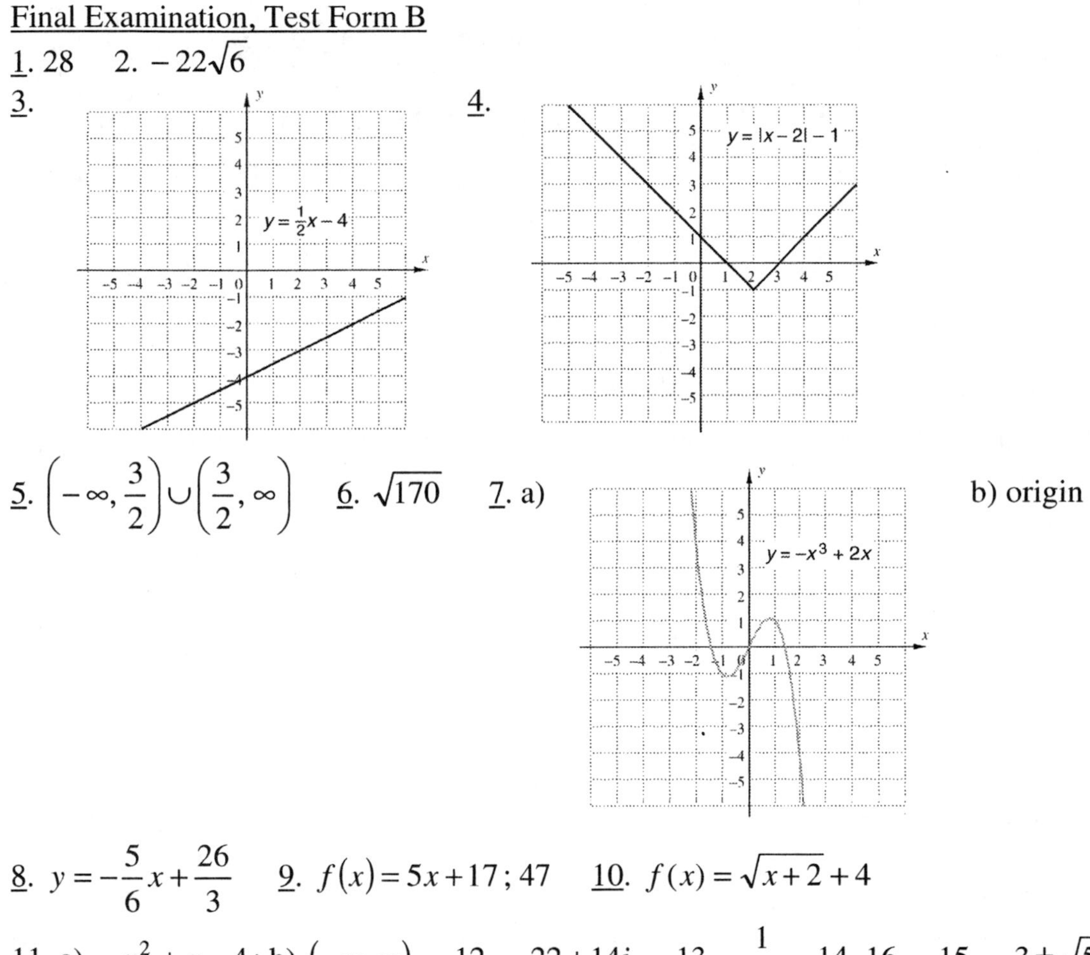

5. $\left(-\infty, \frac{3}{2}\right) \cup \left(\frac{3}{2}, \infty\right)$ 6. $\sqrt{170}$ 7. a)   b) origin

8. $y = -\frac{5}{6}x + \frac{26}{3}$ 9. $f(x) = 5x + 17$; 47   10. $f(x) = \sqrt{x+2} + 4$

11. a) $-x^2 + x - 4$; b) $(-\infty, \infty)$ 12. $-22 + 14i$ 13. $-\frac{1}{2}$ 14. 16   15. $-3 \pm \sqrt{5}$

16. $\left[-2, \frac{9}{4}\right)$

17. a) $(2,4)$; b) $x = 2$; c) maximum $= 4$; d) $(-\infty, 4]$; e)

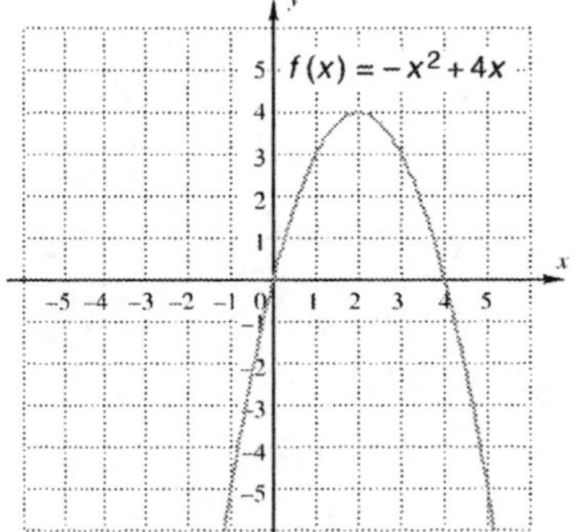

Final Examination, Test Form B (continued)

18. $5\frac{1}{4}$ laps 19. Not possible 20. $6x^2+x-1$, R 4 21. $f(x)=\dfrac{-36}{(x-3)(x+6)}$

22. a) 3 or 1; b) 2 or 0 23. Yes

24.

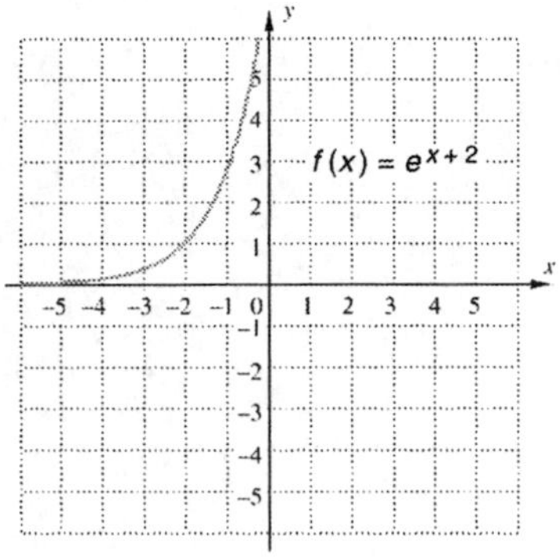

25. $-\dfrac{6}{11}$ 26. $e^{0.1}\approx 1.1052$ 27. 0.86135

28. a) 5.8%; b) 12.0 yr 29. No solution 30. $\left(-1, 6, \frac{1}{2}\right)$

31. Not possible 32. $\begin{bmatrix} -\frac{5}{2} & \frac{3}{2} \\ -2 & 1 \end{bmatrix}$ 33. –6

34. Side opposite the existing fence: 250 ft; other sides: 125 ft

35. Cakes: 130; muffins: 70 dozen; $365 36.

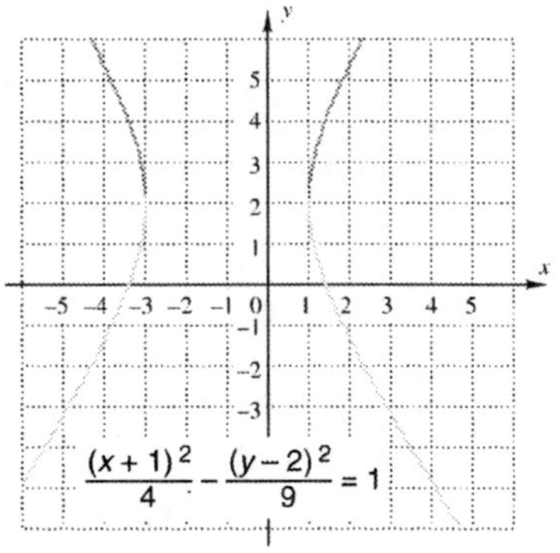

37. $(4,-6)$; 9 38. $6\frac{3}{4}$ in. 39. $(16,-1), \left(-\frac{1}{2}, 32\right)$ 40. 17 41. 250,500 42. 94 43. 75

44.
$S_n: n^2 > n$ for $n > 1$

$S_2: 2^2 > 2$

$S_k: k^2 > k$

$S_{k+1}: (k+1)^2 > k+1$

1. Basis step: $2^2 > 2$ is true.
2. Induction step: Assume S_k is true. Deduce S_{k+1}.

$k^2 > k$

$k^2+1 > k+1$

$k^2+2k+1 > k+1$ Since $k > 1$

$(k+1)^2 > k+1$

45. 56 46. $16x^4-32x^3+24x^2-8x+1$ 47. ${}_5C_4 \cdot {}_5C_2 = 50$ 48. $\dfrac{3}{26}$ 49. 8

50. –106, 94

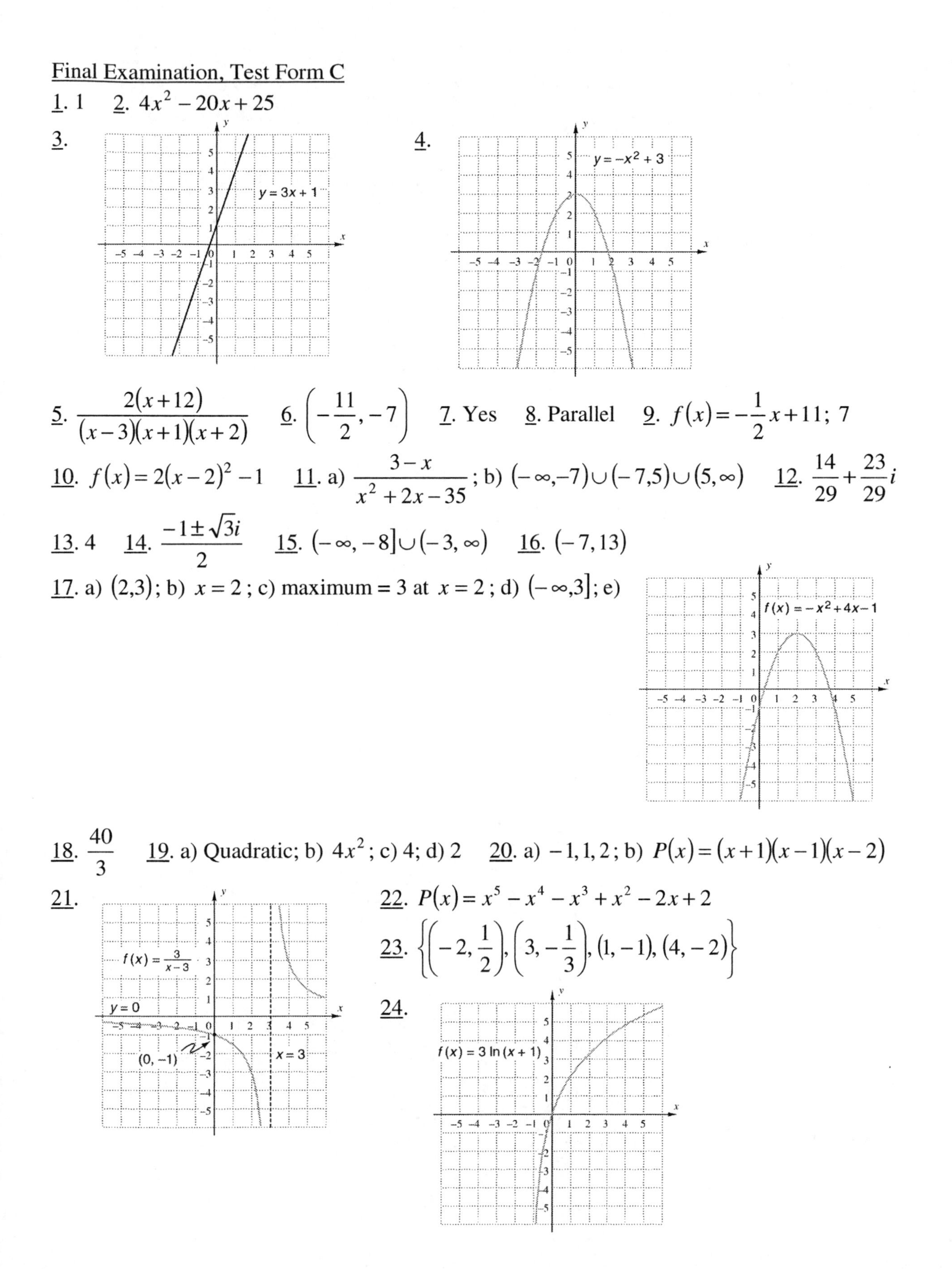

Final Examination, Test Form C

1. 1 2. $4x^2 - 20x + 25$

3.

4.

5. $\dfrac{2(x+12)}{(x-3)(x+1)(x+2)}$ 6. $\left(-\dfrac{11}{2}, -7\right)$ 7. Yes 8. Parallel 9. $f(x) = -\dfrac{1}{2}x + 11$; 7

10. $f(x) = 2(x-2)^2 - 1$ 11. a) $\dfrac{3-x}{x^2+2x-35}$; b) $(-\infty,-7)\cup(-7,5)\cup(5,\infty)$ 12. $\dfrac{14}{29} + \dfrac{23}{29}i$

13. 4 14. $\dfrac{-1 \pm \sqrt{3}i}{2}$ 15. $(-\infty, -8]\cup(-3, \infty)$ 16. $(-7, 13)$

17. a) $(2,3)$; b) $x = 2$; c) maximum = 3 at $x = 2$; d) $(-\infty,3]$; e)

18. $\dfrac{40}{3}$ 19. a) Quadratic; b) $4x^2$; c) 4; d) 2 20. a) $-1, 1, 2$; b) $P(x) = (x+1)(x-1)(x-2)$

21.

22. $P(x) = x^5 - x^4 - x^3 + x^2 - 2x + 2$

23. $\left\{\left(-2, \dfrac{1}{2}\right), \left(3, -\dfrac{1}{3}\right), (1, -1), (4, -2)\right\}$

24.

Final Examination, Test Form C (continued)

25. $e^8 \approx 2980.9580$ 26. 16 27. $2\log x + \frac{1}{2}\log y - 3\log z$

28. a) $P(t) = 4000e^{0.026t}$; b) \$5187.72 29. $(-1, 5)$ 30. $\left(\frac{2}{3}, 5, -1\right)$ 31. Not possible

32. $\begin{bmatrix} \frac{3}{2} & \frac{1}{2} \\ -\frac{5}{4} & -\frac{1}{4} \end{bmatrix}$ 33. –80 34.

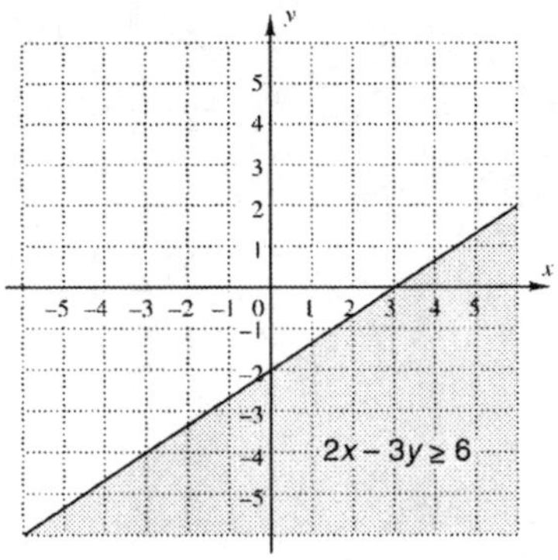

2x – 3y ≥ 6

35. Maximum: 14.8 at $(2.8, -3.2)$; minimum: –16 at $(0, 8)$ 36. c 37. b 38. d 39. a

40. $(-2, 6), (4, -42)$ 41. 6 42. -21 43. \$10,299.71 44. $\frac{7}{9}$

45. $S_n: 2+4+6+\cdots+2n = n(n+1)$

$S_1: 2 = 1(1+1)$

$S_k: 2+4+6+\cdots+2k = k(k+1)$

$S_{k+1}: 2+4+6+\cdots+2k+2(k+1) = (k+1)(k+1+1)$

1. Basis step: $2 = 1(1+1) = 1\cdot 2$ is true.

2. Induction step: Assume S_k is true. Deduce S_{k+1}.

$$\begin{aligned} 2+4+6+\cdots+2k &= k(k+1) \\ 2+4+6+\cdots+2k+2(k+1) &= k(k+1)+2(k+1) \\ &= k^2+k+2k+2 \\ &= k^2+3k+2 \\ &= (k+1)(k+2) \\ &= (k+1)(k+1+1) \end{aligned}$$

46. $x^4 - 4x^3a + 6x^2a^2 - 4xa^3 + a^4$ 47. $26^3 \cdot 10^3 \cdot 26 = 456{,}976{,}000$ 48. $\frac{1}{2}$ 49. $\frac{1}{4}$

50. $(9, \infty)$

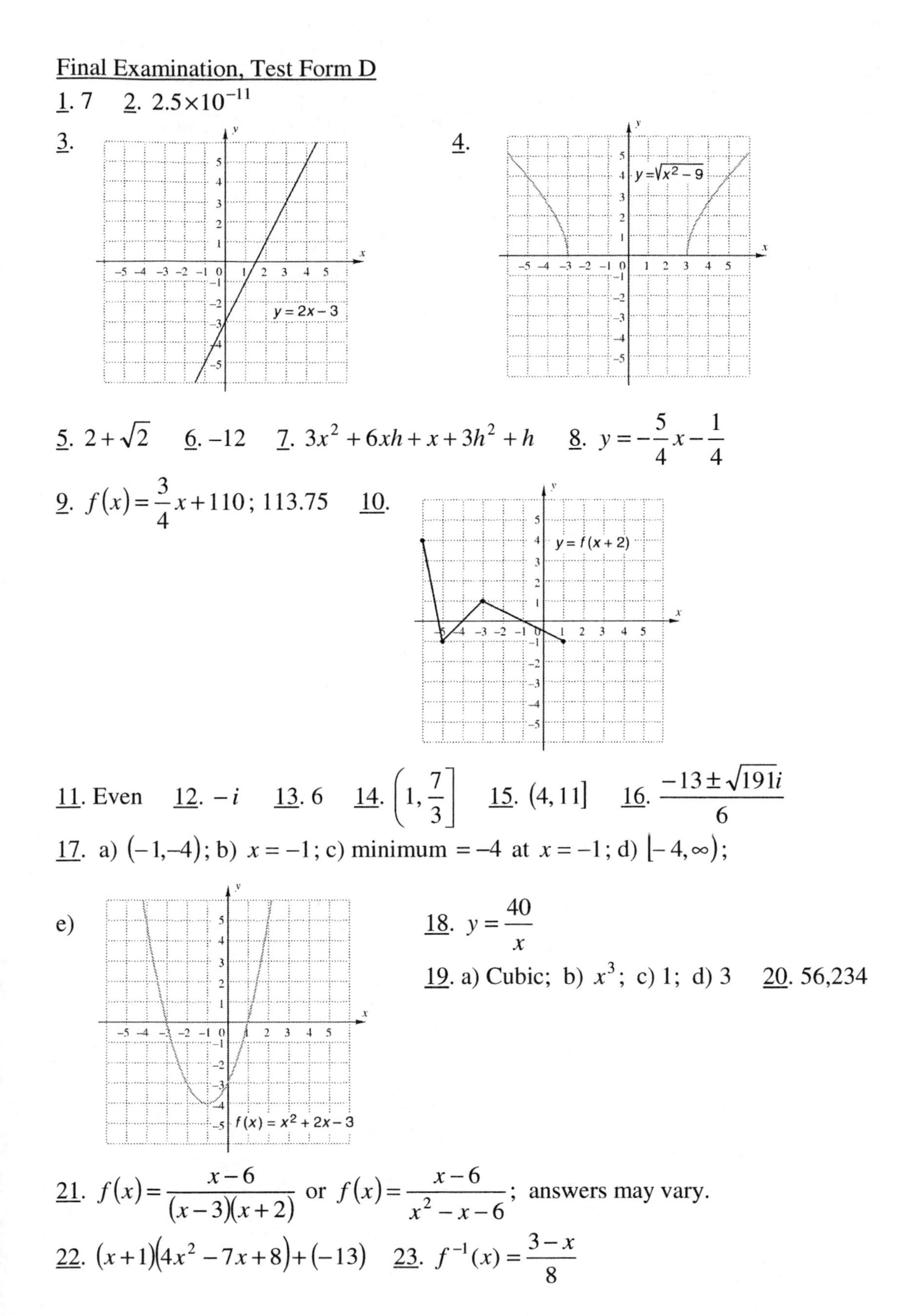

Final Examination, Test Form D

1. 7 2. 2.5×10^{-11}

3.

4.

5. $2+\sqrt{2}$ 6. -12 7. $3x^2+6xh+x+3h^2+h$ 8. $y=-\frac{5}{4}x-\frac{1}{4}$

9. $f(x)=\frac{3}{4}x+110$; 113.75 10.

11. Even 12. $-i$ 13. 6 14. $\left(1,\frac{7}{3}\right]$ 15. $(4,11]$ 16. $\frac{-13\pm\sqrt{191}i}{6}$

17. a) $(-1,-4)$; b) $x=-1$; c) minimum $=-4$ at $x=-1$; d) $[-4,\infty)$;

e)

18. $y=\frac{40}{x}$

19. a) Cubic; b) x^3; c) 1; d) 3 20. 56,234

21. $f(x)=\frac{x-6}{(x-3)(x+2)}$ or $f(x)=\frac{x-6}{x^2-x-6}$; answers may vary.

22. $(x+1)(4x^2-7x+8)+(-13)$ 23. $f^{-1}(x)=\frac{3-x}{8}$

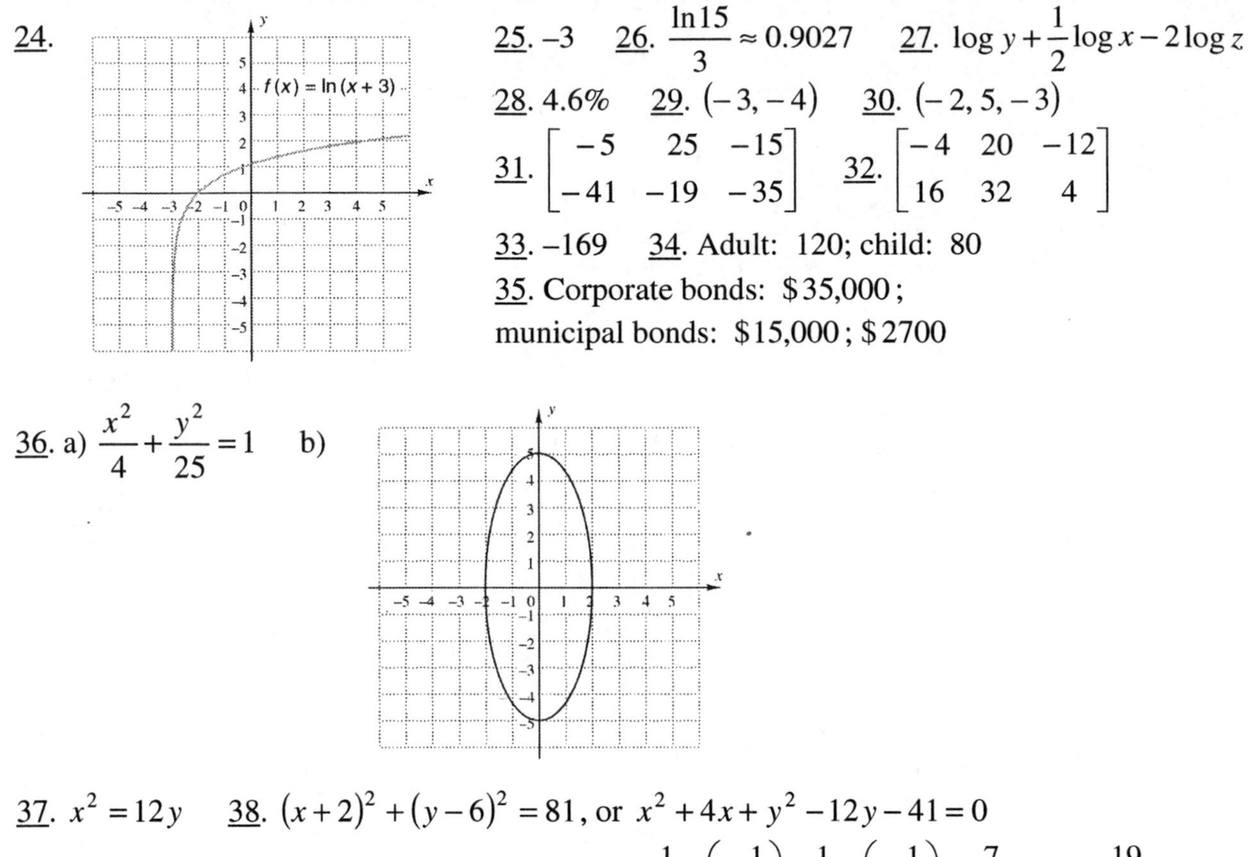

24. (graph)

25. –3 26. $\frac{\ln 15}{3} \approx 0.9027$ 27. $\log y + \frac{1}{2}\log x - 2\log z$

28. 4.6% 29. $(-3, -4)$ 30. $(-2, 5, -3)$

31. $\begin{bmatrix} -5 & 25 & -15 \\ -41 & -19 & -35 \end{bmatrix}$ 32. $\begin{bmatrix} -4 & 20 & -12 \\ 16 & 32 & 4 \end{bmatrix}$

33. –169 34. Adult: 120; child: 80

35. Corporate bonds: $35,000; municipal bonds: $15,000; $2700

36. a) $\frac{x^2}{4} + \frac{y^2}{25} = 1$ b) (graph)

37. $x^2 = 12y$ 38. $(x+2)^2 + (y-6)^2 = 81$, or $x^2 + 4x + y^2 - 12y - 41 = 0$

39. $(-5,-2), (-5,2), (5,-2), (5,2)$ 40. –42 41. $\frac{1}{3} + \left(-\frac{1}{4}\right) + \frac{1}{5} + \left(-\frac{1}{6}\right) = \frac{7}{60}$ 42. $\frac{19}{4}$

43. $5,750,000

Final Examination, Test Form D (continued)

44. 11. $S_n : 1+4+7+\cdots+(3n-2)=\frac{n(3n-1)}{2}$

$S_1 : 1=\frac{1(3\cdot 1-1)}{2}$

$S_k : 1+4+7+\cdots+(3k-2)=\frac{k(3k-1)}{2}$

$S_{k+1} : 1+4+7+\cdots+(3k-2)+[3(k+1)-2]=\frac{(k+1)[3(k+1)-1]}{2}$

1. Basis step: $1=\frac{1(3\cdot 1-1)}{2}=\frac{1(2)}{2}=1$ is true.
2. Induction step: Assume S_k to be true. Deduce S_{k+1}.

$$1+4+7+\cdots+(3k-2)=\frac{k(3k-1)}{2}$$

$$\begin{aligned}1+4+7+\cdots+(3k-2)+[3(k+1)-2] &= \frac{k(3k-1)}{2}+[3(k+1)-2]\\ &= \frac{3k^2-k}{2}+\frac{6k+2}{2}\\ &= \frac{3k^2+5k+2}{2}\\ &= \frac{(k+1)(3k+2)}{2}\\ &= \frac{(k+1)[3(k+1)-1]}{2}\end{aligned}$$

45. 15 46. 256 47. 27,405 48. $\frac{2}{3}$ 49. 16 50. $(1, \infty)$

Final Examination, Test Form E

1. b 2. b 3. a 4. b 5. a 6. d 7. c 8. d 9. c 10. b 11. a 12. d 13. c 14. b
15. d 16. a 17. d 18. b 19. a 20. c 21. a 22. b 23. c 24. d 25. d 26. b
27. c 28. b 29. a 30. b 31. a 32. c 33. c 34. d 35. c 36. c 37. c 38. b
39. c 40. a 41. c 42. c 43. a 44. d 45. a 46. d 47. c 48. b 49. c 50. a

Final Examination, Test Form F

1. c 2. d 3. d 4. d 5. b 6. c 7. c 8. a 9. c 10. b 11. d 12. b 13. d 14. a
15. b 16. a 17. c 18. a 19. d 20. c 21. d 22. d 23. b 24. c 25. a 26. d
27. a 28. d 29. c 30. c 31. a 32. b 33. a 34. d 35. d 36. a 37. c 38. b
39. a 40. d 41. a 42. c 43. d 44. b 45. d 46. c 47. d 48. b 49. a 50. b